This book was made possible through the generous assistance of:

Eastman Kodak Company

Aer Lingus

JOHN **JAMESON** & SON
IRISH WHISKEY

Ryan Hotels

INTERNATIONAL FUND FOR IRELAND

Bord Fáilte
Irish Tourist Board

Dan Dooley
RENT-A-CAR

Northern Ireland
Tourist Board

Galen Rowell

Copyright © 1991 Collins Publishers San Francisco.
All rights reserved, including the right of reproduction
in whole or in part in any form.

"Epic" by Patrick Kavanagh copyright © Peter Kavanagh,
Hand Press, New York. Reprinted by permission.

Library of Congress Cataloging-in-Publication Data
A day in the life of Ireland / photographed by 75 of the world's
leading photojournalists on one day, May 17, 1991.
    p. cm.
    ISBN 0-00-215951-1
    1. Ireland—Description and travel—1981- —Views. 2.
Ireland—Social life and customs—20th century—Pictorial works.
I. Collins Publishers San Francisco.
DA982.D38 1991
941.5—dc20   91-24485

Printed and bound in Japan, first printing August 1991

10 9 8 7 6 5 4 3 2 1

Previous page: The road to Ballinskelligs from Bolus Head,
County Kerry. *Photographer:* **Galen Rowell, USA**

This page: Deenish Island from Hog's Head, Kerry.
Photographer: **Patrick Tehan, USA**

A Day in the Life of Ireland

Photographed by 75 of
the world's leading photojournalists on
one day, May 17, 1991

CollinsPublishersSanFrancisco

A Division of HarperCollins*Publishers*

Ballyferriter, County Kerry: Clearly not a morning person, two-year-old Sibeal O'Sullivan hitches a ride with her father Michael for a tour of the lands near their home. *Photographer:* **Annie Griffiths Belt, USA**

Aughinish Island, County Limerick: First light strikes
the translucent walls of a bauxite storage facility at the
Aughinish Alumina Plant in the Shannon estuary.
Photographer: **Volker Hinz, Germany**

Ballinskelligs, County Kerry: Sunrise over the ruins
of St. Michael's Abbey.
Photographer: **Galen Rowell, USA**

Maynooth, County Kildare: Seminarians
exit the sacristy following morning mass.
Photographer: **John Loengard, USA**

Steve Krongard

When I first travelled to Ireland more than 20 years ago I carried a copy of Patrick Kavanagh's poems with me everywhere I went. I also arrived with a cassette tape of the great American jazz artist, Ben Webster, playing beautiful late night, soft ballads, with just a few select members of the legendary Duke Ellington orchestra. You simply have not lived until you hear Ben Webster, and his friends, play their own unique version of "A Londonderry Air" on a quiet, near-empty early morning road as you wind your way, for the first time, across county lines into the far, far North. What a wonderful tape! Ben Webster was, and remains, a genius; but it was Patrick Kavanagh who first gave Eileen and me a text for the Ireland then opening at our feet.

One of Patrick Kavanagh's poems has stayed with me through all the ensuing years. It is a famous poem. It also goes straight to the heart of the book you now hold in your hands. Patrick Kavanagh called the poem, simply, his "Epic."

I have lived in important places, times
When great events were decided, who owned
That half a rood of rock, a no-man's land
Surrounded by our pitchfork-armed claims.
I heard the Duffys shouting 'Damn your soul'
And old McCabe stripped to the waist, seen
Step the plot defying blue cast-steel—
'Here is the march along these iron stones'
That was the year of the Munich bother. Which
Was more important? I inclined
To lose my faith in Ballyrush and Gortin
Till Homer's ghost came whispering to my mind
He said: I made the Iliad from such
A local row. Gods make their own importance.

Kavanagh was born in County Monaghan, and something about that rural condition caused him to keep his own earlier rhythm against the sound of a modern Dublin bawling in the streets. You will find few, if any, screaming headlines in Kavanagh's work. Like most of the photographers featured in this collection, Patrick Kavanagh authored a poetry of ordinary things.

May 17, 1991 was a quiet day in the life of the Irish people. The government did not fall. The economy did not encounter any sudden upsets. It barely even rained. But what, then, did transpire on the day the photographers came into this country? Well, it was magic.

A priest got a haircut.
A young women rode her horse on the beach.

A fiddle maker made a fiddle.
A farmer in the West bought more cows.

Factory workers in Belfast built an airplane.
An aging woman in Mayo prayed for our sins.

In Dublin, women played bingo.
In Ulster, an Orange man beat an old drum.

Peter Curtin took a bath in Clare.
John McGrath earned his pay in Cork.

And, in Labasheeda, Frank O'Dea, the schoolteacher, awoke with a yawn ...

The photographers who captured each of these poems are Kavanagh's children. The pace of this book is Kavanagh, all the way. This is, after all, Ireland. Settle into these pictures slowly; for then, and only then, you will surely begin to hear photographs sing.

— Bob Callahan

A Day in the Life of Ireland

14 February 1991

Dear Photographer,

It is a great pleasure to invite you to participate in the 11th book in the *Day in the Life* series. *A Day in the Life of Ireland* will utilize the creative talents of 75 of the world's leading photojournalists, 60 international joined by 15 Irish, to capture on film the spirit of Ireland as it moves towards the 21st century.

This year marks the 10th anniversary of the first *Day in the Life* project, *A Day in the Life of Australia*. We thought very carefully about which country we would like to photograph for this milestone year. Ireland was an easy choice. Like Australia, Ireland has always had a special appeal for photographers, and its historical and natural landscapes are among the most dramatic in the world.

Ireland today is a land of fascinating paradox. Despite its claim to the title "the young Europeans" (half of its population is under 25), the country follows the rhythms of one of the most ancient cultures in Europe. From Arranmore Island to the pubs of Dublin, from the shipyards of Belfast to the farmlands of County Kerry, the challenge of *A Day in the Life of Ireland* will be to capture on film the complexity of a nation whose family album ranges from James Joyce and William Butler Yeats to Sinéad O'Connor and U2.

The key objective of this project is to create a superior photographic document which celebrates Ireland and its citizens. We also want to continue the camaraderie which has characterized previous *Day in the Life* projects and to provide a group of talented individuals with the opportunity to work together.

We are not setting out to make the definitive statement about Ireland. That would be impossible. Nor will we concentrate on the rich, the famous or the powerful. Instead, we ask that you apply your skills to one of the toughest jobs in photojournalism: to make extraordinary pictures of ordinary, everyday events.

Although you will receive a specific assignment, you're free to photograph whatever you discover on shoot day—the assignment is just a starting point. All we ask is that you make great pictures.

Following the shoot, your work will be reviewed by a distinguished group of picture editors including:

Christiane Breustedt, *Geo*
Sandra Eisert
Michele McNally, *Fortune*
Kathy Ryan, *New York Times Magazine*
Dieter Steiner, *Stern*

Guy Cooper, *Newsweek*
Colin Jacobson, *The Independent Magazine*
Karen Mullarkey, *Sports Illustrated*
Michele Stephenson, *Time*

Collins Publishers San Francisco, 50 Osgood Place, San Francisco, California 94133, 415-788-4111, Fax: 415-788-3651

Richard Eskite

The sponsors of *A Day in the Life of Ireland*—Eastman Kodak, Aer Lingus, Jameson Irish Whiskey, Ryan Hotels, The International Fund for Ireland, Bord Fáilte/Irish Tourist Board, Dan Dooley Rent-a-Car and the Northern Ireland Tourist Board—understand that the participants in this project are journalists, and they have agreed, without exception, not to exert influence over the editorial process. As with all of our previous projects, we have no intention of producing a travelogue or a collection of postcards.

Of course, there is no guarantee that every photographer will get a picture in the book. That depends not only on your hard work and creativity, but also on what kind of luck (and weather) you have on Friday, May 17.

The schedule: On Sunday, May 12, photojournalists from 12 countries will fly to Dublin via Aer Lingus. Later in the day there will be a general briefing session held at the Gresham hotel where you will receive 50 rolls of Kodak film and information about your assignment. Monday there will be a photography workshop for school kids hosted by Kodak and the *Evening Press*, followed by a group portrait at the Merrion Square government buildings. On Tuesday you will travel to your shooting location (we will provide you with a car courtesy of Dan Dooley Rent-a-Car if your assignment requires it). If your assignment is in Northern Ireland, you will attend the Kodak-*Belfast Telegraph* children's photography workshop before going to your assignment location.

Wednesday and Thursday are research days for you to check out the assignment we have given you and to explore the area for more ideas. The shoot begins at midnight on Thursday and ends at midnight Friday. On Saturday you will return to Dublin for film drop and debriefing before heading home.

Each *Day in the Life* book has posed a unique set of challenges, and *A Day in the Life of Ireland* will be no exception. In a land so rich in history and pastoral splendor—a land so often photographed—you'll need all the resourcefulness and inspiration you can muster to present a fresh perspective. At the same time, there are few better places to create poetry with a lens.

At this writing, 30 of us at Collins Publishers are busy putting all the pieces in place to make sure the shoot goes smoothly. We hope you will be able to lend us your skills, and believe you will be as captivated by Ireland as we are.

Best regards,

Jennifer Erwitt
Project Directors

Tom Lawlor

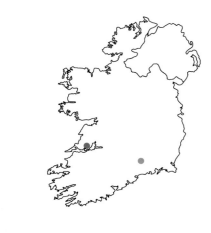

● *Left*

Morning comes a bit early to the home of Frank and Philomena O'Dea in La- basheeda, County Clare. A lifelong educator, Frank has been a teacher at the local primary school for the last 14 years. While he also serves as principal of the 68-student school, the bulk of his day is spent in the classroom, where he teaches students in the fifth and sixth classes, aged 10 to 12, in subjects including English, Irish, environmental studies, and Christian doctrine.
Photographer:
Gerd Ludwig, Germany

● *Following page*

Sarah Walsh, 4, and her sister Marie, 5, dress themselves before breakfast at their home in Callan, County Kilkenny. After breakfast, it's off to Scoil Mhúire, a state-supported pri- mary school run by the Sisters of Mercy at a nearby convent.
Photographer:
Joe McNally, USA

Joe McNally

● *Above, top*

Schoolboys like 13-year-old Ross Browne, here tidying up before his first class, have attended the Portora Royal School in Enniskillen, County Fermanagh, since the year 1608. In the 19th century, the school attracted the sons of wealth and breeding, earning it the nickname "the Eton of Ireland." Now, Portora Royal—which counts Oscar Wilde and Samuel Beckett among its former pupils—concentrates on educating the youth of Fermanagh.
Photographer:
Mark S. Wexler, USA

● *Above*

School doesn't start until 9:30 a.m., but, says Labasheeda teacher and principal Frank O'Dea, "at this time of year, because the weather is good, the kids come to school early to play in the basketball court." That means no time for breakfast this morning. O'Dea returns home at 3:30 to begin grading papers and preparing for the next day.
Photographer:
Gerd Ludwig, Germany

● *Right*

With three minutes to go before the school bus arrives, the Bothwell children of Dundalk, County Louth, finish off breakfast while mother Margret keeps an eye out the window. Sarah and Douglas, 17 and 16, at the table, attend Dundalk Grammar School; Alec, 15, the Marist College. An official at the local horse track, Margret usually works out of their home—except on race days, like today.
Photographer:
Diego Goldberg, Argentina

● *Left*

Belfast crossing guard Alfie Mc-
Quillan holds back one of his
young charges at the corner of
Whiterock Road and Falls Road,
his station for the past five years.
There are two principal systems
of public education in Northern
Ireland: a "controlled" system
administered by the State, and a
"maintained" system administered by the Catholic Church.
Both systems are financed with
public funds and are free to all
students. Only about 2,300
of Northern Ireland's 334,000
schoolchildren attend "inte-
grated" schools, where both
Protestant and Catholic pupils
are taught the same curriculum
in the same classrooms, together.
Photographer:
Andy Levin, USA

● Above

The town of Cobh belongs to the sea. Its Royal Cork Yacht Club dates from 1720; the first vessel to cross the Atlantic entirely under steam, the *Sirius*, departed from here in 1838; and with its natural deep-water anchorage, the port became an embarkation point for dozens of ships setting sail for America during the 1840s and 1850s. The *Titanic* stopped for cargo in Cobh, then known as Queenstown, on its only voyage in 1912, and hundreds of victims of the *Lusitania*'s demise were buried here after that ocean liner was torpedoed by a German submarine in 1915. Roamed by ghosts, Cobh is nevertheless a popular holiday resort today.
Photographer:
Chuck O'Rear, USA

● Right

Holding to perfect decorum, young men of the Monaghan Collegiate School quietly await their morning bus on the steps of the downtown courthouse.
Photographer:
Gary Matoso, USA

It's a quick hop across the
Irish Sea to the Isle of Man for
Archie Alderdice, owner of a
car-repair garage in the town
of Kilkeel near the Mourne
Mountains. The 1948 Aeronca
four-seater is the fifth plane
Alderice has owned since
obtaining his pilot's license in
1963, but he pays a price for
the convenience of using the
field behind his house as a
runway: it usually takes him
15 minutes or so to clear away
a local farmer's sheep before
he can take off.

Photographer:
**Gerry Fitzgerald, Northern
Ireland**

● *Left*

Eight-year-old Bridget Harty of Askeaton, County Limerick, can look forward to growing up in an era when opportunities for women are greater than at any time in Irish history. She's already too late to be Ireland's first woman president, though: Mary Robinson took that title in December 1990.
Photographer:
Brian Lanker, USA

● *Above*

Mary Kane surveys her corner of Belfast's Upper Shankill district from her home on Woodvale Street. For years a bastion of the Protestant working class, the Shankill now faces problems nearly as intractable as those experienced in the nearby Catholic neighborhood known as the Falls. Despite a succession of well-intentioned redevelopment schemes, a lack of inhabitable, affordable housing has led to the exodus of thousands of people from the neighborhood since the mid-1970s; vacant lots, bricked-up schools, and scattered families are the result. Unlike the Falls, which suffers from a lack of employment for its youthful population, fully a quarter of those left behind in the Shankill are retired.
Photographer:
James Meehan, Ireland

● Left

With shearing season just a few short weeks away, a shepherd on a moped prods a gaggle of sheep up the main street of Dingle, in Kerry. The town is located in the heart of one of the country's largest *gaeltachts*, areas receiving state subsidies for the preservation and advancement of the Irish language. Although one-third of the Republic's residents say they speak Irish, the number of people who actually use the language on a daily basis probably stands at less than one percent of the population.
Photographer:
Annie Griffiths Belt, USA

● Right

With the spire of Shandon Cathedral, home of the famous Shandon Bells, looming in the background, steel workers in Cork end a long night's journey into day. Their work on the night shift complete, they leave the ferry that brings them back to the mainland from the Irish Steel Limited plant on Haulbowline Island in Cork Harbour. Founded in 1947, Irish Steel operates the only steel mill in the whole of Ireland.
Photographer:
Chuck O'Rear, USA

Guglielmo de' Micheli

● Left

The business is butchering at Dempsey's Grocers & Victuallers in Killala, County Mayo, but flowers are Nula Dempsey's real love. "I have them in the window seven days a week," she says. Despite the floral touch, Dempsey says it's not easy making ends meet—largely because of competition from the supermarket eight miles up the road.
Photographer:
Simon Callan, Ireland

● Right

Tomás Tuipéar, who describes himself as a "bilingual sign writer," puts the finishing touches on a sign in his home town of Clonakilty, County Cork, as local restaurateur Kevin O'Crowley looks on. Some 60 percent of the town's storefronts boast Tuipéar's handiwork, and now the fourth-generation sign painter's fame has spread abroad: merchants in London, Boston, and San Francisco have hired him to paint their signs as well.
Photographer:
Jim Richardson, USA

● Previous page

A veteran of 25 years spent teaching red dogs new tricks, Owen Lane puts a fleet of Irish setters through their paces in the Comeragh Mountains in southeastern Ireland. Lane, the Honourable Secretary of the Irish Red Setter Club, trains the bird dogs for field trialing competition, mock hunts in which setters are disqualified for overlooking birds hidden in the brush, scaring them away, or making any movement at the crack of a rifle. When hunting season arrives, dogs like these are used to hunt grouse in the mountains, and pheasants and snipe in the stubble below.
Photographer:
Guglielmo de' Micheli, Italy

● *Above*

Pride of place: No smudge escapes the scrutiny of Madge Redpath at her home in Belfast's Upper Shankill district. Scrubbing the doorstep on hands and knees is part of a daily ritual in certain of the city's neighborhoods.
Photographer:
James Meehan, Ireland

● *Right*

Ireland's first recorded cricket match took place in Dublin's Phoenix Park in 1792, pitting the Gentlemen of Ireland—polite nomenclature for a group of amateurs—against the Military of Ireland. Never as popular as indigenous sports such as hurling and Gaelic football, the game nearly died out altogether when the British Army, within whose ranks it was most popular, withdrew from the south of Ireland in the 1920s. The sport has enjoyed a modest resurgence in more recent times, however, claiming more than 20,000 players today. Here Jack Sweetman grooms the pitch at a hotbed of young cricket talent, the Headfort School in Kells, County Meath. Because the ball bounces once on its way from bowler to batsman, it is essential that the ground between them be absolutely free of defects.
Photographer:
Billy Stickland, Ireland

Eli Reed

● *Previous page*

Paul Kelly, 27, often walks his daughter Caoimhe, 5, to her school bus stop in the morning in order to see her safely across several streets in the Derry housing estate where they live.
Photographer:
Eli Reed, USA

● *Above*

Linda Kelleher, 17, and her sister Sandra, 21, ride a double-decker public bus from Cross-haven, where they live with their parents, to morning classes at University College, Cork. Linda is just finishing her first year in college; Sandra, a student of Spanish and psychology, is in her third. Founded in 1845 as Queen's College, UCC is, together with Dublin and Galway, one of three campuses comprising the Republic's 20,000-student National University. The state meets about three-quarters of the National University's operating budget; tuition, which typically runs about £1,300 a year depending on the course of study, covers the rest. While students from disadvantaged backgrounds are still under-represented in the Irish university system, women now make up almost half of all students at the highest educational levels.
Photographer:
Rick Smolan, USA

● *Right*

Students try their best to remain orderly during morning assembly at Headfort, a distinguished all-boarding prep school at the primary level in Kells, County Meath. Boys and girls aged 7 to 14 come to Headfort from Ireland and England to prepare for Eton, Harrow, and other private secondary schools. Less than 100 students attend the school, where tuition runs more than £5,000—almost $7,500—a year.
Photographer:
Billy Stickland, Ireland

● *Far left*

Trading is civilized on the Dublin Stock Exchange, where today Liam Jones presides from beneath a portrait of James Marshall Murray, president of the exchange in the late 19th century. Aside from the computerized information on the television screens, things look much the same as they did under Murray's reign: traders must remain seated while buying and selling securities during the 45-minute trading sessions each morning and afternoon, and current prices are recorded on a chalkboard. In 1990, 12 member firms trading in the shares of 117 Irish companies conducted transactions worth an average of £15 million each day.
Photographer:
Frank Miller, Ireland

● *Left*

Since 1979, Charles Haughey of the Fianna Fáil party has served three terms as Prime Minister, or Taoiseach—an Irish word meaning "chief." Fianna Fáil, or the Soldiers of Destiny, was founded in 1926 by Eamon de Valera, a principal shaper of modern Ireland and author of the Republic's 1937 Constitution; the party has been the country's dominant political force ever since.
Photographer:
Tom Lawlor, Ireland

● *Above*

Budding computer jockeys hone their skills at the Christian Brothers School in Tralee, County Kerry.
Photographer:
Bradley Clift, USA

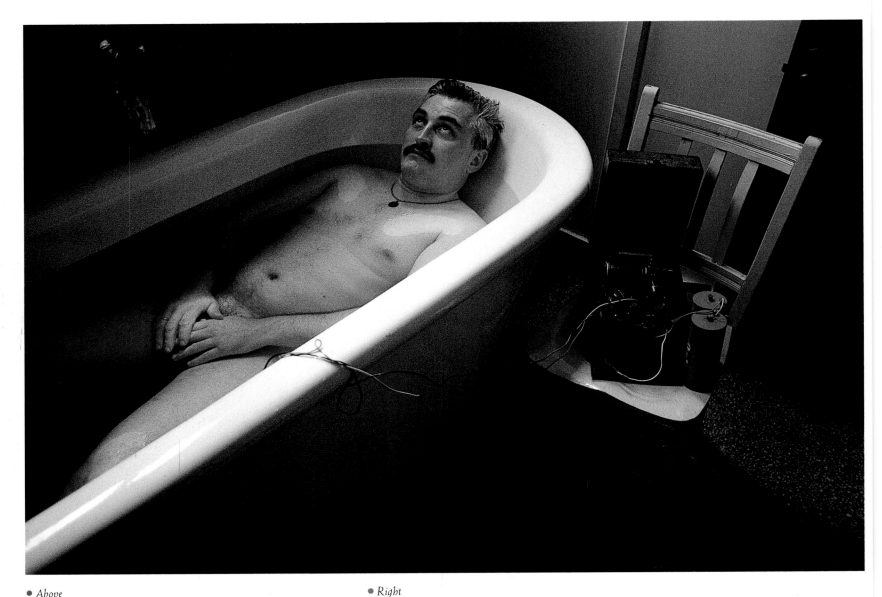

● *Above*

Shock value: Eyes rolled heavenward, Peter Curtin undergoes a 20-minute sulphur bath at the Spa Wells in Lisdoonvarna, the only spa in Ireland. The battery-powered electrodes connected to his feet and buttocks provide him with an extremely low-voltage charge—enough, says spa director Christine O'Neill, to invigorate his muscles, but not nearly enough to harm him. Visitors to the spa can also take the waters in more prosaic fashion by simply imbibing the sulphur water, iron water, or magnesia water straight from the tap at one of the Spa Wells pump houses.
Photographer:
David C. Turnley, USA

● *Right*

No highbrow establishment: Barber John Cronin takes a little off the top at the shop he has operated in Clonakilty with his brother Dan since 1945. The parish priest, the Reverend Jerome Casey, stops in regularly for a haircut and an eyebrow trim while he catches up on the news.
Photographer:
Jim Richardson, USA

● *Left*

The semicircular ring fort known as Dún Aengus dates back to the first century B.C., making it one of the oldest known human settlements in Ireland. Historians believe that the fort, perched 300 feet above the waves on Inis Mór in the Aran Islands, may once have been fully circular, with the missing sections having fallen into the sea long ago due to erosion of the massive limestone cliffs.

Photographer:
Georg Gerster, Switzerland

● *Above*

Last of a breed, John Murphy, John Griffin, and Michael Griffin fish for salmon with draft nets on the River Laune in County Kerry. For 300 years, the Murphy and Griffin families have been dragging the 150-foot-long nets along the river using small boats. On an average day, the three men drag the river eight times, but more often than not the nets come up empty. Larger, sea-going boats with drift nets miles long, Murphy says, have stripped the fishery of virtually all its salmon. He doesn't expect a new generation of draft fishermen on the Laune: "We're losing money," he says, "so we'll get no young people to take it up."

Photographer:
Nutan, Ireland

● *Above*

Despite its 2,500 miles of coastline, Ireland has only in recent
times begun fully to tap the
wealth of the seas. In a country
of self-sufficient farmers, fishing
was at best a local industry for
many years—well-equipped to
meet the needs of small coastal
communities, but hardly those
of a hungry nation. Now, says
Phena O'Boyle of the Irish Sea
Fisheries Board, with huge
factory ships and a thriving
fish industry based out of
ports like Killybegs, in County
Donegal, where these fish pour
out of their containers, "we're
acting like an island should."
Photographer:
Péter Korniss, Hungary

● *Right*

As many as seven tons of
salmon meet their end each
harvest day at the Clare Island
Sea Farms on Achill Island,
where it is Joe Cooney's job to
drain the fish of their blood
before transferring them to a
bin of salt water and ice. The
salmon are raised at sea in
underwater cages for as long as
two years, growing to a weight
of about eight pounds each;
once Cooney and his co-
workers wield their knives, the
fish are sold to smokehouses
and fresh-fish wholesalers both
for domestic consumption
and for export to France, the
United States, and Germany.
Photographer:
Michael Bryant, USA

Where thirty years ago, the word "crafts" in Ireland suggested cloth donkeys and miniature shillelaghs produced in bulk for tourists, recent years have seen a revival of genuine craftsmanship. "I'm carrying on an earthenware tradition that dates back 250 years," says potter Stephen Pearce, who turns out three distinctive lines of glazed terra cotta from a studio in Shanagarry, County Cork. "There was a terrible slump from 1920 to 1960," he adds, "but now we are in a boom."

With 30 employees, Pearce operates the largest hand pottery studio in Ireland. Here he takes a rest near his home after gathering wild vegetables and greens for a luncheon salad.
Photographer:
Elliott Erwitt, USA

● *Left*

On a visit to the Celtic Helicopter Company, Father Thomas C. Butler of Dublin lends a new twist to the Catholic tradition of blessing the fishing fleets each year.
Photographer:
Tom Lawlor, Ireland

● *Below*

The dandelion's nemesis, Sister Rosario Allen tends the graves of fellow nuns of the Sisters of the Presentation of the Blessed Virgin Mary at the order's convent in Cork. The order was founded by Nano Nagle, one of Ireland's most remarkable religious leaders, whose crypt dominates the small cemetery. Born to a prosperous farming family early in the 18th century and educated in France, Nagle founded nine schools for

poor Catholic children in Cork at a time when Catholic education was illegal in Ireland. At the age of 57, she became a nun and formed the Sisters of the Presentation to provide aid to the least fortunate members of Irish society. In 1805, 21 years after her death, Nagle's community of nuns was officially confirmed by Pope Pius VII.

Photographer:

Rick Smolan, USA

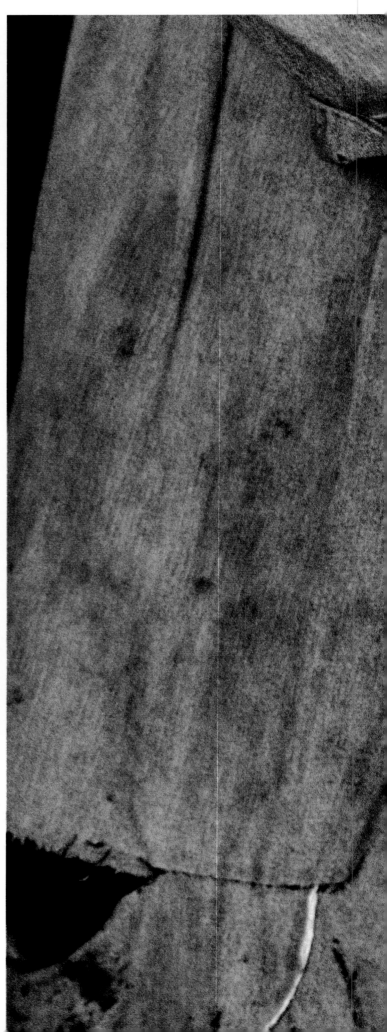

E nlightenment comes from many quarters. Some seek it out in academic pursuits or theological debate; others wait for episodes of mystical transcendence brought on by isolation or asceticism. For Sister Benedict at Kylemore Abbey in western Connemara, insight, such as it is, comes along with a lot of hard work. Sister Benedict was born Maeve O'Beirne in Cambridge, England; she came to Ireland at the age of 10, when her father, a lecturer in law at Cambridge University, acquired a farm in County Meath. Kylemore operated a primary school at the time, and she attended as a boarder. Later, she trained as a barrister at Cambridge; but Kylemore held its grip, and in 1957 she returned to the Abbey to take up life as a Benedictine nun. She has been a full-time farmer ever since, helping provide for the worldly needs of the Abbey's other nuns using little but her own two hands. *Photo essay by:* **Roseanne McGregor, Ireland**

Kylemore was built as a shooting lodge for a wealthy doctor in the 1860s. The Benedictine order acquired it in 1920, and upkeep of the holdings has been a constant challenge ever since. Some funding comes from tuitions and education subsidies; other income flows from donations and from a small crafts shop.

Throughout the year, Sister Benedict rises as early as 5:00 a.m. to start her working day. Kylemore keeps 150 acres of grazing lands; a typical morning finds the Sister watering and feeding the cattle, milking the cows, churning the cream into butter, and tending to rows of rhubarb and parsley in the estate's former rose garden. Occasionally, the grounds take on a spiritual side of their own: "Sometimes, when it's quiet," Sister Benedict muses, "I can hear the ladies having their tea parties."

Brian Lanker

● *Previous page*

Laundry dries quickly on a
windy day near Doolin, in
County Clare.
Photographer:
Brian Lanker, USA

● *Left*

Samuel Stevenson finds a quiet place to practice in the glass house behind his home in Broughshane, County Antrim. While the greenhouse helps his tomatoes and cucumbers grow, it's equally useful in seasoning the six or seven violins he makes each year; the sun darkens the wood to a rich brown as the varnish dries. Of course no fiddle is ready until Stevenson has tested it—by playing it in the greenhouse. Once they pass muster, the instruments sell for £250 and up depending on the wood and detailing.

Photographer:

Barry Lewis, Great Britain

● *Above*

Bono, the driving force behind the rock band U2, takes a break from recording the group's latest album in a private house in County Dublin. Considered one of the premier bands of the past decade, U2 has helped make Dublin an epicenter of world rock and roll.

Photographer:

Tom Lawlor, Ireland

Cats have it all over their canine cousins where bicycling postman John Farrelly of County Westmeath is concerned. Farrelly, one of 8,000 people in Ireland who work for the national mail service An Post, delivers the mail five days a week to familiar faces like Rathowen's Kathleen Glennon—often by hand. An Post moves about a million pieces of mail a day.
Photographer:
John Carlos, Ireland

The boat to Tory Island delivers mail, food, and other supplies twice a week from the Irish mainland eight miles away. When the ship comes in, the island's 125 residents gather to unload the goods and catch up on the news; whoever gets to the mail sack first drags it to the tiny post office for distribution. In the wintertime, the social gathering sparked by the arrival of supplies takes place less frequently; stormy seas dictate that shipments come in by helicopter—and only once every two weeks. The residents of Tory are an independent lot; they speak in their own Irish dialect, and when they travel to the mainland to escape the winter storms, they say they are going "over to Ireland."
Photographer:
Peter Turnley, USA

● *Left*

Butcher to the town of
Ballydehob, in County Cork,
Connie O'Sullivan comes by
his trade honestly: his father
was a butcher, as were all the
O'Sullivan men before him,
stretching back at least 200
years. Connie and his wife
Mary run the store together
six days a week—plus a half-
day on Sunday—and have
trained each of their six
children to run the business,
guaranteeing the availability
of high class victuals in
Ballydehob for at least one
more generation.
Photographer:
Eddie Adams, USA

● *Above*

The South Eastern Cattle
Breeding Society in Dovea,
County Tipperary, is one of
four artificial-insemination
breeding stations in the Republic of Ireland. In peak
seasons, the station services
more than 14,000 cows per
week. But first, of course,
there is this business with the

bulls. The bull here is a prize
Hereford. His companion is a
man named John McGrath. It
is McGrath's job to provoke
the bull to a high state of ex-
citation such that, as plant
manager Dermot Cahill puts it,
"any port in a storm will do."
McGrath points out, "It's not
everyone who would stand
under a bull. You need to be
very agile." He has been in his
position since 1982.
Photographer:
Randy Olson, USA

● *Left and above*

Men at work: Local farmers and livestock dealers gather at the auction ring in Ennistymon, County Clare, to trade stories and cattle. Cattle auctions in the west of Ireland date back many centuries; descriptions of the marts, and of the festivals and ceremonies which surrounded them, can be found in Ireland's earliest books. In Ennistymon, some 300 to 400 animals might be sold on a typical auction day, which takes place once every two weeks in the summer and once a week in the fall. The cows, bullocks, and heifers are penned in before being weighed and driven into the ring by an auction employee known as the Ringman, who escorts each animal for one lap around the premises and out again while the bidding goes on.
Photographer:
Stephanie Maze, USA

● *Above*

The potato is not native to Ireland; it was brought from South America in the 16th century. By the mid-19th century, however, it was the only food available to one-third of the Irish population, who as tenants to colonial landlords were obliged to pay rent in other crops. The onset of a blight lasting from 1845 to 1849 led to the Great Famine, in which a million people in Ireland starved to death and another 1.5 million set sail for the United States.

Today, the tuber remains a staple of Irish cuisine: the average person eats over 300 pounds a year, after boiling them, steaming them, baking them, mashing them, or slicing them and deep-frying them as "chips." Here, Seamus Whelan sorts seed potatoes on a farm in Thurles, County Tipperary.
Photographer:
Randy Olson, USA

● *Right*

A throwback to another era, Martha Esler, 79, tends the small family farm in County Antrim where she and her brother Paul, 81, have lived their entire lives. The pair, neither of whom ever married, live without electricity, cut their own peat for fuel, bake their own soda bread, and grow virtually all their own food. Martha and Paul play checkers or read each night by the light of an oil lamp and, says their friend and doctor Tony Redmond,

"are very happy people." Paul occasionally drives a tractor to the nearby village of Brough-shane, but his involvement with modern technology ends there: "Someone gave them a portable radio about twenty years ago," says Redmond, "but they never turn it on."
Photographer:
Barry Lewis, Great Britain

● Left

Ireland's traditional thatched-roof cottages now exist mostly in the minds of tour directors. In fact, they're considered such a fire hazard that Irish companies will no longer insure them. Today, thatchers like Paddy Mullins of Carraroe, County Galway, ply their trade with reeds, rather than straw; and instead of using the traditional clay or mud, they set the reeds in wire atop a zinc-asbestos roof. The thatch itself serves no particular purpose except to please the eye. "It's not the old way," says Máirtín Davy of Radio na Gaeltachta, the nearby Irish-language radio station, "but nothing really is in Ireland."
Photographer:
Bruno Barbey, France

Alan Lewis

● *Previous page*

Rising some 300 feet above industrial Belfast, the twin gantry cranes Samson and Goliath at the Harland and Wolff shipyards rank among the city's proudest landmarks. Designed and manufactured by Germany's Krupp Ardelt and controlled from driver's cabs like the one here, the mammoth structures move about the yards on half-mile tracks and are capable of lifting 840 tons apiece. Large sections of vessels known as weldments are fabricated under cover in the yard, then maneuvered into place by the cranes for final assembly.
Photographer:
Alan Lewis, Ireland

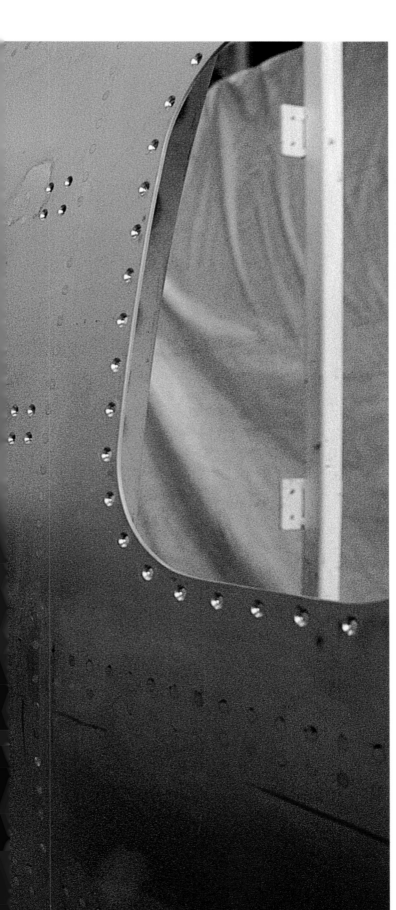

● *Left and above*

Graham Cully and Samuel Gibson check out a fuselage panel (*left*) at Short Brothers, which bills itself as both the largest private company in Northern Ireland and the oldest aircraft manufacturer in the world. The 9,000 workers at the East Belfast plant, like the men working on a Fokker 100 wing section (*top*) and a Shorts Tucano Turboprop Trainer (*above*), turn out commercial and military aircraft for clients around the world; components of the Patriot missiles used by allied forces during the Persian Gulf War were built at Short Brothers, and one of its corporate ancestors built the plane flown by the Wright Brothers at Kitty Hawk in 1903. The firm, which the British government sold to Canada's Bombardier Company as part of the Thatcher government's privatization strategy in 1989, has long attracted the scrutiny of activists seeking integration of the overwhelmingly Protestant work force. Company officials point to equal-opportunity hiring practices which have led to a doubling over the past decade in the numbers of Catholics working at the plant, to about 12 percent of the total. Many observers see a need for the appointment of Catholics to executive positions in the company, however, and for the size of the Catholic work force to rise to a point where it approximates the proportion of Catholics living in Northern Ireland—a figure near 40 percent.
Photographer:
Misha Erwitt, USA

Clutches of the devil: Two years ago, Liam Farrelly and his wife Mary bought St. Dominic's, a deconsecrated Catholic church in Kenagh, County Longford, turning it into their home as well as the site of their auto-repair business. Drivers who think only miracles can keep their old cars running have come to count on Liam, who knows St. Dominic's well: as a youngster, he served in the venerable building as an altar boy.
Photographer:
Joyce Tenneson, USA

● *Above*

Francis Finneran and Sam
Cairns take a break to contemplate their work at Willie
Conneely's coffin company in
Galway City. A good Irish
coffin, says Conneely, is
distinguished by its shape,
closely following the contours
of the human body, whereas
US-made caskets tend to
resemble mere oblong boxes.
Conneely and his four em-
ployees turn out seven or
eight coffins a week, by hand.
"My favorite part," says
Conneely, "is shining them
up at the end."
Photographer:
Joe O'Shaughnessy, Ireland

● *Following pages 78-79*

One of Ireland's eeriest places,
the Burren—which takes its
name from the Irish word
boireann, or "rocky land"—
stretches for 100 square miles
in County Clare. Stepped layers of limestone and shale play
host to the country's rarest
flora, and countless caverns and
stone forts dot the landscape.
Photographer:
Georg Gerster, Switzerland

● *Following pages 80-81*

The hands of a farmer: Michael
Giblin of County Leitrim.
Photographer:
David Peterson, USA

Georg Gerster

David Peterson

● Previous page

For one day each July, known locally as Reek Sunday, the slopes of 2,513-foot Croagh Patrick swarm with thousands of climbers intent on paying homage to Ireland's patron saint. At the summit of the Reek, open-air masses are said continuously through the day to mark the event, with some pilgrims making the two-hour climb barefoot. On a damp, foggy May 17, however, 13-year-old Shane Cunningham of nearby Westport had Croagh Patrick pretty much to himself. *Photographer:*

Don Doll, S.J., USA

● Below

No one knows who first had the idea of harvesting for fuel the thick mats of sodden, partially decomposed mosses, genus *Sphagnum*, that fill Ireland's boggy lowlands. Once cut into pieces, stacked, and drained, then dried on the hearth or in the sun, however, turf burns with a slow, even flame that has fueled both agriculture and industry in Ireland for centuries. As Ireland's appetite for electricity has grown, so has pressure to exploit this ready source of fuel. Bord na Móna, the state-owned company set up for this purpose in the Republic in 1946, has perfected machinery and techniques for large-scale harvesting of the peat, even building its own rail line to facilitate extraction. Once dried and pulverized, the moss is blown into electrical generators operated by the Electricity Supply Board, replacing the equivalent of approximately a million tons of oil each year that would otherwise be imported.

Such natural bounty comes at a price, however: 8,000 acres of bogland are sacrificed

to the cause annually, and depending on climate and local growing conditions, the bogs can be expected to regenerate only with the passage of hundreds or thousands of years, if at all. Bord na Móna's harvest will cease as the available turf runs out, although its technology has already been exported to other boggy nations including the Soviet Union and East Africa's Burundi.

Photographer:
Georg Gerster, Switzerland

● *Right*

John Haran digs deep into history while cutting turf for use at the inn he operates near Milltown Malbay in Clare. Formed through the encroachment of vegetation on glacial lakes, peat bogs have yielded remarkable finds over the years. Botanists prize evidence of ancient plant and animal life, and archeologists have found boats, weapons, and human bodies, all well preserved by the acidic waters.

Photographer:
Stephanie Maze, USA

● *Above, top*

At last count, the Republic of Ireland was home to 3.5 million people and 4.8 million sheep. Within the sheep industry, valued at £250 million per year, wool plays a modest role; lamb chops, and mutton, rank at the top of the menu.
Photographer:
David Peterson, USA

● *Above and right*

Pat Byrne of Kilcar, County Donegal, clips his sheep by hand, aiming to remove the fleece in one piece (*above*). A contractor working with electric shears can take off a sheep's coat in about a minute; it takes Byrne and his hand shears about 10 times as long. Few of the Republic's 52,000 sheep farmers go to such great lengths to recover the wool. For many of them, in fact, the value of a fleece on the open market is so low—currently about £1.50—that it's more economical to send their flocks to the slaughterhouse without shearing them at all.

After carding and spinning, the wool winds up in the nimble hands of people like Siobhán and Con McBrearty, who live down the road (*right*). In many parts of Ireland, knitting is taught in schools, to boys as well as girls. But "very few men," says neighbor Denis Lyons, "are as skilled at knitting as Con."
Photographer:
Péter Korniss, Hungary

Following page

Ernie Patterson is a bit of a renaissance man. In 1980, he constructed a full-scale replica of the first airplane built and flown in Ireland, and flew it on the original route from Dundrum Bay to Newcastle in County Down. His work in the breeding and preservation of rare strains of sheep has led to appearances on Irish television and visits with farmers in Scandinavia. As for the motorbike, he finds that with 600 animals spread out over 200 acres, it simplifies a big job—but the wheelie is just for fun.
Photographer:
Doug Menuez, USA

87

Doug Menuez

● *Above and right*

Though charged with defending the nation the Republic's all-volunteer Permanent Defence Force has never come under attack. Instead, the 13,000 troops making up the Army, Naval Service, and Air Corps spend their time patrolling the border, chasing away foreign fishing trawlers, conducting search-and-rescue missions, containing oil spills, guarding prisons, and training, training, training. In part because the Republic of Ireland is officially neutral—it is not a member of NATO or any other military alliance—Irish forces have been called upon by the United Nations several times over the past 30 years to serve on peacekeeping missions in Africa, the Middle East, Southwest Asia, and Central America. Here, officer candidates from the Military College in the Curragh undergo tactical training in the Wicklow Mountains.
Photographer:
Claus C. Meyer, Germany

● *Left*

Maurice Mills, a 49-year-old alderman in Ballymena, County Antrim, adjusts the sash, bowler, and gloves that identify him as a member of the Protestant organization known as the Orange Order. The Order traces its roots back to 1795, when it was formed to promote Protestant interests in the north of Ireland, taking its name in honor of William of Orange. Since the Orange Order is a secret society, Mills won't say what the emblems on the sash mean, except to acknowledge that 635 is his lodge number. He does allow, however, that Protestantism has a glorious history in Ireland: St. Patrick, he maintains, was a Protestant, despite having lived 1,000 years before the Reformation.
Photographer:
Barry Lewis, Great Britain

● *Above*

In Banbridge, County Down, May 17 saw the initiation of 22 boys as young as eight years old into a new Orange Order "junior lodge." Following administration of the secret rituals and oaths by a Deputy Grand Master of Ireland, the boys are expected to attend monthly meetings, and may take part in an array of "youth club activities" as well. Each pays 10 pence a month in dues.
Photographer:
Doug Menuez, USA

The longest and widest main street in all of Ireland runs through Cookstown, County Tyrone. Photographer Pedro Coll had the disconcerting experience here of having a rifle pointed at him by a young soldier. Not to worry, says an information officer with the British Army: the soldier is merely "using the rifle's telescopic sight to gain a better view of a subject, presumably your photographer!"
Photographer:
Pedro Coll, Spain

the half-hour session.

Prior to 1975, inmates detained for politically-motivated acts of violence and conspiracy in Northern Ireland received privileges not granted ordinary prisoners. Thereafter, political convicts—Loyalist and Republican—were "criminalized," assigned to ordinary cells and required to live and work like other inmates. A series of protests seeking changes— such as the right to wear one's own clothes and exemption from prison work—culminated in the 1981 hunger strikes, when 10 Republican prisoners died. Many of their demands have since been met.
Photographer:
Nicole Bengiveno, USA

● *Below*

Armed British soldiers are a common sight for residents of parts of Belfast and other areas of the North—often spilling out of armored cars or helicopters on searches and patrols. Their presence is particularly resented in the working-class Catholic neighborhoods where it is also most apparent. Many people in other areas, however, see the projection of force as essential in maintaining their own security against the threat of Republican violence
Photographer:
Misha Erwitt, USA

● *Left*

Nowhere is the youthful character of Ireland's population more apparent than on Dublin's principal shopping thoroughfare, Grafton Street. Some of the young people attend nearby Trinity College; most converge on the pedestrian mall to visit the shops and restaurants, see friends, and hang out. In the countryside, the picture looks very different. Many rural areas have experienced an exodus of young people, often to points abroad; and despite the congestion on Grafton Street,

the Republic of Ireland's population density, at 130 citizens per square mile, is actually the lowest in the European Community. Still, and perhaps fittingly in a land whose population actually dropped by more than half from 1841 to 1961, the Republic is currently the only EC nation where births outnumber deaths.

Photographer:
Paul Chesley, USA

● *Above*

Two members of Ireland's youth culture—and one of a generation yet unreckoned—step smartly through St. Stephen's Green in Dublin. The Green was first laid out as a public park in 1880 by businessman and politician Sir Arthur Edward Guinness, who had headed his family's famous brewery from 1868 to 1877. On a sunny day, the gardens, bandstands, and lakes make the Green a popular crossroads for tourists, punks, housewives, lunching businesspeople, students, politicians, pets, musicians, and small children of every persuasion.

Photographer:
Steve McCurry, USA

● *Left*

Father and daughter share a tender moment in Dublin, where seven-year-old Grace Buckley is a student and outpatient at the Central Remedial Clinic. Grace, who has cerebral palsy, can't speak, walk, or sit up straight; father Paul, a prison officer, works a swing shift in order to spend more time with her. "Grace is definitely a daddy's girl," says Paul's wife Bríd.

The smiling face on Grace's wheelchair is intended to keep her fingers out of the spokes, but it serves another purpose as well. Before the disk was installed, according to Bríd, other children would meet Grace and ask what was wrong with her; now, the first thing they say is "Look at those wheels!" As for the doll, "Susie," it is Grace's mouthpiece to the world. Susie is a "talking" doll, and Grace signals Paul and Bríd by moving Susie in such a way that the doll makes noise. Before she got the doll, all she could do to get her parents' attention was to cry.
Photographer:
Lynn Johnson, USA

● *Above*

Business is booming for Colette Fleming of the Wee Care private day nursery in Belfast. In Ireland, both north and south, the child-care industry has grown rapidly as more women have taken jobs outside the home. In Northern Ireland, in fact, there are more professional baby-sitters, or childminders, per child, than in any other part of the United Kingdom. In 1978, there were some 700 registered child-minders caring for about 1,300 children in Northern Ireland; a decade later, the number of childminders had risen to 2,900 and the number of children to more than 7,500.
Photographer:
Andy Levin, USA

● *Above*

A dance to summer: May 17 was the last day of classes at the Nano Nagle School in Cork, inspiring students to seek out partners for a lunch-hour whirl.

With half the population under the age of 28, the preoccupations of Ireland's youth can't be taken lightly. A recent poll for the *Irish Independent* revealed that the Republic's unemployment rate—now at 17 percent, highest in the European Community—is the main worry of those aged 15 to 24. AIDS is the second greatest area of concern among those surveyed, a majority of whom also disagreed with the Catholic Church's stand on contraception. Politically, only one in five said they feel allegiance to any of the Republic's current political parties, and only 15 percent said they were "very concerned" about the issue of a united Ireland.

Photographer:
Rick Smolan, USA

● *Left*

David O'Callaghan, 13, makes the rounds of St. Finbarr's Hospital in Cork, selling sweets, pies, and sandwiches. But David is no ordinary peddler: he's one of about 100 boys from disadvantaged backgrounds who attend the St. Francis Training Centre, a vocational school led by an engaging priest known as Father Roch. "The boys themselves run the place," says the modest Father, by electing a Central Council which makes the rules and doles out punishments for transgressions. Aside from their coursework, the boys, who are organized into competing 15-member "clans," operate two bakeries that help support the Centre financially while teaching good management practices.
Photographer:
Rick Smolan, USA

● *Above*

With his aristocratic ancestors keeping watch, six-year-old François O'Neill hides from family cook Sylvia Hamilton before a dinner party at the O'Neill home, Cleggan Lodge, in Broughshane. François's father Hugh heads the Northern Ireland Tourist Board, and both his grandfather and great-grandfather served in Northern Ireland's parliament.
Photographer:
Barry Lewis, Great Britain

Above: Amateur boxer Danny Boyd, 16, of the St. George's Boxing Club in Belfast. *Photographer:* **Andy Levin, USA**
Right: Retired pipefitter Michael Hayes, 74, at home in Gneevgullia, County Kerry. *Photographer:* **Patrick Tehan, USA**

● *Right*

Like many rural families, the Vials of Killybegs in County Donegal manage a sizable menagerie, sharing their estate with ducks, chickens, muscovies, four ponies (Shetland and Connemara), two dogs, a cat, and some lambs. On May 17, while her husband Bill, a fisherman, was away at sea, Gerardine Sharkey Vial decided to give her neighbors a treat, and invited the local blacksmith for a visit. Five children showed up to have their ponies' feet examined, and each left with a new set of shoes. Soon after, Gerardine, an admirer of all things equine, departed for the horse and pony show then getting under way in Letterkenny—leaving one of her own steeds behind to tend the lawn.

Photographer:

Péter Korniss, Hungary

● *Above*

Judy Sheridan, 6, attends
ballet lessons in a converted

● Above

● Following page

George Steinmetz

Children of lighthouse keepers themselves, Larry and Pauline Butler raised 15 sons and daughters at a lighthouse in Clonakilty, County Cork. "What else are you going to do in a lighthouse?" asks Larry. *Photographer:* **Jim Richardson, USA**

During the '40s and '50s, Jim Tady Willie O'Connor, here with his wife Breda in Gneevgullia, County Kerry, ran the local ballroom for dances on Sunday afternoons. Staging the dances at night, the parish priest felt, might be leading the flock into temptation. *Photographer:* **Patrick Tehan, USA**

William and Edith Walkingshaw of Ballymena, County Antrim, raise harriers, or hounds for hunting hare. The canine specimen in the window, however, is not for sale. *Photographer:* **Barry Lewis, Great Britain**

Lucky dog: Charles Plunkett was working as caretaker at Ely Lodge on Lough Erne in Fermanagh when its owner, the Duchess of Westminster, passed away and left the entire estate to him in her will. *Photographer:* **Alan Lewis, Ireland**

● *Above, top*

Two young lads work on their green thumbs outside the Mace Supermarket on Andersonstown Road in West Belfast.
Photographer:
Andy Levin, USA

● *Above*

Proprietor of a grocery store on wheels, Robert Baldrick, 64, reflects on changes in the business he's run for almost 30 years in Letterkenny, County Donegal. "People have their own cars now," he says. "They can get what they need at the supermarket." But there's still enough demand to keep 20 or more grocery vehicles on the road in Letterkenny alone, and Baldrick continues to work five full days a week supplying customers on his route with their regular orders. "It's a service," he insists. "They're depending on me."
Photographer:
Bill Frakes, USA

● *Right*

The Moore Street Market in Dublin swarms with characters recalling the legendary Molly Malone, who pushed her wheelbarrow through the streets in the late 1600s. Though her song now rings out at official celebrations, Malone might find selling her wares somewhat tougher now that police require vendors to work from fixed locations and arrest those without licenses.
Photographer:
Paul Chesley, USA

• *Above*

A city of bridges, Dublin stands neatly divided north and south by the River Liffey. Rising in the Wicklow Mountains, the river is navigable only for a short distance where it merges with the waters of Dublin Bay. Long-distance water travellers with time on their hands are better off on the nearby Grand Canal, which makes use of natural and artificial waterways as it threads its leisurely way across the country, through dozens of locks, to the Shannon River estuary.

Photographer:
Georg Gerster, Switzerland

At the center of Inis Mór in the Aran Islands stands the well-preserved Celtic fort known as Dún Oghill. The nearby tower served as a lighthouse in the 1800s, but its position at the center of the island actually made it a hazard to shipping. During the Second World War it was used as a lookout for spotting German submarines. Today it stands watch mainly over stone walls and wildflowers.

Photographer:
Georg Gerster, Switzerland

The limestone surface of Inis Meaín, like all the Aran Islands, was scoured by glaciers during the last Ice Age, some 10,000 years ago. For centuries, island residents used the abundant rocks left over to wall off their fields, and laboriously fertilized the land each spring using seaweed and debris tossed ashore by the rough North Atlantic.
Photographer:
Monica Almeida, USA

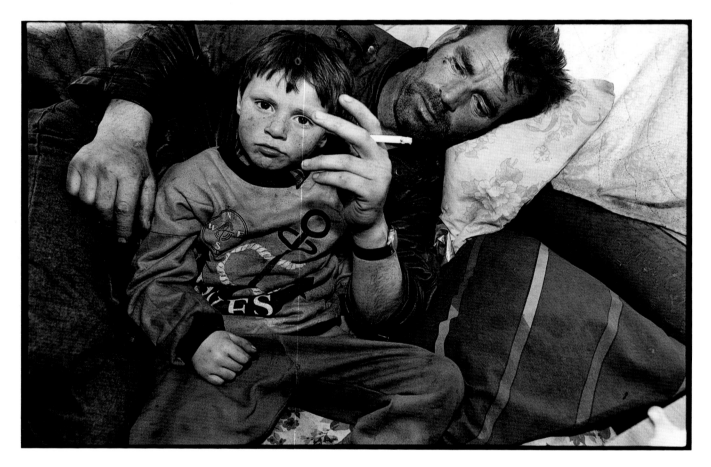

The Travellers make up Ireland's single largest ethnic minority. Though Irish in origin, they possess their own language (known as Gammon, Shelta, or simply the Cant), history, and culture dating back to the 12th century. Like the Gypsies of the European continent, many of the island's 21,000 Travellers live in roadside encampments, often without electricity or plumbing. Some move constantly; others stay put for months or years. While a large percentage depend on public assistance, many also earn money through trades such as scrap dealing, horse trading, and tin working. Travellers face a typical range of discriminatory behavior in their dealings with the "settled community": some bars and restaurants refuse to serve them, social welfare offices set aside special hours for them, and residents' groups often oppose Travellers' "halting sites" in their areas. Of course most Travellers would give much to escape their poverty and poor living conditions; they prefer to do so, however, without sacrificing their nomadic way of life.

Above, Michael Joyce shares a quiet moment with his son Patrick at a trailer camp in Dublin's Finglas district. At right, young Martin Gavin hangs from a makeshift jungle gym erected at an encampment in Cara Park. Some 80 percent of Travellers are under 25 years of age; 55 percent are children under the age of 14. *Photo essay by:* **Mary Ellen Mark, USA**

At far left, Michael Joyce embraces his father Christie, better known as Chappie; above, Bernard and Mary Joyce and their son John pass the time at home—in this instance, an abandoned car in Finglas. At left, Margaret Joyce models the dress she'll wear for her first Holy Communion.

● *Above and right*

Hail the Huntsman: With four months to go before the beginning of fox-hunting season, Robert Walker of the East Down Foxhounds Club takes his hounds for a training walk as assistant Bryan McDowell trails behind. Walker, who has been a Huntsman for more than 40 years, leads fox hunts twice a week from September to March, though he stresses that the joy of the hunt is in the chase: the objective is not to kill the fox. As for the hounds—don't let Walker hear you call them dogs—they range in age from two to eight years old, reaching the peak of their skills between the ages of three and six.
Photographer:
Doug Menuez, USA

John Colman, his daughter Terry, and three river guides consider their catch from the River Moy in Foxford, County Mayo. *Photographer:* **Mike Bunn, Great Britain**

Tim Finney shows off his prize Irish wolfhound Benjamin, 5, in Naul, County Dublin. *Photographer:* **Michael Lutzky, USA**

R.G. Reade, William McCrory, Richard Mulholland, and Brian Mulholland stalk the feral pigeon. Ballymena, County Antrim. *Photographer:* **Barry Lewis, Great Britain**

"Lenny" of the Waterford Wheelers minds his Harley-Davidson Evolution Softail in Kilmeadan, County Waterford. *Photographer:* **Rick Rickman, USA**

● *Left*

Like many amateur boxers, 24-year-old Pat McKeown is, according to coach Michael Hawkins, one of "the rougher kids." In McKeown's hometown of Belfast alone, there are 21 boxing clubs, all located in working-class neighborhoods and claiming several dozen members each. In international competition Ireland fields one team, with fighters from both Northern Ireland and the Republic.
Photographer:
Andy Levin, USA

● *Above*

A young girl displays her First Communion dress for friends near Claremorris, County Mayo.
Photographer:
Raphaël Gaillarde, France

● *Above*

The day before their first Holy Communion, twin brothers Seosaimh and Dara Ó hIarlaithe practice their most angelic smiles at St. Joseph's National School in Dingle. Ninety-four percent of the Republic's population is Catholic.
Photographer:
Annie Griffiths Belt, USA

● *Right*

Children learn traditional Irish dance under the tutelage of 82-year-old Dan Furey, who comes to their school in Labasheeda once a week to play the fiddle and teach the steps. Dance instruction is an integral part of physical education classes in Ireland. These students, who are learning a combination of jigs and reels known as the "Clare Sets," stand to join a growing list of Furey pupils who have gone on to win awards at *fheiseanna*—dance and music festivals—all over Ireland.
Photographer:
Gerd Ludwig, Germany

● *Left*

Gotcha! Niall Cawley, 11, uses a rural squirt gun on his brother David, 9, as mother Nora and brothers Tony, 7, and Stephen, 3, look on. It's never hard to find a brother or sister to tease around the family farm in Westport: Nora and her husband Michael have 14 children of their own, plus a neighbor's child they took in after his mother died. Meals on the 63-acre farm are served in shifts, and all the kids help out with the chores before and after school.
Photographer:
Don Doll, S.J., USA

● *Below, left*

Style savvy comes at an early age to brothers Jason and Darren O'Driscoll, aged five and two, of the Mitchels Crescent housing estate in Tralee, County Kerry.
Photographer:
Bradley Clift, USA

● *Below*

Neil Johnston and William Spence devise a makeshift playground along Riga Street, off the Shankill Road in Belfast. Neil and William face uncertain odds as their education continues: in 1990, only 13 students in their district progressed to selective secondary schools; fully half the children in the district left school with no academic credentials at all.
Photographer:
James Meehan, Ireland

● *Right*

Music is a way of life for punk rockers Emily Dawson and Deko Doyle of the Paranoid Visions, but it's no way to make a living. "It's more to do with expressing ourselves," says Doyle, wearing the leather collar. To conserve cash, the couple share a tiny "bedsit" apartment in Dublin's Rathmines district. Doyle makes a little extra money as a sound engineer for the F.O.A.D. record label that produced the group's four records, while Emily works part-time cleaning houses. Both receive government assistance as well.

For years, Doyle and his friends encountered hostility from hooligans, vigilantes, and the law, treatment which Doyle attributes mostly to their appearance. As the band has gained exposure in newspapers and on television, however, attitudes have changed. "Once people get to know you, they aren't afraid," he says. Here one fearless neighbor stops to chat with Deko and Emily and their friends David Murphy ("Plop"), Skittles Bates, and James Davern.
Photographer:
Paul Chesley, USA

● *Above*

The spirit of a traditional Irish wake—intended to bid good-bye in as joyous and festive a manner as friends and relatives could provide—lives on in many a grand and colorful grave. The cemetery in Quilty, County Clare, is the site of an elaborate floral shrine to the memory of Peggy Downes.

Photographer:
Stephanie Maze, USA

● *Right*

After digging the grave them-selves, James Ward's friends and neighbors in the small village of Arigna, County Leitrim, carry his body to the village cemetery for burial. Ward, 81, worked in the local coal mine, which shut down in 1990, leaving most of the villagers unemployed.

Photographer:
**Crispin Rodwell,
Great Britain**

● *Following pages 146-147*

Her walls a shrine to her family and her faith, Mary Moran of County Mayo says the rosary while son Tommy has a cup of tea. As often as her health permits, Mary visits the shrine at nearby Knock, where parishioners reported seeing an apparition of the Virgin Mary on August 21, 1879. One hundred years later, Pope John Paul II came to Knock on the first-ever trip to Ireland by a Pope.

Photographer:

Raphaël Gaillarde, France

● *Following pages 148-149*

In northeastern Ireland, spring arrives with a burst of color as fields of rape, known in the United States as colza, come into flower. Its seeds are pressed elsewhere in Europe to make an oil for cooking, sometimes marketed as "canola" oil.

Photographer:

Doug Menuez, USA

● *Left*

The Reverend Robert E. Lee offers an alternate form of confession, known as "reconciliation," at his parish church, Cill Treasa (Church of Theresa), in Ros a Mhíl, County Galway. While confession is traditionally heard in a darkened booth, with a grille separating priest and penitent, Father Lee says face-to-face reconciliation is "grand"—and, he insists, "quite private." But it's not private enough for many of his parishioners, especially older churchgoers, who continue to opt for the darkness and ostensible anonymity of the traditional confession box.

Photographer:

Bruno Barbey, France

● *Above*

Eileen French and her daughter Joanne attend regular sessions at the Derry Well Woman center. The center offers courses in nutrition, stress management, child health, and other subjects as well as counseling, support groups, and referrals for women in Derry and the surrounding area.

Photographer:

Eli Reed, USA

Raphaël Gaillarde

Doug Menuez

D on't expect Michael and Joan Curtin to expound on the bucolic joys of life down on the farm. Like many thousands of farmers in Ireland, the Curtins, of Kinshanny, County Clare, know all too well the odds against them—from the vagaries of the harvest to the prices they'll get for their cattle. And with 11 children to support, most of whom work on the farm themselves already, there is little room for error.

Farming is big business in Ireland, accounting for more than 10 percent of GNP and over 40 percent of all exports—and yet it hangs by a thread, dependent on the muscles and endurance of families like the Curtins. Only about one-fifth of family-operated farms generate income greater than £10,000 per year for their owners; three-fifths produce less than £5,000. With the aging of the rural population and the consolidation of farmlands into larger, more efficient units, many of the smaller operations will undoubtedly vanish in years to come. That doesn't make things any easier, however, for those who remain. The unification of European markets, in particular, comes as a double-edged sword. While opening up new markets for Irish farm products, it puts families like the Curtins in direct competition with large farming enterprises hundreds or thousands of miles away—businesses offering economies of scale unknown in County Clare.

Above, Joan and Michael Curtin line up with *most* of their brood. From left: Róisín, 2; Donncha, 8; Madeline, 6; Fergus, 17; Martina, 18; Conor, 15; Sinéad, 12; Gráinne, 10; Stephen, 11. Missing: Siobhán, 16, and Deirdre, 14. At right, getting to bedtime comes down to a test of wills between Michael and Róisín. *Photo essay by:* **David C. Turnley, USA**

Meals come in shifts in the Curtin household. The kitchen table only seats four or five, and Joan starts cooking in the early hours to get the whole pack off to school on time. After school, it's time for tea; Stephen takes care of Donncha while Madeline waits her turn. Róisín, of course, waits for no one.

After having their tea, the children head out to do chores. Stephen brings his father sandwiches and a bottle of hot tea with milk, wrapped in a sock to retain the warmth out on the bogs. Taking advantage of the light, Michael will work late into the evening in the exhausting task of cutting turf by hand.

David C. Turnley

● *Right*

The castellated mock-Tudor outlines of Kylemore Abbey loom large in western Connemara, where 175 girls from Ireland, Spain, Mexico, the Netherlands, France, Germany, Sweden, and the United States come to attend the prestigious school operated by sisters of the Benedictine order. The foreign students, and those from other parts of Ireland, live on site, paying tuition as they would for any other boarding school; for a few lucky Irish girls, however, Kylemore is the local high school, and fees are covered by the state. The abbey's location in a remote, misty region insures that aside from schoolwork, little remains to distract the young mind— though an occasional gab session isn't out of the question.
Photographer:
Roseanne McGregor, Ireland

For hundreds of Irish schoolchildren, May 17, 1991 was a day to remember. At the Belfast Telegraph/Kodak Workshop and the Evening Press/Kodak Dublin Workshop, each received a Kodak 335 camera, two rolls of Ektapress film, and a lesson from one of the world's great photographers. Some of their best work appears here, selected from more than 450 rolls exposed by Ireland's photojournalists of the future.

Niall Kearney, 10, Stillorgan

Melissa Lynch, 8, Dublin

Kaitriona Kelly, 10, Dublin

Garrett Fitzgerald, 10, Belfast

Rachel Anne Andrews, 10, Ballycarry

Carla Mohan, 11, Belfast

Sarah Wallace, 11, Monkstown

Brian Holland, 9, Lucan

Kellie McAllister, 14, Belfast

Joanne Treacy, 11, Blackrock

Ryan Rogan, 11, Belfast

Sharon Carty, 11, Celbridge

● *Left*

Horsing around near Shannon,
County Limerick.
Photographer:
Volker Hinz, Germany

● *Left*

Horse racing is serious business in the Curragh, a grassy basin in County Kildare renowned as a base for training and breeding some of the world's finest animals. Groundwater percolating up through layers of limestone yields a high-calcium drink to build strong equine bones, and an abundance of natural turf makes for ideal running surfaces. Here two young jockeys at the John Ox stable go over their training schedule for the day.
Photographer:
Jay Dickman, USA

● *Below and following page*

Competition is keen both on and off the track as a steeple-chase event gets under way in Dundalk. About 350 licensed bookmakers roam a circuit of Irish horse tracks throughout the racing season, taking bets from all comers and paying out on the spot. A government-backed Racing Board runs its own betting operation, known

as the Tote, but five times as much business passes through the hands of the private bookies. Together, the two systems turned over £120 million in 1990. Another £300 million passed through off-track betting parlors strategically situated on streetcorners throughout the land.

Photographer:
Diego Goldberg, Argentina

Diego Goldberg

Fresh from a spin around the village of Cill Rónain, Dublin school girls Heather Victors, Siobhán Kane, and Aoife O'Halloran chat with local resident Rory Beatty in front of the bike shop where he works. Tourism, fishing, and the manufacture of the distinctive Aran sweaters are the main industries here on Inis Mór, largest of the Aran Islands off Ireland's west coast. Some things have changed little since playwright John Millington Synge visited the island and memorialized its natives nearly a century ago: the 300 or so residents still speak Irish, and continue to look upon the mainland as a slightly foreign land, separated from them by more than waves alone.
Photographer:
Monica Almeida, USA

● *Above and right*

Get me to the church on time: As her five-year-old son Brian looks on, Mary Morrissey performs a last-minute repair to her sister Letitia's dress (*right*) before they set off for Letitia's May 17 wedding to Terry Walsh in Kilkenny. Later, at the reception, a tired Brian—who served as page boy at the wedding—leans against his mother on the dance floor, while Terry, his tie askew, celebrates with old friend Peter Byrne. The tie between Letitia and Terry is meant to last: divorce is prohibited by the Republic's Constitution, and a 1986 referendum to amend the law was voted down by nearly a 2-1 margin.
Photographer:
Joe McNally, USA

● *Following page*

Delia and Jack Davis of Lakyle,
County Clare evoke a poem by
William Butler Yeats:

*When you are old and grey and full
of sleep,*
*And nodding by the fire, take down
this book,*
*And slowly read, and dream of the
soft look*
*Your eyes had once, and of their
shadows deep ...*

Photographer:
Gerd Ludwig, Germany

Patrick Tehan

● *Previous page*

Looming off the coast of County Kerry, the two rock formations known as the Skellig Islands are often called "the last parish before Brooklyn." The only parishioners allowed on Little Skellig are birds, 18,000 gannets and puffins for which the island is an official sanctuary. Visitors are welcome on the larger Great Skellig, however—home to the remains of St. Finian's Abbey, one of the oldest monastic sites in the Christian world. The larger island is also known as Skellig Michael, in honor of Saint Michael, patron of high places and guardian against the powers of darkness.
Photographer:
Patrick Tehan, USA

● *Right*

Since medieval times, when St. Patrick is said to have fasted for 40 days at this site, Catholic pilgrims have come to Lough Derg in Donegal to contemplate the language and mysteries of the soul. Guides like caretaker Jamesie Monaghan take the visitors from the shore of the lake to tiny Station Island, one-half mile out, where for three days they eat only dry bread and drink black tea, travel barefoot, sleep in spartan conditions, and spend their conscious hours engaged in a ritual of prayer. Seamus Heaney's long poem "Station Island" is based in part upon this voyage, which thousands make each year.
Photographer:
Alan Lewis, Ireland

Famed women's fashion designer Richard Lewis holds forth from the sofa as Ireland's glitterati gather to share gossip and drinks at the home of art collectors Cecil and Monika Murray, in Dublin's Rathgar District. The German-born Murray, clasping the hand of a guest from her perch next to Lewis, later recalled the evening as "a good Irish party: we scheduled it from 6:00 to 8:00 p.m., but most people didn't show until 7:30 and didn't leave until 11:30."
Photographer:
Paul Chesley, USA

Life imitates art outside Clerys, one of Ireland's leading department stores. For generations, the centrally-located store on O'Connell Street has served as a meeting place for Dubliners, who rendezvous beneath its outdoor clock before going off for the evening—or catching the bus home.
Photographer:
Steve McCurry, USA

● *Left*

Since the Gulf War, Paddy Burke has taken a lot of kidding from regulars at the pub he owns on Clear Island, at the southern tip of Ireland, for his resemblance to a well-known American general. "People have taken to calling me Norman," he says.
Photographer:
Eddie Adams, USA

● *Above*

Historians say that when the English soldiers of Henry II first arrived in Ireland in the 12th century, they raved about the charms of a drink called *uisce beatha* (literally, "waters of life"). The word *uisce* may be the source of the English word "whiskey"; in any event, off-duty British soldiers in Northern Ireland can still be found celebrating the joys of an ancient custom.
Photographer:
Mark S. Wexler, USA

● *Left*

Sheep farmer Alex O'Boyle
and retired sea diver John
Murray enjoy a pint at Hugh
McIlwaine's Mariner's Bar in
Waterfoot, County Antrim.
Proprietor McIlwaine had
sailed around the world by
the age of 17, and eight years
later was one of Ireland's
youngest sea captains. When
his father died a decade ago,
McIlwaine came home to
run the family pub.
Photographer:
Brendan Murphy, Ireland

● Far left

The Most Reverend John Buckley, Auxiliary Bishop of Cork, puts a little body Irish into his follow-through in a road bowling match against Frank Nash, Lord Mayor of Cork. Players in the ancient game—which has survived only in counties Cork and Armagh—hurl a 28-ounce metal ball over a long course laid out over public roads. The goal: to reach the end of the course with the least number of tosses, or lofts.

Photographer:
Eric Lars Bakke, USA

● Above

Fans call hurling, Ireland's national game, the fastest team sport in the world. Players on the 15-member teams use sticks called "hurleys" to move a leather ball three inches in diameter toward the opponent's goal, where they try to send it either over the crossbar, for a point, or under the crossbar— a far more difficult feat—for a three-point goal. Here the Kilcormac team in County Offaly, one of about 3,000 local clubs in Ireland competing under the auspices of the Gaelic Athletic Association, or GAA, hones its skills.

Photographer:
George Steinmetz, USA

● Left

There's no such thing as a professional hurler—even on the best teams, all the players are amateurs—but that doesn't stop Irish boys from dreaming of making it to the top, or Irish grandfathers from teaching them the basics of the game. While soccer and Gaelic football compete for the title of Ireland's most popular sport, hurling is certainly the most ancient: some historians have traced the game back to the second century before Christ. Girls and women play a slightly scaled-down—but equally robust—version of the game known as camogie.

Photographer:
Andy Levin, USA

Randy Olson

● *Previous page*

Legend has it that the Rock of Cashel, which rises 200 feet above the surrounding plain in County Tipperary, was formed when the Devil, flying overhead with a rock in his mouth, saw Saint Patrick preparing to build a new church and opened his mouth in shock—dropping the stone to the ground. Nowadays, the Rock is dominated by a Romanesque church, a medieval cathedral, a 12th-century Round Tower, and a 15th-century Hall of Vicars.
Photographer:
Randy Olson, USA

● *Left*

Meals are a time of thanks for the Stuarts of Kiltamagh in County Mayo—Michael, Angela, and their 11 children. Angela credits their faith for seeing them through hard times since Michael was laid off from his job at a nearby textile factory several years ago: the whole brood goes to Mass twice weekly, and to the shrine at nearby Knock several times a year.
Photographer:
Raphaël Gaillarde, France

● *Above*

Decked out in a goalkeeper's jersey from England's popular Liverpool Football Club, 12-year-old Michael Finn watches television on the family farm near Thurles in County Tipperary. The Republic of Ireland has two state television stations, but viewers in many parts of the country can also pick up four British channels and eight British satellite stations—making the exploits of Roseanne, Cliff Huxtable, Sam and Diane, Bart Simpson, and Phil and Oprah as familiar in Ireland as anywhere in the world.
Photographer:
Randy Olson, USA

● *Right*

"Our kitchen is our living room," says Bernadette Duhig of Limerick City as she curls daughter Elizabeth's hair on the eve of the seven-year-old's First Communion. "It's the biggest room in the house, so the kids play in here." As nine-year-old Martin steals a snack, father Patrick hoists Lynsey, 2, on a broom handle. Elsewhere in the kitchen frolic two other red-clad two-year-olds, Luke and Lee, who are identical twins born along with Lynsey. "It was a shock at first," says Bernadette of bearing triplets, "but it's worked out well. Patrick and I are just mad about the kids." Luke, she says, is inclined to be bossy toward the more placid Lee. Mischievous Lynsey, however, is the terror of them both: "She kills the two boys," Bernadette laughs. "She's a bully."

Photographer:
Dana Fineman, USA

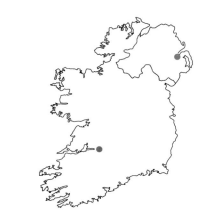

● *Left*

Limerick, its residents say, is home to Ireland's most beautiful women, lending cachet to the annual Miss Limerick contest. With a helping hand from stylist Dave Murphy, 16-year-old Mary Hogan prepares for the swimsuit segment of the competition. The judges later disqualified Hogan for not meeting the contest's minimum age requirement of 17—but not without encouraging her to come back next year.
Photographer:
Dana Fineman, USA

● *Above*

Actors Richard Attlee and P.S. Gibbon of the English Shakespeare Company prepare for an evening performance of Ben Jonson's *Volpone* at the Grand Opera House in Belfast.
Photographer:
James Meehan, Ireland

● *Above*

Nicknamed "The Housewife's Choice" because of his long-running morning radio show, Gay Byrne works a night shift too: he's the host of the "Late Late Show," the Friday evening program that critics have called the most influential in the history of Irish television. An estimated one-third of Ireland's viewing public tunes in each week as Byrne, here interviewing author Patricia Scanlon, chats up the stars—and discusses political and social issues—as he has for the past 30 years.
Photographer:
Jean-Pierre Laffont, France

● *Right*

You can go home again: Although urban development has destroyed many of their homes and old haunts along Dublin's Buckingham Street, dozens of people who grew up in the neighborhood return on Friday nights to play bingo at Macushla Hall. One of the largest and most raucous bingo games in Dublin, it is populated by characters straight from the pages of a Sean O'Casey play—who depend on the weekly event to keep in touch with old friends. All proceeds from the game go to benefit the foreign missions of the Passionist order.
Photographer:
Lynn Johnson, USA

● *Above*

The three men and a lady of the band Engine Alley rev it up during a gig at the Bridge Hotel in Waterford. The lads, from Kilkenny—Eamonn Byrne on bass, Canice Williams on vocals, and Brian Kenealy on lead guitar—joined 17-year-old Emmaline Duffy Fallon from Dublin, who handles the drums, to form the band in 1989. Engine Alley recently signed an international record deal with Mother Records, a label set up by U2 to help promote new Irish rock talent.
Photographer:
Rick Rickman, USA

● *Right*

Carrying a drum weighing more than 30 pounds, a member of Lodge 770 of the Orange Order practices for a competition in Crewe, County Antrim. Contestants are judged on tone and rhythm in their use of the Lambeg drums—modified versions of those used in William III's victory in 1690 at the Battle of the Boyne. Each year on July 12, some 100,000 members of the Orange Order march in deafening parades at locations all over Northern Ireland.
Photographer:
Barry Lewis, Great Britain

● *Right*

On Achill Island in County Mayo, a 21st-birthday surprise party comes with a twist: the invasion of eight Strawboys in hats of straw and long white gowns. The custom is said to date back to the 18th century, when masked rustlers preying on a landlord's cattle escaped capture by ducking into a packed wedding celebration and joining in for a dance or two. Today's Strawboys come equipped with an accordionist and a repertoire of traditional steps to entertain the guests.

Photographer:
Michael Bryant, USA

● *Above*

Former All-Ireland fiddle champion Jim McKillop fires up a reel at a house party in Broughshane, where guests stayed until 4:00 in the morning playing accordions, guitars, banjos, fiddles, and the shallow goat-skin drum known as a *bodhrán*. Traditional music today ranks among Ireland's leading cultural exports, a phenomenon many observers trace to the efforts of noted composer and jazz pianist John Reidy. As musical director of the Abbey Theatre in the mid-1950s, Reidy formed an orchestra of traditional musicians, the Ceoltóirí Chualann, to relearn and re-arrange traditional tunes. Reidy soon adopted the Irish version of his name, Seán Ó Riada; after his death in 1971, a group of musicians from his original orchestra went on to gain international fame under their new name, the Chieftains.
Photographer:
Barry Lewis, Great Britain

● *Above*

Music transcends political and religious differences in a Belfast kitchen, where a self-described "psycho country" band known as Ten Wheels for Jesus rehearses for an upcoming club date. It's not unusual for Catholics and Protestants in Northern Ireland to play in bands together, says Ten Wheels guitarist Paddy Calvert: "The music," he says, "is an escape from all that." The Irish and Scottish base of much of American bluegrass and country music is now celebrated by musicians on both sides of the Atlantic, and traditional chords and tunes figure prominently in the contemporary music of bands including the Waterboys, U2, and the Pogues, and in the singing of Christy Moore, Mary Black, Sinéad O'Connor, and Van Morrison.

Photographer:
Andy Levin, USA

● *Above*

Dublin women give new
meaning to the term "pool
party" as they applaud a model
showing off the latest in bikini-
wear. The women had spent
most of the evening buying
lingerie at a sales party inside
a private home before retiring
to the empty swimming pool
out back for the grand finale.
Photographer:
Tom Lawlor, Ireland

● *Right*

As on any Friday night in
Ireland, entertainment-seekers
on the 17th of May found no
lack of diversions. In Belfast, it
was Rhythm & Blues Night at
Nelson Mandela Hall on the
campus of Queen's University.
In Dublin, a German expres-
sionist version of O'Casey's
The Plough and the Stars (in which
all the leading women sported
shaven heads) filled the Abbey,
and a brilliant exhibition of
political art found an unusual
venue at the old Kilmainham
Jail. Out in Milltown Malbay,
it was enough to dance the old
Clare Sets once more, to the
tune of the fiddle and pipes.
Photographer:
Stephanie Maze, USA

Prime time at a Travellers site in Tullamore, County Offaly.
Photographer: **George Steinmetz, USA**

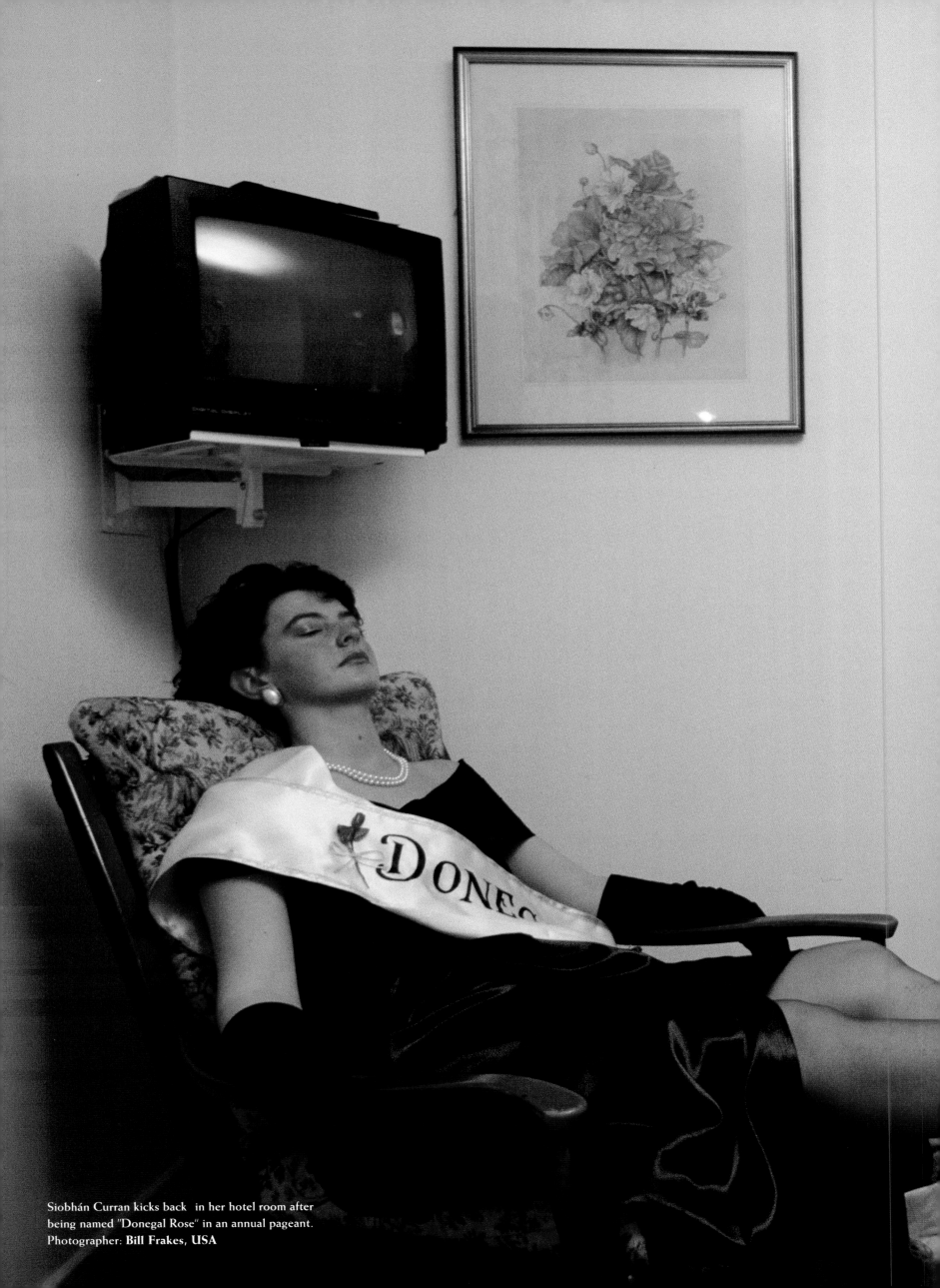

Siobhán Curran kicks back in her hotel room after
being named "Donegal Rose" in an annual pageant.
Photographer: **Bill Frakes**, USA

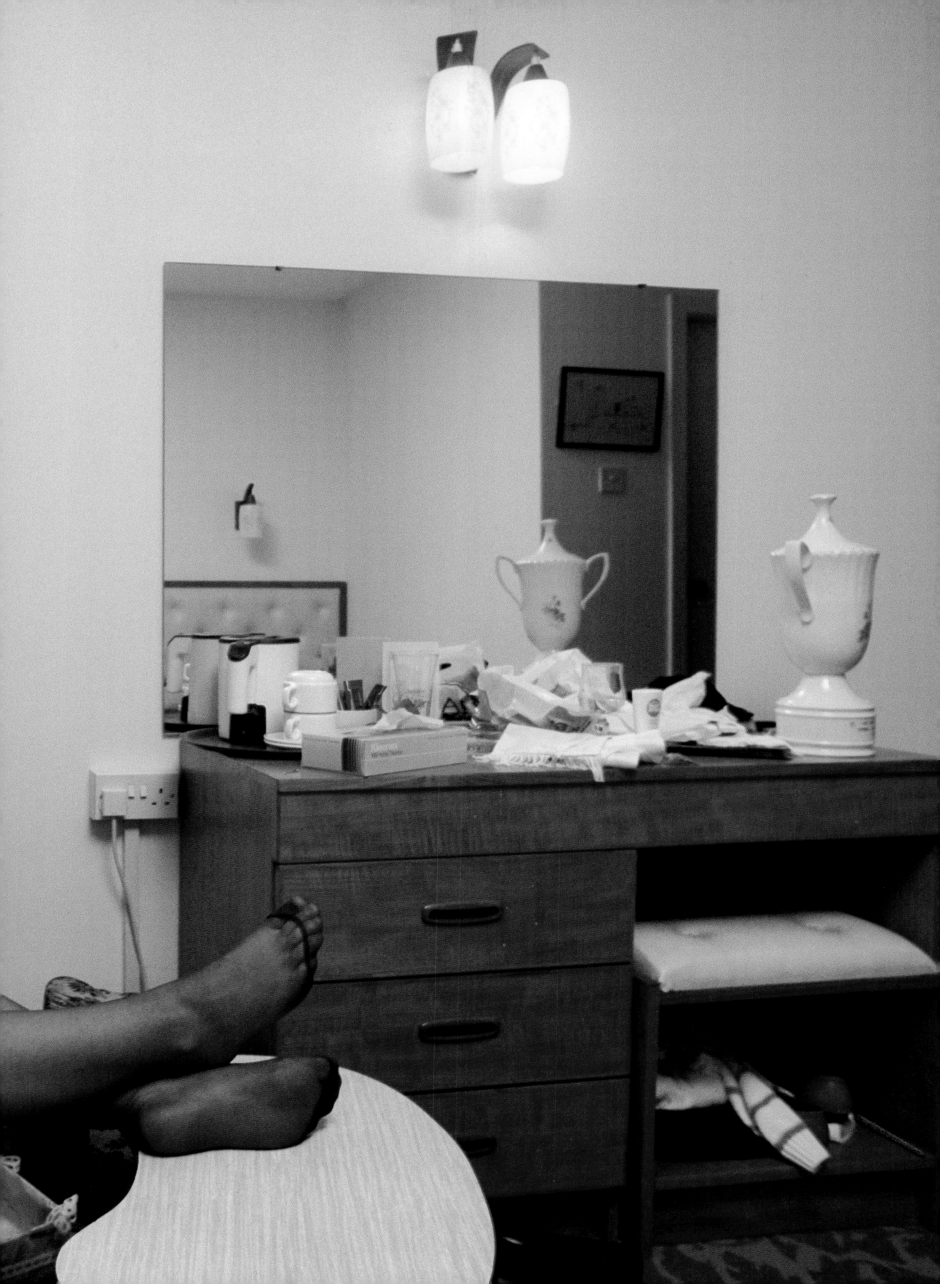

INCEPTVM EDWARD·F·VI· AN·I

Steve Krongard

Photographer Locations

To shoot *A Day in the Life of Ireland*, more than 75 photographers from 13 countries flew to and from Ireland on one carrier—Ireland's own Aer Lingus. With its extensive route network, modern equipment, and staff of 7,000 serving 4 million passengers each year, no airline was better equipped to handle the extraordinary requirements of this uniquely Irish undertaking.

1 Eddie Adams
2 Monica Almeida
3 Eric Lars Bakke
4 Bruno Barbey
5 Nicole Bengiveno
6 P.F. Bentley
7 Torin Boyd
8 Michael Bryant
9 Mike Bunn
10 Cyril Byrne
11 Simon Callan
12 John Carlos
13 Paul Chesley
14 Bradley Clift
15 Pedro Coll
16 Guglielmo de' Micheli
17 Jay Dickman
18 Don Doll, S.J.
19 Elliott Erwitt
20 Misha Erwitt
21 Tina Etheridge
22 Brian Farrell

23 Dana Fineman
24 Gerry Fitzgerald
25 James Fraher
26 Bill Frakes
27 Raphaël Gaillarde
28 Sam Garcia
29 Georg Gerster
30 Diego Goldberg
31 Bill Greene
32 Annie Griffiths Belt
33 Volker Hinz
34 Graciela Iturbide
35 Kenneth J. Jarecke
36 Lynn Johnson
37 Péter Korniss
38 Steve Krongard
39 Jean-Pierre Laffont
40 Brian Lanker
41 Tom Lawlor

42 Andy Levin
43 Alan Lewis
44 Barry Lewis
45 John Loengard
46 Gerd Ludwig
47 Michael Lutzky
48 Mary Ellen Mark
49 John Marmaras
50 Gary Matoso
51 Stephanie Maze
52 Steve McCurry
53 Roseanne McGregor
54 Joe McNally
55 James Meehan
56 Doug Menuez
57 Claus C. Meyer
58 Frank Miller
59 Kai H. Mui
60 Brendan Murphy
61 Nutan
62 Randy Olson
63 Chuck O'Rear

64 Joe O'Shaughnessy
65 Tony O'Shea
66 Graeme Outerbridge
67 David Peterson
68 Bill Pierce
69 Eli Reed
70 Jim Richardson
71 Rick Rickman
72 Crispin Rodwell
73 Galen Rowell
74 Joe St. Leger
75 Rick Smolan
76 George Steinmetz
77 Billy Stickland
78 Patrick Tehan
79 Joyce Tenneson
80 David C. Turnley
81 Peter Turnley
82 Mark S. Wexler

Sam Garcia, Cork

Torin Boyd, Donegal

P.F. Bentley, Antrim

Cyril Byrne, Cavan

Kai H. Mui, Wicklow

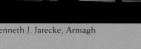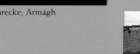

Kenneth J. Jarecke, Armagh

Tina Etheridge, Laois

Brian Farrell, Donegal

Graeme Outerbridge, Derry

Graciela Iturbide, Tyrone

• Tory Island/81

Ballycastle/6

• Buncrana/7

Portstewart/66

• Derry/69

• Glens of Antrim/60

• Finner Camp/22

DERRY

• Ballymena/44

• Letterkenny/26

ANTRIM

DONEGAL

• Lough Neagh/15

• Killybegs/37

TYRONE

• Belfast/5,20,42,55

• Lough Derg/43

• Omagh/34

• Manorhamilton/67

• Enniskillen/82

ARMAGH

DOWN

• Culleens/25

• Sligo/38

TERMANAGH

• Monaghan/50

• Castlewellan/56

• Killala/11

SLIGO

MONAGHAN

• Ballyconnell/10

• Crossmaglen/35

• Rostrevor/24

• Keel/8

• Lough Arrow/9

CAVAN

• Dundalk/30

• Carrick-on-Shannon/72

LEITRIM

MAYO

• Westport/18

• Knock/27

ROSCOMMON

LONGFORD

LOUTH

• Kells/77

• Longford/79

• Kylemore Abbey/53

MEATH

• Mosney/47

Roundstone/64

WESTMEATH

• Mullingar/12

• Kilkieran/4

GALWAY

• Maynooth/45

• Galway/29,49

• Dublin/13,36,39,41,48,
52,58,65,68

DUBLIN

• Inishmore/2

OFFALY

KILDARE

• Birr/76

• The Curragh/17

• Glendalough/57

• Lisdoonvarna/80

• Doolin/40

LAOIS

• Ballyhnan/21

WICKLOW

CLARE

• Milltown Malbay/51

CARLOW

• Arklow/59

• Limerick/23,33

TIPPERARY

• Kilkenny/54

• Labasheeda/46

• Thurles/62

KILKENNY

LIMERICK

WEXFORD

• Tralee/14

• Dingle/32

• Waterford/71

• Killorglin/61

• Killarney/78

WATERFORD

• Dungarvan/16

KERRY

CORK

• Ballinskelligs/73

• Cork/31,63,75

• Ballincollig/3

• Shanagarry/19

• Kinsale/28

• Clonakilty/70

• Naval patrol/74

James Fraher, Sligo

• Cape Clear/1

Bill Greene, Cork

Joe St. Leger, Cork

John Marmaras, Galway

Bill Pierce, Dublin

Tony O'Shea, Dublin

1. Eric Lars Bakke

1. Karen Bakke and Linda Lamb start setting up at the *Day in the Life* offices in Dublin.

2. Linda Lamb

2. The first wave of project staff arrives on site. Harry Browne, Lynn Geldof, Monica Baltz, Róisín Hannigan, Lisa Pereira, Patti Richards, Jennifer Erwitt, Bill Messing, Tom Lawlor, Jim Jennings.
3. Jennifer Erwitt, Patti Richards, and Bill Messing take advantage of a lithic feature atop a grassy crag in Kerry.
4. Lynn Geldof and Lisa Pereira work out assignments with Tom Lawlor.
5. Cathy Quealy and Monica Baltz reconnoiter the coastline at Glasdrumman, County Down.

3. Rick Smolan

4. Rick Smolan

5. Jennifer Barry

I n the early hours of May 17, 1991, Doug Menuez, an award-winning American photographer from Mill Valley, California, found himself riding along country roads in County Down in Northern Ireland, following a local milk carrier as she travelled about on her morning routes. Menuez was only one of more than 75 internationally-acclaimed photographers moving quickly now in the approaching Irish dawn.

Menuez had come to County Down as a photographer for *A Day in the Life of Ireland*, the renowned book series which commenced with *A Day in the Life of Australia* 10 years ago. Over the years, shoots in China, the Soviet Union, the USA, and seven other locations had won high praise for the series around the world. While everything about this project had been planned in great detail in the months, weeks, days, and hours leading up to this actual moment, Menuez, a veteran of eight of these shoots, was already beginning to improvise.

"You stop to talk to somebody, you're in a big hurry, and all you want is one piece of information," Menuez would recall during a debriefing session the next day in Dublin, "and instead you find out about 20 different things. This went on all day for the three days I was there." The milkwoman was only the first in a series of assigned subjects Menuez was due to shoot on May 17. Others included the ferry across Strangford Lough and an initiation ceremony at an Orange Order junior lodge. Serendipity plays a central role in every *Day in the Life* shoot, though, and anything else he might find would be fair game.

"I found out where people ride their horses on the beach for exercise. I found out about a new helicopter school, the only one in Northern Ireland. And then I found out about this huntsman. He's a very prominent local character. He looks as though he's lived a very fast, full, extraordinary life with the richest people in the world. He was with the Bass family and the Pulitzer family in St. Louis, running hunts for them. First I got him working with the dogs. I got down on dog level, and the dogs are very sensitive, very skittish. No, not dogs. They're called hounds. They look like big beagles. And here's this guy, this grand old gray-haired guy on a white stallion with 50 hounds and another stallion behind him, and they're coming down the lane with hedges on either side, and we pass this bright yellow colza field in flower, beneath the mountains of Mourne. It was really rich visually. We're not trying to shoot clichés. But when you're out in the countryside of Ireland, it's beautiful."

A Belfast-based photographer for Britain's *Daily Mail*, Alan Lewis, was delighted to see the foreign photographers like Menuez coming to Ireland with their eyes open. "When they arrived, I thought some of them might go looking for stereotypes," says Lewis. In most of the country, that means thatched cottages and misty fields of green; in Northern Ireland, perhaps, it means predictable images of conflict. "In talking to them afterward," says Lewis, "I found that people whose assignments didn't work out still came back with nice pictures. Some of them said they'd be back to do more work on their own. And I sure didn't hear anyone complaining about the kind of reception they got."

Improvisation was not part of Lewis's strategy. Using local contacts built up over many years, he worked out 12 different assignments for himself, covering more ground on the shoot day while travelling from Belfast to Donegal than did any of the other photographers. "Trying to squeeze everything in was like a military operation. But the contacts I had lined up were brilliant. I made sure I was always at a place within 15 or 20 minutes of schedule, and they were all exactly where they had to be."

Lewis had ideal weather for his morning visit to the Harland and Wolff shipyards in Belfast; as he moved west, though, the clouds closed in, and his Lough Derg sunset didn't materialize. But not to worry: "The two caretakers had gone out and turned on every light in the premises. It had taken them an hour and a half. When I left at 11:00 p.m., they were going back out to turn them all off." For Alan Lewis, this was clearly a day in a lifetime: "It gave me an opportunity to take shots that wouldn't get in my own paper, to indulge myself—in the company of other photographers whom we here have admired for years."

A Day in the Life of Ireland is surely not *Ulysses*, but the masterpiece by Irishman James Joyce does bear similarities to the book you hold in your hand. The novel takes place from morning to midnight on a single day (some 87 years too soon), unfolding its insights from within the minds of a few quite ordinary, though memorable, Dublin characters.

In Labasheeda, County Clare, German photographer Gerd Ludwig came upon one such character in the local schoolmaster, Frank O'Dea. "One thing was very hard to get across," Ludwig explained in Dublin, the day after the shoot. "When I got to Labasheeda, everyone wanted to show me the landscape and seaside. It took me a long time to get past that. But my contact was really great. Frank O'Dea is the principal of the local school. He is also one of the teachers. I shot a lot on him. In a way he is a typical schoolteacher. He always stands with his feet at a 90-degree angle. Belly in, chest out.

"I actually sneaked into his bedroom in the morning, before he and his wife Philomena woke up, and just started shooting as he was lying there in bed yawning. He was very nice not to kick me right out of there. After he got up, his tie around his neck but not tied yet, I photographed him as he stood in the kitchen shaving with an electric shaver. Because the plug kept coming out of the wall, he had to stand there shaving with one arm held out to hold it in.

"I shot a lot in the school itself. Then an 80-year-old fellow, Dan Furey, came to school to play the fiddle, and teach Irish dance to the students. Little ones doing Irish dance. And then an Irish lesson. People were very friendly. At another dance that night, they gave a speech, and I got a little love letter from a girl at the school—a thank-you note with drawings of flowers, and a message: 'We'll remember you for a long time'."

For these photographers, the Irish certainly lived up to their reputation for hospitality—hardly surprising, given the excitement that even an album of photographs generates in so many Irish homes. But what sort of experience was this for their hosts? Tom and Breda Kirwan, together with their children Mandy, Laura, and Anna, hosted *Day in the Life* newcomer Tina Etheridge, from the US, at their home in County Laois. "Tina was just lovely," says Breda. "She was obviously very excited the night before the shoot, and she didn't have a lot to say." Six-year-old Mandy was especially thrilled when she arrived at school the next day with a personal photographer in tow.

After an exhausting shoot, Etheridge arrived back at the Kirwans' home and plopped down with Tom and Breda in front of the TV. "She was like a different person, so relaxed, and chatting away with us." The hard part for all concerned came on the 18th, when the photographer had to get back to Dublin to deliver her film; she stayed with the Kirwans for the morning, took a long walk with them, and left with new friends and a new fascination with a side of Ireland and a part of the country which tourists rarely see. The Kirwans were charmed.

Not every photographer is so lucky. Even some *Day in the Life* veterans had to throw up their hands at times as prepared assignments went haywire. Diego Goldberg of Argentina was the victim of just such an assignment while trying to photograph a chicken farm at dawn in County Louth.

"The shoot was scheduled from 4:30 to 6:30 a.m. There were 7,000 chickens there ready to be picked up and taken away. The chickens each have to be picked up by hand while they're asleep. Otherwise they start running around, and it would be a mess. It was a mess anyway. The stench was unbelievable, mostly ammonia. We all wore masks. It was surreal. Ridiculous. We were all in this huge shed, 60 meters long by 20 meters wide, full of chickens, in total pitch darkness. I couldn't see my hands in front of me.

"Because it was so dark, I asked the guy, 'Can you turn the lights on a little?' So he would turn the lights on a little bit, just a faint

6. Rick Smolan

7. Cathy Quealy

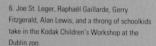

6. Joe St. Leger, Raphaël Gaillarde, Gerry Fitzgerald, Alan Lewis, and a throng of schoolkids take in the Kodak Children's Workshop at the Dublin zoo.
7. The Children's Workshop in Belfast came with its own parachute.
8. Jean-Pierre Laffont imparts a few trade secrets to a workshop participant in Dublin.
9. Jenny Barry and Carole Bidnick make a new acquaintance in Belfast.

8. Cyril Byrne

9. Andrew J. Hathaway

10. Bill Kirk

10. Photographers shooting in Northern Ireland converged at the Crown Bar in Belfast before setting off on assignment.

213

11. Andrew J. Hathaway

12. P.F. Bentley

11. Barry Lewis digs into his last repast before the shooting begins.

12. Many hands make light work as the book goes together in San Francisco.

13. Misha Erwitt

13. Eli Reed and Andy Levin settle in for the ride from Dublin to Belfast.

14. Steve Krongard and Andrew Hathaway take a break following the group portrait at the Government Buildings in Dublin.

15. Galen Rowell gets close with an historic personage.

14. Pedro Coll

15. Paul Chesley

glow inside, and all the chickens would wake up and go 'buck, buck, buck'. Then he would turn it down again, and they would go 'do, do, do', and go back to sleep. And then he would try again, and they would all start up again. So I shot from the hip. It was so dark I doubt if I got a thing." Goldberg, thankfully, would have better luck that afternoon at the horse races in Dundalk.

It is an article of faith among the *Day in the Life* organizers that each photographer selected for the shoot has the talent to turn potential disasters like Diego Goldberg's into spontaneous acts of genius improvisation. If one assignment isn't working—and the lack of any light whatsoever can be a problem—photographers are instructed just to move on to the next.

Photographers go into the field with as many as a dozen possible assignments. In Ireland, these shooting subjects were researched weeks in advance by a team of crack Assignment Editors working out of a stone tower—fully computerized with 15 top-of-the-line Macintoshes, of course—at the Industrial Development Authority's Pearce Street Enterprise Centre in Dublin. And an eclectic lot they were: Harry Browne, a transplanted American, freelances at the *Irish Times*; Lynn Geldof had just completed a four-year stint in Cuba researching a new book; Jim Jennings came from "The Late Late Show" at the RTE television studios, where he is senior researcher; Lisa Pereira is a freelance writer who comes to Ireland via Trinidad and Paris.

For six feverish weeks prior to May 17, the Assignment Editors worked with Managing Editor Bill Messing, and the project's Co-Directors, Irish photographer Tom Lawlor and Collins's Jennifer Erwitt, to come up with issues and ideas that might help yield an overview of daily life as actually experienced by the Irish people in the spring of 1991. Tom Lawlor, in particular, was adamant that the shoot capture the new, and increasingly aggressive, modern Ireland. Rather than shooting the standard dreamy, romantically-draped series of portraits that have gone into so many books on Ireland in the past, he insisted that *A Day in the Life* balance green pastures with urban hustle, rural farmers with modern technology, Aran fishermen with contemporary Dublin businessmen, if Ireland as it is today were to be portrayed accurately in the pages of this book.

One tenet held sacred throughout, however: that whatever its ambitions, *A Day in the Life of Ireland* would never claim to be the definitive work on this most complicated land. Building the shooting list might best be likened to the painting of a pointillist picture, where each of the hundreds of assignments adds imperceptibly to the whole. Because at its best, there is no such thing in photojournalism as a sure thing (except that even the most carefully laid plans are sure to go awry), all the Assignment Editors labored under strict instructions to look first for the decisive image. How the pieces fit together in the book would be solved later.

In the months leading up to the shoot, eight separate sponsors signed up in support of *A Day in the Life of Ireland*: Eastman Kodak Company, Aer Lingus, Jameson Irish Whiskey, the Ryan Hotel Group, the International Fund for Ireland, Bord Fáilte/Irish Tourist Board, Dan Dooley Rent-a-Car Limited and the Northern Ireland Tourist Board. Each brought its unique strengths to the task of carrying out the project; but as one measure of the special regard which *A Day in the Life* has earned over the years, no project sponsor sought to influence the content of the book. That task was best left up to the picture editors flown to San Francisco after the shoot just for the purpose of sorting through the 100,000 available frames and choosing the strongest images from among them. Arguments in-house over individual photos could, and did, often last well into the night. But every discussion centered on the merits of a particular photo, without regard for the countless political considerations surrounding each frame.

But all of that was still a distant prospect in the final days before the shoot. At about 10:00 in the morning on May 14, 1991, Jennifer Erwitt could be found sitting by herself at her desk in Dublin and laughing into her computer. A careful and usually reserved administrator, Erwitt was asked if she had snapped, and finally lost her mind. No, she replied; this was the morning when all of the photographers were supposed to report to their contact people in the field, and one of her best photographers, Pulitzer Prize-winning David Peterson from the *Des Moines Register*, who had asked to explore the farming communities of the Midlands, had just called in. Instead of catching a shuttle across town to pick up his rental car, Peterson had somehow boarded the wrong bus and wound up in Belfast. Now he wished to know how best to get to Leitrim. Erwitt was loose, but cautious. So far, things had been going too well.

Mistaken bus rides would prove to be the least of her problems. In Cookstown, on the shoot day, Spanish photographer Pedro Coll spent the morning focusing his camera on a public checkpoint manned by members of the British Army. As Coll looked through his lens to snap the shot, he was shocked to see a British soldier looking down the barrel of a modern automatic rifle through his own telescopic lens directly at Coll. "It was very interesting at the checkpoint," Coll would say later. "People were looking at us like we were crazy. One lady came past us and said, 'If you have no problems, you are looking for them now'."

British photographer Barry Lewis found things somewhat more hopeful. Lewis spent most of his day in County Antrim, with members of the Orange Order. In the evening his hosts threw a small party in his honor. "People gathered in someone's kitchen, and the party went on until 5:00 in the morning. What surprised me was how close the farmers—the working farmers, whether they're Catholic or Protestant—can be when they're playing music. There is this kind of musical link. There was one fiddler—he was clearly the best musician—and I'm sure he was Catholic. But we never talked about it. We talked about everything else. It was 5:00 a.m., and everyone was still talking. It was lovely."

No matter where they went in Ireland, the photographers could not stop talking about the warmth and generosity of the Irish. Sometimes clichés come about because they prove true so often. "I was wondering why people were smiling in my photographs," mused Hungarian photographer Péter Korniss. "Then I realized that it wasn't because I made them smile, but because they are really open. I was born in Transylvania, and I came from the same sort of people. I'm not talking about Budapest. Budapest is different. I have been living in Budapest since I was 14. But still all my friends in Budapest are from Transylvania. They are so open, so warm-hearted, and that's what I experienced here."

As the day unfolded before us, it may have fallen to Lynn Johnson to capture the true heart of this wonderful country. A two-time World Press Photo Foundation honoree from Pennsylvania, Johnson is also a recipient of the distinguished Robert F. Kennedy Award for outstanding coverage of the disadvantaged. It was no surprise, then, that she chose to spend her day at a very special clinic for disabled people outside of Dublin.

"I made the choice to shoot the Central Remedial Clinic. It's a very diverse place. They work with adults; they work with children. It's a massive operation, though it still feels like home and family. Such a massive operation that I couldn't really cover it all, so I concentrated on the school. The relationship between the teachers and the children, and the volunteers and the children— it's really moving. There's something different here in Ireland. There's a strong confidence level in these kids. It's a joyful place.

"After school I went home with a family where the mom is a nurse. She works one week out of the month, and her husband is a corrections officer at a local prison. Their little girl is named Grace, and she is a precious child. She's in a big wheelchair, and the wheelchair has a big old smiley face that covers the entire wheel. I photographed this little girl and her dad reading in their garden, and they had the most extraordinary relationship. A totally non-verbal, absolute heart-to-heart connection with each other. You could see it in their eyes. I love the people here. It was a great day."

It *was* a great day.

—Bob Callahan

16. Claus C. Meyer

17. P.F. Bentley

16. Claus Meyer's new friends from the Military College.
17. Part of the task of keeping 3,000 rolls of film straight fell to Linda Lamb, here at the Gresham Hotel in Dublin.
18. Sam Garcia, Bill Pierce, and Eddie Adams trade stories from the shoot.
19. Colin Jacobson searches for the one true image at the Collins offices in San Francisco.

18. Linda Lamb

19. P.F. Bentley

20. P.F. Bentley

20. Staring into bright light at tiny pictures for a solid week is enough to drive anyone crazy, but the *Day in the Life* picture editors hold it together long enough for one last shot.

Photographers' Biographies

Eddie Adams
American/New York, New York
With a Pulitzer Prize, three George Polk Memorial Awards, a World Press Grand Award, and six New York Press Photographer of the Year Awards to his credit, Adams is one of the most decorated and published photographers in the United States. He has photographed leaders in all fields, from heads of state to superstars of film, sports, and high fashion. He is founder and director of the Eddie Adams Workshop, a yearly event designed to promote development of talented new photographers.

Monica Almeida
American/New York, New York
Almeida began her career at the *Los Angeles Times*, where she was part of the team of journalists awarded the 1984 Pulitzer Prize for coverage of California's Hispanic community. She was a staff photographer for the *New York Daily News* for five years and currently works as a freelancer covering a variety of news and feature stories.

Eric Lars Bakke
American/Golden, Colorado
During his 18-year career, Bakke has covered events ranging from the World Series and the Super Bowl to insect infestation in Utah and fire storms in Yellowstone National Park. His work is published in an array of magazines including *National Geographic*, *Sports Illustrated*, and *Boys' Life*, and he recently completed coverage of the Soviet Union for a new textbook. He is a member of the Picture Group photo agency.

Bruno Barbey
French/Paris
Barbey became a professional photographer after studying at the École des Arts et Métiers in Vevey, Switzerland, and became a full member of the Magnum photo agency in 1968. His work has been featured in dozens of books and periodicals. He was awarded the French National Order of Merit in 1985.

Nicole Bengiveno   Soviet Union 1988

Nicole Bengiveno
American/Brooklyn, New York
Bengiveno joined the *New York Daily News* in 1986 after eight years with the *San Francisco Examiner*. She was named Bay Area Press Photographer of the Year in 1979. In 1985 she was a finalist for the W. Eugene Smith Award for her work on the AIDS epidemic, and in 1987 and 1989 she won first-place honors in feature photography from the New York Associated Press for her work from the Soviet Union. This is her tenth *Day in the Life* project.

P.F. Bentley
American/Stinson Beach, California
Bentley is a *Time* magazine photographer whose assignments have included election coverage in both El Salvador and Panama. His awards include first-place honors in the National Press Photographers Association Pictures of the Year competition in 1984 and 1988 for his coverage of the U.S. presidential campaigns. Ireland is his seventh *Day in the Life* book.

Torin Boyd
American/Tokyo
Boyd began his career as a surfing photographer at the age of 17 in Cocoa Beach, Florida. Based in Tokyo since 1986, he specializes in work on modern-day Japan for clients including *U.S. News & World Report*, *Forbes*, *Fortune*, and *Winds*, and for numerous corporate publications. Ireland is his seventh *Day in the Life* project.

Michael Bryant
American/Philadelphia, Pennsylvania
A staff photographer at the *Philadelphia Inquirer*, Bryant was named Pennsylvania Photographer of the Year in 1988. He worked for the *San Jose Mercury News* from 1980 to 1986, during which time he was named Photographer of the Year in both California and Michigan.

Mike Bunn
British/Dublin
Educated in figure drawing, Bunn travelled around the world three times by the age of 21 and then settled in Spain. Today he is a highly regarded fashion and location photographer whose work has been used to illustrate three books—including one on his favorite pursuit, fishing. He spends any free time in the west of Ireland, in and around Sligo.

Cyril Byrne   Aran Islands 1985

Cyril Byrne
Irish/Dublin
Byrne has been a staff photographer with the *Irish Press* newspapers since 1973 and was a founding member of the Press Photographers Association of Ireland. He has numerous lectures, workshops, and exhibitions to his credit and has worked extensively in the Aran Islands. He was named Ireland's Photographer of the Year in 1983.

John Carlos
Irish/Dublin
Carlos began his career with the *Connacht Tribune* and the *Irish Times* and has since contributed to many other publications including the *New York Times* and the London *Sunday Times Magazine*. He has covered assignments in Ethiopia, Yemen, and Cuba, winning two Irish Press Photographer of the Year awards. He is currently a staff photographer with Dublin's *Sunday Tribune* and is working on a book with the poet Mary O'Malley.

Paul Chesley
American/Aspen, Colorado
Chesley is a freelance photographer who has worked with the National Geographic Society since 1975, travelling regularly to Europe and Asia. Solo exhibitions of his work have appeared in museums in London, Tokyo, and New York. Ireland is the tenth *Day in the Life* project for Chesley, who is also a frequent contributor to *Fortune*, *GEO*, *Travel & Leisure*, *Life*, and *Stern*.

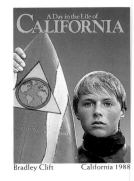
Bradley Clift   California 1988

Bradley Clift
American/Hartford, Connecticut
Clift acquired an interest in photography at an early age when his father and older brother built a darkroom in their home. The holder of a journalism degree from the University of Minnesota, Clift is now a staff photographer for the *Hartford Courant*. In 1986 he won the National Press Photographers Association Photographer of the Year award and a World Press Photo Foundation award; in 1987 he won the Robert F. Kennedy Award for Photojournalism. The cover of *A Day in the Life of California* features one of his works.

Pedro Coll   Sierra Leone 1985

Pedro Coll
Spanish/Mallorca
A lawyer by training who abandoned his practice at the age of 28 to take up photography, Coll has traveled on assignment to five continents since 1975. Specializing in travel industry and editorial work, he is represented by photo agencies in Barcelona, London, Frankfurt, New York, Milan, Tokyo, and Melbourne.

Guglielmo de' Micheli
Italian/Florence
De' Micheli began publishing his photography in 1979, at the age of 17. In addition to his work for corporate clients in Europe, his pictures have appeared in *Forbes*, *Sports Illustrated*, *Life*, the *New York Times Magazine*, and other publications. Recently he also served as production manager on a Bill Moyers film on the Renaissance.

Jay Dickman

American/Littleton, Colorado

A 1983 Pulitzer Prize winner and gold medalist in the World Press Photo Foundation competition, Dickman was a newspaper photographer in Dallas for 16 years before moving to Denver to devote himself full-time to a career as a freelancer. His work appears in *National Geographic*, *GEO*, and *Life* and has been honored by Sigma Delta Chi, the Society of Professional Journalists. He has participated in eight *Day in the Life* projects.

Don Doll, S.J.   Alaska 1989

Don Doll, S.J.

American/Omaha, Nebraska

A professor of fine arts and photography at Creighton University, Doll has worked extensively among native peoples including Alaska's Athapaskan Indians and Yupik Eskimos and South Dakota's Sioux. In the 1989 Pictures of the Year competition, sponsored by the National Press Photographers Association, he won first place in the magazine feature photograph category for "Myrtis Walking Eagle Attending Christmas Mass" from the Collins book *Christmas in America*.

Elliott Erwitt

American/New York, New York

Erwitt was born in Paris, grew up in Milan, moved to the United States at age 11, and has been an obsessive traveller ever since. Exhibitions of his work have appeared in museums and galleries throughout the world, including New York's Museum of Modern Art, the Smithsonian Institution, the Chicago Art Institute, and the Kunsthaus Zürich. A large retrospective exhibition of his work took place in Paris, Cologne, and Tokyo in the fall of 1988 to accompany publication of his book *Elliott Erwitt/Personal Exposures*.

Misha Erwitt

American/New York, New York

A native New Yorker, Erwitt has been taking pictures since he was 11 years old. His work has been published in *American Photo*, *Esquire*, *People*, *USA Today*, and *Manhattan, inc.*, and he has participated in eight *Day in the Life* projects. He is affiliated with the Magnum photo agency and is the son of fellow *Day in the Life* photographer Elliott Erwitt.

Richard Eskite

American/San Francisco, California

Eskite is best known for his corporate and advertising still-life photography. He has received awards from Printing Industries of America, Inc., Consolidated Paper Companies, Inc., and the San Francisco Art Directors Club. His clients include Apple Computer, Del Monte Foods, Ghirardelli Chocolate, Levi Strauss, and the Raychem Corporation.

Tina Etheridge

American/Gilroy, California

Etheridge worked in retirement planning for 11 years before switching careers in 1990 to take a position as a staff photographer for the *Gilroy Dispatch* in California. Her work at the Eddie Adams Workshop the same year earned her a fellowship with Eastman Kodak and a place on *A Day in the Life of Ireland*.

Brian Farrell

Irish/Dublin

Farrell spent the early 1980s as a freelancer working extensively in Northern Ireland for national and international publications including *Time* and *Newsweek*. He joined the *Independent* newspapers in 1986 and published a book about the island of Inishbofin in 1988.

Dana Fineman

American/New York, New York

A member of the Sygma photo agency, Fineman studied at the Art Center College of Design in Pasadena. Her work appears regularly in *New York*, *People*, *Time*, *Newsweek*, and *Stern*. In May of 1986, following shoot day for *A Day in the Life of America*, she married photographer Gerd Ludwig with 200 of the world's best photojournalists covering the wedding.

Gerry Fitzgerald   Belfast 1986

Gerry Fitzgerald

Northern Irish/Belfast

Fitzgerald has covered the Troubles in Northern Ireland for 15 years, the last 12 as a staff photographer for the *Belfast Telegraph*. A graduate of the University of Ulster's College of Art & Design, he has published extensively in British and international media including the *International Herald Tribune* and *USA Today*. Among his recent awards are Northern Ireland News Picture of the Year and Feature Photographer of the Year.

James Fraher

American/Grayslake, Illinois

A photographic educator and professional photographer for over 15 years, Fraher is the creator of the current exhibition "The Blues Is a Feeling." His photographs have appeared in *Living Blues*, *Downbeat*, the *Chicago Tribune*, the *Atlanta Journal/Constitution*, and the *Chicago Reader*, as well as on numerous record album covers.

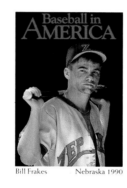

Bill Frakes   Nebraska 1990

Bill Frakes

American/Miami, Florida

Frakes has been a staff photographer for the *Miami Herald* for 12 years and is a frequent contributor to *Sports Illustrated* and other publications including *Time*, *Newsweek*, *Life*, and *Business Week*. His recent coverage of the two-minute Kentucky Derby horse race required the operation of 38 cameras by remote control. In the National Press Photographers Association's Pictures of the Year competition, he was named Newspaper Photographer of the Year in 1982, and his magazine sports portfolio took first place in 1989. His work appears on the cover of the Collins book *Baseball in America*.

Raphaël Gaillarde

French/Paris

Gaillarde is a leading news photographer with Gamma Presse Images. His coverage of world events has appeared in magazines all over Europe including *Paris Match*, *Le Figaro*, and *GEO*, and in the World Press Photo Foundation competition he received the 1990 Oskar Barnack award. He has participated in eight *Day in the Life* projects.

Sam Garcia

American/Melville, New York

Formerly an Atlanta-based freelance photographer, Garcia is now on staff with Nikon Professional Services. In his 15 years with Nikon he has covered most major sporting events, including four Olympic Games, and he has trained America's space shuttle astronauts to use 35mm still equipment. Ireland is the eighth *Day in the Life* project for Garcia, who is also on the faculty of the Eddie Adams Workshop.

Georg Gerster   1990

Georg Gerster

Swiss/Zumikon

A veteran aerial photographer with numerous books to his credit, Gerster has freelanced as a writer and photographer since receiving his Ph.D. in German literature from the University of Zurich in 1956. He is a frequent contributor to *Neue Zürcher Zeitung*, *National Geographic*, and *GEO*. His work has also been published in the London *Sunday Times Magazine*, *Paris Match*, *Epoca*, and *Omni*, and by Time-Life Books.

Diego Goldberg

Argentine/Buenos Aires

After beginning his photographic career in Latin America as a correspondent for *Camera Press*, Goldberg moved to Paris in 1977 as a Sygma staff photographer. In 1980 he moved to New York, only returning to his native Argentina in 1985. His work has been featured in the world's major magazines, and in 1984 he won a World Press Photo Foundation award. He is the only person to have participated in all eleven *Day in the Life* projects.

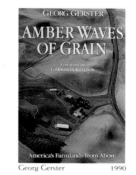

Bill Greene   Puerto Rico 1990

Bill Greene

American/Boston, Massachusetts

A graduate of the University of Massachusetts at Amherst, Greene was named New England Photographer of the Year four times in a row while at Quincy's *Patriot Ledger*. He has won Photographer of the Year honors from the Boston Press Photographers Association five times, and in 1987 he was named Photographer of the Year by the National Press Photographers Association. Greene is currently a staff photographer for the *Boston Globe*.

Annie Griffiths Belt

American/Silver Spring, Maryland

After graduating from the University of Minnesota with a degree in photojournalism, Griffiths Belt began her career with the *Worthington Daily Globe* in southern Minnesota. In 1978 she began assignment work for *National Geographic* and has since worked on more than two dozen magazine and book projects. She has received awards from the National Press Photographers Association, the Associated Press, the National Organization for Women, and the White House News Photographers Association.

Volker Hinz
German/New York, New York
For the last 17 years Hinz has been a staff photographer for *Stern* magazine. His pictures also appear in many other news and feature magazines including *Vanity Fair, Time, Newsweek, New York, Life, Paris Match,* and *GEO.*

Graciela Iturbide
Mexican/Mexico City
The recipient of the Grand Prix Award from the French Ministry of Culture in 1989, and the recipient of the International Award from Japan the next year, Graciela Iturbide is the author and creator of four books of her own photos, including the widely acclaimed *Women of Jochitan.*

Kenneth J. Jarecke   Beijing 1989

Kenneth J. Jarecke
American/New York, New York
Since joining Contact Press Images in 1986, Jarecke has travelled around the world covering major political events, from Haitian elections to the upheaval in Lithuania and the uprising in China's Tiananmen Square. Recently his work as a contract photographer for *Time* has resulted in a World Press Photo Foundation award for a picture illustrating the controversial "Rotten Apple" cover story and taken him to the Persian Gulf as a member of the U.S. press pool.

Lynn Johnson
American/Pittsburgh, Pennsylvania
Johnson is the recipient of two World Press Photo Awards as well as the winner of the Robert F. Kennedy Award for her coverage of the disadvantaged. Formerly on staff at the Pittsburgh Press, she is currently a contract photographer for Black Star. Her work has been featured regularly in *Life, National Geographic, Fortune, Smithsonian,* and the *New York Times Magazine.*

Péter Korniss   Hungary 1983

Péter Korniss
Hungarian/Budapest
Korniss began his career as a dance photographer. Later he spent thirteen years photographing Eastern Europe's disappearing traditional peasant life, and then another eight years photographing migrant workers in Hungary. He has published four books and exhibited widely on these and related subjects. A 1983 World Press Photo Foundation Award winner, Korniss publishes regularly in *GEO, Forbes, Fortune,* and many other magazines.

Steve Krongard   Miami 1986

Steve Krongard
American/New York, New York
One of the country's busiest advertising and corporate photographers, Krongard counts Amtrak, Qantas, and Bell South among his recent clients. He is on the faculty of the School of Visual Arts in New York City. Ireland, where he shot the group portrait which appears on page 208, is his ninth *Day in the Life* project.

Jean Pierre Laffont
French/New York, New York
Laffont attended the prestigious School of Graphic Arts in Vevey, Switzerland and later became a founding member of both Gamma and Sygma photo agencies. He is the recipient of awards from the New York Newspaper Guild and the Overseas Press Club of America; he has also received the Madelein Dane Ross Award, the World Press General Picture Award, and the Nikon World Understanding Award. His work appears regularly in the world's leading news magazines.

Tom Lawlor
Irish/Dublin
Lawlor brought the experience of 18 years with the *Irish Times* to his role as Project Co-Director on *A Day in the Life of Ireland.* With assignments in the Soviet Union, Greenland, Bangladesh, and throughout Europe to his credit, he is among the most well-travelled and decorated photographers in Ireland. He was named Ireland's Photographer of the Year in 1982 and published the bestselling book *Dublin: One in a Thousand* to mark the city's millenium anniversary. He currently operates his own studio, accepting corporate, advertising, and editorial assignments.

Andy Levin
American/New York, New York
A nine-time *Day in the Life* participant, Levin has covered a wide variety of medical subjects for news and feature magazines, including stories on a gay AIDS doctor and a nun who operates a clinic for the poor in rural Mississippi. In 1985 he received top honors in the National Press Photographers Association Pictures of the Year competition for his essay on a Nebraska farm family. In 1986 his essay on the Statue of Liberty won similar honors. Today he works on a freelance basis for clients nationwide.

Alan Lewis   Belfast 1984

Alan Lewis
Irish/Belfast
Lewis has covered events in Ireland since 1971, receiving numerous awards including Northern Ireland Press Photographer of the Year in 1976 and All Ireland Photographer of the Year in 1984. He has been chief photographer at the *Daily Mail* for 15 years, and during that time he has worked on assignment as far afield as the upper Amazon in Peru.

Barry Lewis
British/London
Originally a science teacher, Lewis holds a Master's degree from the Royal College of Art and is a founding member of the Network agency. He shoots regularly for *Life, GEO,* the London *Sunday Times,* and the *Observer,* and has photos on display in several U.S. and British museums. He was the 1990 recipient of the World Press Photo Foundation's Oskar Barnack Award for his work in Romania.

John Loengard   Italy 1990

John Loengard
American/New York, New York
A Harvard graduate, Loengard was on the staff of *Life* magazine from 1961 to 1972, during which time *American Photographer* hailed him as *"Life's* most influential photographer." He was the founding picture editor of *People* magazine and later served as picture editor for *Life* after its rebirth as a monthly in 1978. His book *Pictures Under Discussion* won the Ansel Adams Award for Book Photography from the American Society of Magazine Photographers. Today Loengard writes a column for *American Photo* magazine and teaches at the International Center of Photography in New York City.

Gerd Ludwig
German/New York, New York
A founding member of the Visum photo agency in Hamburg, Ludwig is a regular contributor to *GEO, Life, Stern, Fortune,* and *Zeit Magazin.* He is an honorary member of the Deutsche Gesellschaft für Fotografie.

Michael Lutzky
American/Rochester, New York
The youngest participant in *A Day in the Life of Ireland,* Lutzky has interned at the *Seattle Times,* the *Florida Times-Union* in Jacksonville, the *Grand Rapids Press,* and *National Geographic.* He was recently named College Photographer of the Year and has travelled on assignment to Africa for the United Nations.

Mary Ellen Mark   Barcelona 1987

Mary Ellen Mark
American/New York, New York
Winner of numerous grants and awards, including the George W. Polk, Robert F. Kennedy, and Philippe Halsman awards for photojournalism, Mark has exhibited her work throughout the world. Herself the subject of several magazine profiles, she currently contributes to *Life,* the London *Sunday Times, Stern, Vanity Fair,* and the *New York Times.*

John Marmaras   Sydney 1990

John Marmaras
Australian/Sydney
Marmaras spent eight years in London and thirteen years in New York before returning to his native Australia. He has worked on assignment for *Time, Newsweek,* the *London Daily Telegraph,* the London *Sunday Times, Fortune, Esquire,* and *Sports Illustrated.* Ireland marks his fourth *Day in the Life* project.

Stephanie Maze
American/Washington, D.C.
Maze was a staff photographer for the *San Francisco Chronicle* from 1973 to 1979. Since then she has been a freelance photographer for *National Geographic,* working in numerous Spanish-speaking countries. She has covered three Olympic Games, and she won a first-place award from the White House Press Photographers Association in 1985.

Steven McCurry

American/New York, New York

McCurry started out as a beat photographer for the local paper in King of Prussia, Pennsylvania, where he worked for two years before setting out for India in 1978 as a freelancer. Since 1982, he has pursued stories of conflict along the Afghan border, in Kampuchea, and in Baghdad, Beirut, and the Sahel for *National Geographic* and other publications. His awards include Magazine Photographer of the Year in 1984, the Overseas Press Club Robert Capa Gold Medal in 1980, and an unprecedented four first places in the World Press Photo Foundation awards in 1985.

Roseanne McGregor

Irish/Grimsby, England

Following a stint in a commercial studio and three years studying photography in Edinburgh, McGregor became the first female staff photographer to work with Ireland's *Independent* newspapers. She earned two national press photography awards before returning to Scotland to specialize as a fashion photographer. She recently opened a new studio in partnership with a graphic design and advertising agency.

Joe McNally   Texas 1990

Joe McNally

American/New York, New York

McNally started his career in 1976 with the *New York Daily News* and went on to spend two years as a still photographer with ABC-TV. He has been a magazine freelancer since 1981, publishing pictures primarily in *Life*, *National Geographic*, and *Sports Illustrated*. Affiliated with the Sygma photo agency, McNally won first prize in magazine illustration in the 1988 University of Missouri Picture of the Year awards.

James Meehan   Dublin 1990

James Meehan

Irish/Dublin

Though trained as an engineer, Meehan turned to a career in photography in 1981 and later co-founded the InPho agency with fellow *Day in the Life* photographer Billy Stickland. He was named Ireland's Press Photographer of the Year in 1989 and is current president of the Press Photographers Association of Ireland. He works regularly for the *Sunday Business Post* in Dublin, and he serves as a contract photographer for Reuters.

Doug Menuez   California 1989

Doug Menuez

American/Sausalito, California

Formerly with *USA Today*, Menuez now works on assignment around the world for *Time*, *Newsweek*, *U.S. News & World Report*, *Fortune*, and other news magazines. In 1987 he established Reportáge, a full-service corporate photojournalism agency specializing in the design and production of annual reports, brochures, and photo essays. In 1989 Menuez co-directed *15 Seconds: The Great California Earthquake of 1989*, a book project that sold 70,000 copies and raised more than $500,000 for earthquake relief.

Claus C. Meyer

German/Rio de Janeiro

The winner of many prizes and awards, Meyer was selected in 1985 by *Communications World* as one of the top annual-report photographers in the world. His color photography has been recognized by Kodak and Nikon, and in 1981 he won a Nikon International Grand Prize. He has published several books on Brazil.

Frank Miller

Irish/Dublin

A staff photographer with the *Irish Times*, Miller has received awards including News Picture of the Year and Feature Picture of the Year from the Press Photographers Association of Ireland. He specializes in feature and human-interest stories from daily life in and around Dublin.

Kai H. Mui

American/Rochester, New York

A photographer by training, Mui is responsible for the art direction of all image advertising worldwide for Eastman Kodak's Professional Photography Division. Among those efforts are profiles of some of the leading lights in each area of professional photography, including several *Day in the Life* veterans.

Brendan Murphy

Irish/Belfast

Murphy was a local publican in Belfast for years before embarking on a new career as a freelance press photographer in 1972. Following a long association with the *Irish News*, a morning daily, he became picture editor of that paper in 1980. He designed his own assignments for *A Day in the Life of Ireland*, exploring the Glens of Antrim.

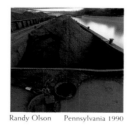
Randy Olson   Pennsylvania 1990

Randy Olson

American/Pittsburgh, Pennsylvania

A graduate of the University of Kansas, Olson worked at the *San Jose Mercury News*, West Virginia's *Charleston Gazette*, the *Milwaukee Journal*, and the *West Palm Beach Post* before joining the staff of the *Pittsburgh Press*. He received the Robert F. Kennedy Award for social documentary in 1991, and he freelances for *National Geographic*, *Fortune*, and *Time*. While teaching photojournalism at the University of Missouri, he received a National Archives grant for work with the Pictures of the Year archives.

Chuck O'Rear   Napa Valley 1989

Chuck O'Rear

American/St. Helena, California

O'Rear has photographed stories around the world for *National Geographic* for more than 20 years. His home in California's Napa Valley wine region has provided him with a base from which he has produced books both on nearby Silicon Valley and on the local vineyards—including *Napa Valley* from Collins Publishers.

Joe O'Shaughnessy

Irish/Galway

In addition to his work as a staff photographer for the *Connacht Tribune* newspaper group, O'Shaughnessy serves as a correspondent from the west of Ireland for the *Irish Times* and the *Independent* newspapers. He has won a total of eight awards in competitions sponsored by the Press Photographers Association of Ireland.

Tony O'Shea   Dublin 1988

Tony O'Shea

Irish/Dublin

O'Shea is a freelance photojournalist whose photographs appear regularly in domestic and international publications including the *Sunday Business Post*, the London *Sunday Times Magazine*, London's *Independent Magazine*, and Milan's *Sette*. He has published two books with the writer Colm Toibin, *Walking Along the Border* and *Dubliners*.

Graeme Outerbridge

Bermudian/Southampton

Named Young Person of the Year in Bermuda in 1985, Outerbridge is active in both politics and photography. When not working as chairman of the National Liberal Party, he is usually on assignment for clients including *Vogue*, *House & Garden*, and *Signature*. He has published two books, *Bermuda Abstracts* and *Bridges*; a third, concerning the motion picture *Evita*, is forthcoming.

David Peterson

American/Des Moines, Iowa

Following two years at the *Topeka Capital-Journal* at the start of his career, Peterson joined the *Des Moines Register* in 1977, where he has remained ever since. He is currently Special Projects photographer at that newspaper. A Midwest native, he was awarded the Pulitzer Prize in 1987 for his work on the Iowa farm crisis.

Bill Pierce   Derry 1981

Bill Pierce

American/New York, New York

A graduate of Princeton University, Pierce played backup guitar for Jimi Hendrix before choosing photojournalism as a career. His images of conflict in Beirut and Belfast won him the Overseas Press Club's Olivier Rebbot Award for international photoreportage, and he won the Leica Medal of Excellence in 1989 for his contributions to the project *Homeless in America*. Ireland marks his eighth *Day in the Life* project.

Eli Reed

American/New York, New York

Reed followed up a 1982 Nieman Fellowship with a 1983 Pictures of the Year Nikon World Understanding Award for his coverage of Central America. In 1988 he published the book *Beirut, City of Regrets*. Recent projects include a documentary film on poverty among children, a photo essay on Black America, and unit photography on the Robert Townsend film *The Five Heartbeats* from 20th Century-Fox.

Jim Richardson

American/Denver, Colorado
Freelance photographer Richardson has devoted years to documentary photography of rural life in his native Kansas. His pictures have toured worldwide in the award-winning audiovisual show *Reflections from a Wide Spot in the Road* and have been honored at the World Understanding Contest with three Special Recognition awards. He recently completed coverage of the Colorado River and water issues in the American West for *National Geographic* and is working on a new story on the Oglala Aquifer.

Rick Rickman   Sichuan 1989

Rick Rickman

American/Laguna Niguel, California
During five years at the *Des Moines Register*, Rickman was named Iowa Photographer of the Year three times. In 1985 he brought a Pulitzer Prize in Spot News Photography to the *Orange County Register* for coverage of the 1984 Olympics and was chosen California Photographer of the Year. One of his works from *A Day in the Life of China* was featured on the cover of *Time* magazine.

Crispin Rodwell

British/Belfast
Rodwell has covered events all over Ireland and abroad for 10 years and is currently a contract photographer covering Northern Ireland for the London *Sunday Times*. His work has also appeared in *Time*, *Stern*, and *Paris Match*, and he has illustrated two books on Irish politics.

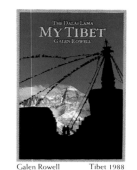
Galen Rowell   Tibet 1988

Galen Rowell

American/Albany, California
Rowell sold his auto repair shop in 1972 to devote himself to mountaineering and photography. He won the first of many *National Geographic* assignments a year later and has since published ten books, including *Mountains of the Middle Kingdom, Mountain Light*, Collins's *The Art of Adventure*, and an extraordinary collaboration with the Dalai Lama entitled *My Tibet*. He has participated in more than 1,000 climbs, including 23 trips to the Himalaya, and was the recipient of the Ansel Adams Award from the American Society of Magazine Photographers in 1984 for his contribution to the art of wilderness photography.

Joe St. Leger

Irish/Dublin
A staff photographer with the *Irish Times*, St. Leger has also worked for the *Irish Press* group and for the Irish broadcasting network RTE. His photographs have received numerous awards in Ireland and elsewhere in Europe. He is currently completing a documentary film, five years in the making, which captures the last of the Galway Hooker boatmen from Connemara.

Rick Smolan

American/Mill Valley, California
Creator of the *Day in the Life* series, Smolan was a founding member of Contact Press Images and one of *Time* magazine's chief photographers in Asia and Australia. In 1985 he was selected as a member of *Esquire* magazine's Register of influential men and women under 40, and in 1990 he co-directed a book project on health care around the world entitled *The Power to Heal*. He is married to Jennifer Erwitt, Project Director of *A Day in the Life of Ireland*.

George Steinmetz

American/San Francisco, California
Before graduating from Stanford University with a degree in geophysics, Steinmetz took two-and-a-half years to hitchhike through more than twenty African countries. His work appears frequently in *Time, Fortune, Life*, and *GEO*. He has recently completed work on a story about alcohol for *National Geographic*.

Billy Stickland   Italy 1990

Billy Stickland

Irish/Dublin
Named Photographer of the Year in 1991 by the Press Photographers Association of Ireland, Stickland is co-founder with fellow *Day in the Life* photographer James Meehan of the InPho sports photo agency in Dublin. His work has appeared in *Time, Stern, L'Equipe, Sports Illustrated*, and the *Observer Magazine*. In 1990 he was awarded first prize for his sports coverage in the World Press Photo Foundation competition.

Patrick Tehan   Missouri 1986

Patrick Tehan

American/Pittsburgh, Pennsylvania
Formerly with the *Orange County Register* and now a staff photographer for the *Pittsburgh Press*, Tehan has won numerous regional and national awards and is a regular participant in *Day in the Life* projects. One of his photographs from *A Day in the Life of America* won top honors in the magazine division of the National Press Photographers Association's Pictures of the Year competition for 1986.

Joyce Tenneson

American/New York, New York
Aside from her work in fine art photography, Tenneson is also active in the fields of fashion, beauty, and portraiture. Named Woman Photographer of the Year in 1990, she lectures frequently at universities and workshops and is the author of three books. Her photographs have appeared in more than 100 exhibitions, and she is a regular contributor to *Taxi, Bride's, L.A. Style*, both the Italian and French editions of *Vogue*, and other publications.

David C. Turnley

American/Paris
Turnley is a staff photographer for the *Detroit Free Press* and is affiliated with the Black Star photo agency. He won the 1990 Pulitzer Prize and the 1989 Overseas Press Club Robert Capa Gold Medal for his images of political and social turmoil in the socialist countries; in 1988, he won Picture of the Year from the World Press Photo Foundation for a photograph of a grieving father following the Armenian earthquake. His most recent book is *Moments of Revolution*, a photographic account of the events in Eastern Europe in 1989, created jointly with his twin brother Peter.

Peter Turnley

American/Paris
Peter Turnley is a contract photographer for *Newsweek*, and his work is distributed worldwide by the Black Star photo agency. He has received numerous awards, including the Overseas Press Club's Olivier Rebbot Award in 1989 and awards from the World Press Photo Foundation. He has photographed more Soviet leaders than any other Western photographer. In 1989 he traveled to China, East Germany, Czechoslovakia, Romania, Hungary, Poland, and the Soviet Union, producing seven cover photographs for *Newsweek*. His work has been published in two books co-authored with his twin brother David, *Beijing Spring* and *Moments of Revolution*.

Mark S. Wexler   Ohio 1990

Mark S. Wexler

American/New York, New York
Wexler travels the world as a photographer for a variety of editorial and corporate clients including *Time, Life, National Geographic, Smithsonian*, and *GEO*. He won three World Press Photo Foundation awards for his work on *A Day in the Life of Japan*.

Contributing Photographers

Simon Callan
Irish/Dún Laoghaire

Brian Lanker
American/Eugene, Oregon

Gary Matoso
American/Paris

Nutan
Irish/Paris

Project Staff

Project Directors
Jennifer Erwitt
Tom Lawlor

Managing Editor
Bill Messing

Design Director
Jennifer Barry

Publicity Director
Patti Richards

Sponsorship Director
Cathy Quealy

Travel Director
Karen Bakke

Office Manager
Linda Lamb

Assignment Editors
Harry Browne
Lynn Geldof
Jim Jennings
Lisa Pereira

Sponsorship Coordinator
Monica Baltz

Film Traffic Coordinator
Andrew J. Hathaway

Sponsorship Consultant
Graeme Outerbridge

Assistant Office Manager
Róisín Hannigan

Project Assistants
Cathy O'Connor
Elaine Mangan

Picture Editors

Christiane Breustedt
GEO

Guy Cooper
Newsweek

Sandra Eisert

Colin Jacobson
The Independent Magazine, London

Michele McNally
Fortune

Karen Mullarkey
Sports Illustrated

Kathy Ryan
New York Times Magazine

Dieter Steiner
Stern

Michele Stephenson
Time

**Photography &
Design Consultant**
Sandra Eisert

Introduction & Story
Bob Callahan

Senior Editor
Bernard Ohanian

Production Director
Lynne Noone

**Design & Production
Assistant**
Cecile Chronister

Researchers
Jim Jennings
Anne Maloney

Consulting Editor
Harry Browne

Copy Editor
Janice Maloney

Proofreader
Jonathan A. Schwartz

Project Logo Designer
Kari Perin

Collins Publishers

Publisher
Lena Tabori

Publishing Adviser
Clayton Carlson

Sales Director
Carole Bidnick

Business Managers
Peter Smith
Diane Lind

Special Sales Manager
Jennifer Ward

Senior Accountant
Jenny Collins

Publicist
David Carriere

Assistant Sales Manager
Maria Hjelm

Accounts Payable Assistant
Jackie Porter

Publicity Assistant
Molly Schaeffer

Assistant Office Manager
Barry Sundermeier

Administrative Assistants
Alan Everton
Lara Morris
Jill Stauffer

Attorneys
Jim Fox
Mathew Martin

Sales Representatives

Mid-Atlantic
Robert Eickemeyer
John Leibfried
Frank Rizzo
Geoffrey Rizzo

Midwest
Jim Lauber
Betty Redmond
Gene Rotenberg
Sean Sullivan

Mountain States
Gordon Saull

New England
Joan Emery
Sam Prosser
Marc Seager

Northwest
Ted Lucia

Southeast
John Genovese
John Mackey
Edward Springer

Southwest
Michael Donahue
Bill McClung
Jim Shepherd
Edward Wood, Jr.

West Coast
Bob Ditter
William Maher
Thomas McFadden
Jan Mutzabaugh
Judy Wheeler

Legal Advisers

Gallens Crowley &
   Chamberlain, Canberra
Goodman Derrick & Co.,
   London
Ross & Hayes, Dublin

Documentary Legal Advisers

Eugene P. Fanning
Mary Swords
Arthur Cox, Dublin

Dai Nippon Printing Co.,Ltd.

Ryo Chigira
Toshihiko Miyazaki
Hiroshi Takada
Michinori Nakamoto
Kenzaburo Osawa
Kikuo Mori
Mitsuo Gunji
Yoshio Akasaka
Yoshinori Katoh

*The one-hour documentary on
A Day in the Life of Ireland
which accompanies this volume was
directed by Michael Tobias and
produced by Red Deer Productions,
and is a production of Collins
Publishers San Francisco in association with WNET/Thirteen.
Originally broadcast on the PBS
Travels series, hosted by John
Heminway.*

Bill Frakes

Sponsors and Contributors

Sponsors
Eastman Kodak Company
Aer Lingus
Jameson Irish Whiskey
Ryan Hotel Group
International Fund for Ireland
Bord Fáilte/Irish Tourist Board
Dan Dooley Rent-a-Car Limited
Northern Ireland Tourist Board

Major Contributors
Belfast Telegraph
Evening Press
Image Photographic Laboratory
The New Lab
Pallas Photo Labs

Contributors
Apple Computer, Inc.
The Bedford Hotel, San Francisco
Galway Irish Crystal
Industrial Development Board
   for Northern Ireland
The Irish Card MasterCard
Industrial Development Authority
   of Ireland
Qantas Airways Limited

Associates
Adobe Systems
Aldus Corporation
All Saints National School
Army Bargains, Dublin
R. & A. Bailey & Co. Limited
Ballymaloe House
Belfast Botanic Gardens
Belleek Pottery
Belltable Arts Centre
Benedictine Sisters
Ben Madigan Preparatory School
Burrendale Hotel & Country Club
Bushmills Irish Whiskey
CAFE/Creative Arts for Everyone
Camerawork Darkrooms Derry
Canon
Cassidy Covers
Celtic Helicopters
Central Remedial Clinic
The Confused Sisters
Copy Service
Corporate Travel Services, Denver
Crent Company
Derry-Boston Ventures
The Divine Word National School
DMF International Limited
Donegall Road Primary School
Dublin Zoological Gardens
Dynamac Computer Products, Inc.
Eddie Adams Workshop
Elmgrove Primary School
Europa Hotel, Belfast
Farallon Computing
Fitzers
Fitzpatrick Hotel Group
Fullerton House Preparatory School
GAA Ash Project, Waterford
Gate Theatre
Glassdrumman Lodge
Tokyo Hilton International Hotel
Holy Rosary Primary School
Irish Country Houses &
   Restaurants Association
Irish Red Setter Club
The Island Players
Iuppa McCarten, Inc.
Just Add Water Acme
   Instant Frolics
Kielty & Dayton
KLP Marketing Network
Kodalux Processing Services

Loch Neagh Fishermen's Co-op
Lundeen Associates, Inc.
Malham Limited
Marathon Petroleum Ireland
Mid-Ulster Mail
Mount St. Michael School
Mullingar Post Office
Northern Ireland Partnership
O'Byrne Hire and Catering Limited
Omnicomp
O'Regan Stables
Our Lady of Bethlehem Abbey
Our Lady's Hospital for
   Sick Children
The Packaging Store
Park Lodge Primary School
Park Public Relations
Patrick Conway Pub
Stephen Pearce Pottery
Pinnacle Type
The Point Depot
Prescott Hotel
Primal Screen
Print Masters
P.S.F. Transcriptions
Rathgar Junior School
Rathowen Post Office
Royal Hospital Kilmainham
Rupert Stanley College
   Performing Arts Department
St. Anne's Primary School
St. Audeon's Primary School
St. Brendan's Primary School
St. Bride's Primary School
St. Fintan's Primary School
St. Peter's Primary School
Scoil Mhúire Mountsackville
   Convent
Scoil Mhúire National School
The Selective Angler
South Presentation Convent
Springhill Primary School
Ten Wheels for Jesus
Toner Marketing Agency
U2
Ulster Museum

Friends and Advisers

Capt. Tom Aherne
Bill Allen
Myrtle Allen
Sister Rosario Allen
John Altberg
Paul Anderson
Michael Archbold
Acheson Armstrong
Comdt. Dave Ashe
Tony Ayton
Anna Maria Bambara
Tony Bambrick
Richard Barkle
James Barlow
Howard Barney
Ed & Rena Barnum
David Barry
John Bastable
Dora Beacom
Jim Beggan
Eddie Bell
Alan Berrigan
David Biehn
Leonard Bierman
Michael Black
Margaret Blair
Peter Block
Gene Blumberg
Amy Bonetti
Bono
Margaret Bothwell
Maria Bourke
Paul Bourke
David Boyce
Padraic Breathnach
Declan Brennan
Jackie Brennan
Amanda & Christoper Brooke
Imelda Brophy

John Brosnan
Gerry Brough
John Brown
Lynda Brown
Russell Brown
Erik Browne
Mary Anne Bryan
Grace Buckley & family
Richard Burrows
Larry & Pauline Butler
Charlie Byrne
Mary Byrne
Tom Cafferkey
Heather Cahoon
Sean Callahan
The Calvey family
Finn Campbell
Jim Campbell
Dorothy Cantrell
Ann Carey
Orla Carey
Guy Carleton
John Carmody
Donal Carolan
The Carroll family
Claire & Patrick Casey
Diane Casey
Mark Cashen
Michael Cass & family
Jane Cassidy
Phillip Cassidy
Glynis Casson
Walter Cavanagh
Vera Cave
The Cawley family
Shirley Christine
Albert Chu
Beth Churchill-Fantz
Harold Clarke
Jim Clarke
John Clarke
Fred Cobain
Derek Cobbe
Bill Coblentz
Veronica Coburn
David Cohen
Connolly Cole
Michael Colgan
Jim Collins
Nuala Collins
John Colman
Peter Connolly
Jack Conroy
Hazel Conway
Tony Corcoran
Ruth Costelloe
Mary Courtney
Joe Cowan
Raymond Coyles
Francis P. Coyne
Phil & Shirley Crabb
George Craig
R.C. Crane
Barbara & Dennis Crossen
Robert L. Crossey
Niall Crowley
Barry Cullen
Kieran Cullen
John Culleton
Tony Culley Foster
The Cunningham family
Edmund Curran
Capt. Seamus Curran
Lizzie Curtain
Michael Daly
Paul Daly
Treena Darcy
Norma Darragh
David Davis
Mairtin Davy
Emily Dawson
Helena & Geordie Dawson
Ray DeMoulin
Ray DiMascio
Chickie Dioguardi
Phinian Dodd
Robert Dogget
Barry Doherty
Colm Doherty
Julie Doherty
Mary Doherty & family
Paddy Doherty
Chris Donegan

Michael Donnelly
Sheila Donnelly
Liam Donohoe
Hilary Donovan
Peter Donovan
Dan Dooley
Pat Dooley
Paul Dooley
Daibhi Doran
Sean Dougherty
Joe Dowling
Deko Doyle
Lesley Doyle
Patricia Doyle
Letitia Doyle & family
Cliona Drew
Gene & Gayle Driskell
Rosemary Duddy
James Duffy
Joe Duffy
John Duffy
Michael Duffy
Dominic Duggan
Martin Dully
Paul Dunne
Rena Dunne
J. Camillus Dwane
Steve Edelman
William Edgar
Liam & Mary Egan
Terry Lynn Ehlers
Ahmed El Habbash
Katrine Ennis
Ellen Erwitt
Paul & Martha Esler
Jim Fahy
Tony Fahy
Willie Farrell
John Farrelly
Jeanne Farruggia
Phil Feldman
MaeBeth Fenton
Sandra Fenton
Paul Ferran
Hilary Finlay
The Finn family
Gerry Finneran
Susan Finnerty
Tim Finney
Susan Fitzgerald
Jim Fitzgibbon
Paddy Fitzpatrick
Cynthia Fitzwilliams
Martin Flaherty
Gerry Flanagan
Peggy Fledderjohn
Michael Forbes
William Fowble
Donal Fox
Karen & Christopher Fox
Séan Frankland
Roll Fricke
Mark Friedman
Patricia Furlong
Andrew Gaffney
Michael Gallagher
Paddy Gallagher
Patricia Gallagher
Tanya Gallagher
Brenda Gallen
Sean Galvin
James Cocker Gammie
Fiona Gannon
Sharon Garrett
Colman Garrihy
Terry Gavin
Len Gaynor
Pauline Geoghegan
Colm Gillespie
Gerry Gillespie
Mary Gosling
Jane & Declan Goulding
Lady Goulding
Lingard Goulding
Frank Graham
Hugh Graham
Katherine Graham
Shay Graham
Liam Green
Mary Grelish
John Gore Grimes
Carolin Grunning
Brian Hajducek
Graham & Joan Hall

Blake Hallanan
David Hammond
Adrian Hanna & family
Brian Hannigan
Pat Hanrahan
John Hanrick
Peter Harbison
Heiner Harding
Ann Harkin
Robert Harkin
Michael Harnett
Comdt. Gerry Harney
Agnes Harrington
The Harty family
Neil Harvey
Donna Haugen
Steve Haugen
Charles Haughey
Patrick & Bernie Haughey
Kieran Haughui
Michael Hawkins
Michael Hayes
Chris Heaney
John Heaphey
Michael Hedigan
Peter Hedigan
Hugh Helm
Tina Helselt
Lord & Lady Hemphill
Ian G. Henderson
Colie Hernon
Frank Hewitt
The Hickey family
Dick Hill
Michele Hill
Fred Hoare
Sam Hoffman
Michael Holland
Tony Hopkins
Derek Hughes
Denis & Kay Hunt
Denis Hunt, Jr.
Tom Hunt, OSA
Sean Hurley
Mary Hurly
Lisa Hussey
Cliff & Mairead Hutchinson
Dan & Sandie Hyland
Tony Hyland
Frances Hynes
Douglas Irvine
Vern Iuppa
Angela Jackson
Kevin Jacobson
Tom Johnson
Tony Jones
Douglas Jordan
Tony Joseph
Denise Joy
Terry Joyce
Troy Kashon
Walter Kavanagh
Juli Kayartz
Tom Keane
Stephen Keating
Brendan Keenan
Michael & Nora Keightley
Louise Kelly
Margaret Kelly
Patricia Kelly
Seamus Kelters
John Kennedy
Kathleen Kennedy
Mike Kennedy
Terry Kennedy
Thomas Kennedy
The Kenny Family
Paddy Keogh
Margaret Kernoghan
Patrick Kerrigan
Brad Kibbel
Mark Lawrence Kidd
Mary Kilbride
The Kirwan family
Larry Kovi
Jeff Kriendler
Dale Kuhns
Darren Laird
Michael Lally
Bernard Lalor
Stuart & Laurina Lamb

Bill Frakes

★

I angled across the parking lot and noticed an arm dangling at an awkward angle from the driver's-side open window of a white Honda Accord. I put my hands on the side of the car and bent down to look inside. There sat the sleazy salesman Randall Swathers. His head lolled to the side at an unnatural angle, his glasses were broken and he had thrown up on himself.

I twisted my head back and forth like at a Ping-Pong match. No one else in the parking lot. Why didn't someone with an annoying cell phone appear when you wanted one?

★

Living with Your Kids Is
MURDER

MIKE BEFELER

TORONTO • NEW YORK • LONDON
AMSTERDAM • PARIS • SYDNEY • HAMBURG
STOCKHOLM • ATHENS • TOKYO • MILAN
MADRID • WARSAW • BUDAPEST • AUCKLAND

Acknowledgments

Many thanks for the assistance from Wendy, Laura, Kasey and Dennis Befeler; feedback from Barbara Graham, Phil Enger, Stuart Bastin, Jodie Ball, Virginia Brost, Jim Munro, Wanda Richards-Seaman and Phil Miller; and editorial support from Deni Dietz and John Helfers.

ONE

My eyes opened in the dim light.

Where the hell was I?

I heard a background rattling hum and smelled a mixture of beer and stale pretzels. All I could imagine was a seedy bar. I blinked, trying to focus. I was wedged in an uncomfortable seat with a man's head lolling on my shoulder.

I squinted and recognized the uniform of a flight attendant, checking seatbelts.

Shit. I was on an airplane. But where was I going?

I couldn't remember.

Think.

I squeezed my eyes shut, then opened them. No clue. All I could remember was that I was Paul Jacobson, too old to be cheek-to-cheek with someone on an airplane.

Something sticking out of my shirt pocket grazed my chin. I grabbed it to find a piece of folded paper. I flicked on the overhead light. Opening the message, I read: "If you fall asleep, you won't remember squat because sleeping causes your short-term memory to do a reset like a VCR when the electricity goes off. You're flying to Denver to live with your son, you old fart. He'll meet you by the fountain in the terminal lobby."

It looked like my handwriting. I turned it over. No other clue.

So I was going to visit my one and only kid, Denny. I couldn't remember how I ended up on this plane, but I could recall my wife Rhonda raising Denny in Los Angeles. After

I retired from my auto parts business, Rhonda and I moved to Hawaii. Then…I felt a pain in my gut. Rhonda died. I had lived on my own after that. An old widower.

Instinctively, I put my hand to my chest. I felt something else in my pocket. I reached in and pulled out a business card—one of those fancy types with a color picture of a man with a black goatee and gold wire-rim glasses. I looked at the head resting on my shoulder. Bingo. Same guy as the picture although he didn't look as pasty in the photograph. Squinting at the card, I read the name. So, Daniel Reynolds, sales representative for Colorado Mountain Retirement Properties, was using my shoulder for a pillow. Without my permission. Crap. And my shoulders had enough trouble supporting my own head.

I peered at the business card again. The tagline stated, "Retire in comfort with your own mountain property."

An old goat like me could sure use some retirement comfort, but it appeared I intended to mooch off my middle-aged offspring. I stuffed the sheet of paper and the business card back in my shirt pocket.

The pilot came on the intercom. "I want to thank all of you for traveling with us today. In particular, my mom happens to be on this flight."

A voice in the row behind said, "That's good news. He'll have to make a smooth landing this time."

I heard some yawns and saw a few arms stretch above the seats as people woke up in the semi-darkened cabin. I looked again at my sleeping companion. I needed to get this lout back into his own space. His greasy black hair would leave a stain on my shirt. I cleared my throat loudly enough to wake a narcoleptic. Nothing. I shrugged my shoulder, but he didn't budge. Then I reached over and shook him. Still nothing. Daniel Reynolds was starting to piss me off.

Taking a deep breath, with a not-too-delicate shove, I pushed Reynolds's head away from me. He flopped over the opposite arm rest with his head blocking the aisle.

A flight attendant, in animated conversation with someone a row ahead, stepped back, and the man's face and goatee nestled comfortably against her butt cheeks. She swung around as if she intended to smack someone, then flinched when she saw my sagging companion.

"I'm sorry," she said, wiping a strand of blond hair from her forehead. She bent down to help straighten the man up.

His glasses slipped off and fell to the floor, but his bulky body remained motionless.

"Sir, are you all right?" the flight attendant asked.

No answer.

She shot upright, erect as a totem pole. "Emil, come quickly!" she shouted.

A male flight attendant dashed down the aisle, skidded to a stop and reached over to examine the man.

"He seems to be unconscious," Emil said, wringing his skinny hands.

"Or dead," a voice said from across the aisle. "The old man next to him gave him a vicious shove."

TWO

A LARGE, SULLEN MAN in dark glasses escorted me and my aging legs through a hallway at the airport, behind one of those doors with signs saying you'd face the wrath of God if you entered.

Our footsteps echoed.

I imagined being locked up and the key tossed away. When we reached another door, I stumbled inside, where a scowling man in a rumpled suit and spotted tie sat across a desk, tapping his fingers on the worn wood surface. A waved hand indicated an unoccupied chair that I plopped down in.

He was a young squirt probably in his late forties, slightly receding brown, curly hair, a squished nose, square jaw and a mole on his left cheek. "I'm Detective Hamilton. Now Mr. Jacobson, please tell me what conversation you had with the man seated next to you on your flight from Honolulu."

"Unfortunately, the only thing I remember is waking up on the plane. This guy in the next seat was slumped against me. All I tried to do was get him off my shoulder."

He put his hand to the stubble of a dark beard that looked like it hadn't been shaved in two days. "And why don't you remember the earlier part of the flight?"

"I have short-term memory loss. I can remember events from my distant past, but any recent thing before I fall asleep is one big blank."

He jotted down a note on a pad. "You don't recall talking with him?"

"No."

He stared at me without smiling. "I find that very unusual. Another passenger reported you had a very heated argument with him after the flight took off."

"Can't help you there, Detective," I said with a shrug. "But I am curious. What did the passenger say we were arguing about?"

"Apparently the man sitting next to you made a comment that old people shouldn't be traveling on their own. You took outspoken exception to that."

"That's understandable. I am an old fart traveling on my own."

"So, Mr. Jacobson. You were overheard arguing with the victim. Later you gave him a shove, and then he's found dead."

"Victim?"

"Yes. We suspect foul play."

I bit my lip. "This is all very confusing."

He held up my ID card. "This indicates you're eighty-five years old."

I ran my hand through my full head of gray hair. "I can't remember exactly, but I'm up there somewhere in geezerland. I know my birth date, but I'm not sure of today's date."

"And what is the purpose of your trip from Honolulu to Denver?"

"I'm going to Boulder to live with my son, Denny."

"How do you remember that if you have a memory problem?"

"Good question." I gave him my most pleasant, stay-out-of-jail smile and handed him the sheet of paper. "I wrote myself a note."

He grunted and read the note. "May I keep this?"

"Fine with me. I'll be happy to autograph it if you like."

"Don't be a wiseass. Your actions with the victim are very suspicious."

I flinched. "Am I a suspect?"

Hamilton stared at me. "Let's just say that I'm very curious about what happened on the plane, and I'll need the address and phone number of where you'll be staying."

I felt a drop of perspiration form on my forehead. "I don't remember, but I may have it written down." I searched through my wallet and found a scrap of paper with Denny's address and phone number.

The detective copied the information onto his notepad.

"Now if you'll point me to the fountain mentioned in the note," I said, "I'm sure my son's wondering where I am. Then you can proceed to find out what happened to Mr. Reynolds."

"That's fascinating, Mr. Jacobson. You claim you don't remember speaking with the victim, yet you know his name."

THREE

SHIT. I COULD HAVE kicked myself. I didn't want to show the business card the victim had given me or else Detective Hamilton might want to confiscate it like he did the note about meeting Denny. Questions flashed though my mind. The police had to be interrogating other passengers. Did someone else see what happened to Reynolds? If Reynolds was the victim of foul play, who could have done it? An old geezer like me couldn't be the only person Hamilton considered suspicious. Still, with the law breathing down my neck, the business card might be the single clue for me to find out more if I had to do something to clear my good name.

"The man's name...I must have overheard it," I said, mumbling.

He eyed me again. "We'll be in touch very soon, Mr. Jacobson."

I gave him another winning smile. "You know where to find me, Detective. I look forward to our next conversation."

After being released, I stood in a hallway for a moment trying to orient myself. I felt a mixture of fear from being questioned concerning a crime and bewilderment regarding so much that I didn't understand. I took a deep breath. I'd have to get my arms around this unexplained circumstance. But first I needed to find my family.

I exited through a doorway into the main terminal and found my way to an open area beneath what looked like a huge white tent. I spotted a sign that read, "Welcome to Denver." I felt oh so welcome.

Wheeled suitcases clacked, and the aroma of cinnamon tickled my nose. I caught sight of a fountain, spitting water in gentle arcs from inches to ten feet in the air. An honor guard of potted plants guarded the fountain, and, as I approached, I noticed strange symbols in gold embedded in the floor tile: an arrow, a mining cart, a tree, a building, a cathedral, a star, a bicycle, a butterfly, a nautilus shell, an airplane, a fish, a canoe, a skier, a chairlift, a sleigh, an oil well and a tractor. I had experienced all of the Denver area without ever having to leave the terminal!

A mob of people wearing boots, sandals and designer jeans gathered there, waiting for arriving passengers to ascend the escalator from the tram below. Above the exit area hung large blue and white gliders. I felt like I'd plopped down in an art deco convention run by reformed pioneers.

I recognized my six-foot-tall son, Denny, his head peeking above the nearby crowd. I waved. As I approached I noticed a tinge of gray in his brown mustache and sideburns. He had aged, or had I forgotten? A skinny girl with a bouncing blond ponytail dashed up and gave me a hug. "Hi, Grandpa." She had bright, shiny brown eyes, even white teeth and a pug nose.

"You look like an older version of my granddaughter Jennifer," I said.

She stomped her foot. "You've forgotten again. I'm twelve."

"I remember a little girl of six."

"That was ages ago, Grandpa. Don't you remember that I visited you last summer?"

"I guess not. There's a lot of blank space in my soggy old brain."

"By the way, your flight came in an hour ago," Denny said. "Where have you been?"

"Just getting acquainted with the local constabulary. Seems the guy sitting next to me died during the flight. The police wanted to talk to me."

"Dad!" Denny said, his eyes going wide. "You're not getting yourself involved in another murder investigation, are you?"

"What the hell do you mean? I don't remember any other murder investigation."

"Grandpa, I'll tell you all about some of your previous adventures, but right now I want to hear what happened on the plane."

"It was a strange situation. I thought the guy fell asleep on my shoulder. Turns out he was dead."

"That's creepy, Grandpa. What happened to him?"

"I don't know."

"Why'd they detain you?" Denny asked.

"Someone claimed I argued with the guy earlier in the flight. Then I pushed him to get him off my shoulder. All that made me seem suspicious."

"I know you didn't do anything wrong, Grandpa."

"Thanks for the vote of confidence. There's a detective who isn't as sure as you are."

"I'll help you if they give you any trouble," Jennifer said, pursing her lips.

"I'm sure you will," I replied.

"Don't you have a carry-on bag, Dad?" Denny asked.

I scratched my head. "I don't know. In all the excitement I left the plane without checking so I have no clue. I wonder if I brought a bag?"

AFTER COLLECTING MY checked luggage, we left Denver International Airport and drove along the Northwest Parkway.

I looked toward the mountains. A trace of snow on the highest peaks. This was going to be different than living in Hawaii. Not that I could remember any recent particulars concerning being in Hawaii.

We pulled into the driveway of a two-story white wood house. The front yard consisted of a neatly mowed lawn adorned with red rosebushes next to the house. Denny parked and unloaded my two suitcases while I strolled along a brick pathway toward the front door, admiring my new home.

The solid wood front door opened. A small white dog shot out like a bullet and screeched to a halt in front of me.

"That's Max," Jennifer said. "He's a West Highland Terrier."

"Hi, boy." I leaned over, and he licked my hand. I watched as he twitched and then jumped up on my leg. He reached all of twenty inches in length with snow-white fur, except for a small black spot on his tail.

"He likes you, Grandpa."

"I have a way with animals. I remind them of dinner."

My daughter-in-law, Allison, strolled out of the house and gave me a kiss. I stepped back to look at her blond hair, done in a flip, and her warm smile and apple cheeks.

"I'm getting quite a welcome," I said.

"Let me show you your new home." She took my hand and led me through a living room with dark blue shag carpet, down a well-lit hallway and into a bedroom on the ground floor. I stuck my head briefly into an adjoining bathroom and noticed that I also had easy access to the kitchen from which the aroma of chocolate chip cookies emerged.

"Now for the rest of the tour," Allison said. We climbed the brown-carpeted stairs and, off the landing, entered a master bedroom.

Jennifer came bouncing up behind me. "Come see my room, Grandpa." She took my hand to lead me to the other end of the second floor hallway. She opened her door and pointed to a collection of stuffed animals. "There are the Hawaiian beanies you gave me."

I looked at a mongoose, myna bird and porpoise, as I scratched my head. "Imagine that."

"You don't remember them, do you, Grandpa?"

"I'm afraid not."

"You'll need to keep a journal while you're here. Like you did when I visited you in Hawaii."

"A journal?"

"You kept a journal to help remember things. You forget overnight, but if you write down what happened during the day before you go to sleep, the next day you can catch up on what you did."

"Seems like a lot of trouble."

"But it works. You have a good memory during the day."

"I don't know," I said, scratching my head.

"I'm going to give you this notebook to write in," Jennifer said. "Then you can leave a note to remind yourself to read it first thing in the morning."

"You're familiar with this procedure?"

"Of course. It's our secret from when I visited you in Hawaii last year."

I shook my head in amazement. My granddaughter knew more about my life than I did.

FOUR

I FELT DISORIENTED and out of control. The confusion of waking up on an airplane, seeing a dead guy in the seat next to me, being questioned by the police and having my granddaughter Jennifer know more concerning my recent past than I did was too much for my tired old brain. I told Jennifer I needed a little time to myself to get unpacked and returned to my room. I started thinking about my experience that morning at the airport. I withdrew the business card from my shirt pocket and inspected it. Who was this guy and what happened to him? Only one way to find out more.

After I called the number on the business card, a pleasant female voice greeted me and informed me I had reached Colorado Mountain Retirement Properties.

"Mr. Daniel Reynolds, please," I said.

There was a pause on the line. "I'm sorry, but Mr. Reynolds is no longer with us."

"He left the company?" I asked.

A pause again. "No. He really left us. He's dead. A heart attack or something."

"That's too bad. I had met him traveling back from Hawaii."

"Yes. He and his boss, Gary Previn, held meetings with prospects in Honolulu this last week."

"May I talk to this Previn fellow?"

"I'm sorry he's not available."

"Is there someone else I can speak with? I'm interested in some property."

Her voice perked up. "Oh, yes. Where are you calling from?"

"Boulder."

"Let me check."

I drummed my fingers on the desk while I waited.

She came back on the line. "There's actually going to be a meeting in Boulder tomorrow. One of our sales representatives, Randall Swathers, will be addressing a group at the Centennial Community Center at 2 P.M. You could attend the presentation and speak with Randall afterwards."

"That would be perfect."

"May I have your name, address and phone number please?"

I gave her the information and hung up.

Later, I asked Denny how to get to the Centennial Community Center.

"It's a short walk. A little way past Jennifer's middle school."

A while later the doorbell rang. Max woofed, raced to the door and skidded to a stop.

I ambled over and opened the door to find a woman in a crisp white nurse's uniform who probably stood five foot even in her stocking feet. She smiled at me.

"Uh-oh," I said. "Did I suffer a heart attack I didn't know about?"

Her dark eyes sparkled. "No, I have an appointment at this address. Is this the Jacobson residence?" Her voice was soft and melodic.

"Oh, good," Allison said. "You're here to set up my father-in-law's medication."

"What's going on?" I asked.

"You need to take pills twice a day," Allison said. "I arranged to have a registered nurse come once a week to set up your medicine. Then I can remind you to take it."

The nurse proceeded to fill a plastic container that had two rows of seven compartments. She stashed the medicine bottles in a cupboard and then explained to Allison and me, "One set of pills each morning after breakfast and the other before dinner. We can start right now." She handed me a glass of water and three horse pills.

"I hate taking pills," I said.

She gave me a winning smile. "A big strapping fellow like you can't be afraid of three little pills."

I couldn't disappoint her, so I managed to swallow the pills without choking to death.

AFTER DINNER, I approached Allison. "As long as I'm going to be bumming off you, I thought I should know the ground rules of your household."

She put her hand on my shoulder. "You're our guest, Paul."

"I don't want to be underfoot, so educate me on your daily routine."

"It's pretty simple. During the week we have breakfast at seven. You can either join us or have cereal later."

"I'm a morning person. I'll probably be up."

"At seven-forty-five Denny leaves for his job, negotiating financial deals to put bread on the table." She smiled. "Then Jennifer walks to school around eight o'clock. Two days a week I leave around one in the afternoon for my volunteer work at Boulder Community Hospital."

"Leaving me all by my lonesome."

She patted my arm. "The rest of the week I'll be here to make sure you don't get in any trouble, Paul."

"I think you're a little late for that."

"Lunch you can fix yourself. A sandwich, soup or whatever you find in the refrigerator."

"I'm a fan of leftovers."

"Dinner's usually around six-thirty, unless Denny's late. I wash on Fridays, so leave anything in the clothes hamper and strip your bed that morning if you want clean sheets."

"I won't remember Fridays from fish filets."

"Then I'll remind you."

"If I'm now part of the household, I need some chores to do."

Allison pursed her lips. Then a smile crossed her face. "I know. You can walk Max. We've all been sharing that."

"Sounds good to me. I like stretching my legs, and the little tyke can join me."

"But there's something you have to do." Allison wagged her finger at me. "In Boulder they're very strict about dog litter. You'll have to take a plastic bag and pooper-scooper from under the sink. I wouldn't want you getting on the wrong side of the law."

"I think I've already done that."

I decided to check out the neighborhood and give Max his first walk. After I assembled all the props and hitched him up, he raced out the door, dragging me behind him. We burst into the dusk as a glow of orange permeated wisps of clouds above. We settled into an intermittent pace of Max dashing forward then screeching to a halt to sniff every bush, mailbox and fire hydrant.

Most of the yards appeared recently mowed and neatly landscaped, with a mixture of flower and rock gardens. We made a wide circle through the neighborhood and on the way back we passed one yard that had a neat row of fir trees lining both sides of a walkway. I thought of Christmas in May.

When we returned home, my jaw dropped in astonishment at the output of that one little dog; he had filled a plastic bag.

THAT NIGHT I wrote down the day's events with a reminder left on top on my nightstand: "Read this, you old poop, and go to the Centennial Community Center at 2 P.M." I even drew myself a map.

THE NEXT DAY, dutifully refreshing my memory by reading my journal entry and wolfing down a hearty breakfast, I sat in the living room of Denny's house and oriented myself to my new domain. The telephone rang, and Allison announced a caller asking for yours truly.

"Who'd phone me here?" I asked

"I don't know, but it's a man who says he needs to speak with you."

"I usually only accept calls from ladies, but, oh well." I picked up the receiver.

"Mr. Jacobson, this is Detective Hamilton from the Denver Police Department. We spoke at Denver International Airport yesterday."

"Yes, Detective."

"I need to ask you some additional questions. I wanted to make sure you'd be home in one hour."

"Let me check my social calendar…you're in luck, Detective. I have an opening. I'll await your visit with bated breath."

By the way he hung up the phone, I didn't think he appreciated my remark. So having to put off any exploration of my environs or romantic trysts, I waited patiently for Detective Hamilton to arrive.

When he pulled up in his deluxe cop car, I happened to be looking out the window, so I watched as he marched up the walkway, adjusting a blue-striped tie. I greeted him at the door sans Max who was out in the backyard. Hamilton didn't look the least bit familiar, but he did match the description I'd written in my diary. He smelled of cheap aftershave lotion and had no five o'clock shadow.

"You do have a mole on your cheek," I said to him.

His hand automatically went to his face. "What's that supposed to mean?"

"See, Detective, I wrote a description of you and what happened to me yesterday."

He dropped his hand. "May we sit down?"

"Standing or sitting. Whatever you prefer, Detective."

I plunked my old body down on the couch, and Hamilton pulled over a chair to face me.

"I need to ask you several questions regarding your background."

"Fire away."

"Did you spend time in the military?"

"Damn straight. I did my duty in the Navy during World War II."

"Combat?"

"No. I handled supply logistics between England and Normandy during the invasion. I pushed paper."

He nodded. "But did you receive any special combat training?"

"Just the usual in basic training and a lot of lifeboat drills. After that I counted pencils and filled out forms."

"Did you ever learn any martial arts, say Judo or Karate?"

"No. My exercise has been limited to golf and walking. Never had any desire to learn how to kick or chop people."

"Unique choice of words, Mr. Jacobson."

I shrugged. "That's what those guys in the white outfits and black belts do, isn't it?"

"You told me yesterday that you didn't know the victim, Mr. Daniel Reynolds."

"That's right. From what I read in my diary, I woke up on the plane and didn't know anything about him."

"Yet, another passenger reported that the two of you argued vehemently over older people traveling on their own."

"Unfortunately, I don't remember that."

"Do you consider yourself a violent man, Mr. Jacobson?"

"I've swatted a few flies now and then."

He glared at me. "And when you get into arguments with people?"

"No, I'm not into the physical stuff. I like cussing and screaming."

"Mr. Jacobson, there remains the matter that you claimed

not to know Mr. Reynolds, yet when I questioned you yesterday, you volunteered his name."

I thought back to my journal. "I have an explanation. Wait here." I lumbered into my room and returned with Reynolds's business card.

"Here." I handed the card to Hamilton. "I found this in my pocket, so he must have given it to me. That's how I came up with the name."

"It would have been helpful if you had mentioned this yesterday."

I sighed, realizing that I would never make Detective Hamilton happy.

He turned the card over in his hands and dropped it back on the end table. "Any final recollections, Mr. Jacobson?"

"No, you've heard everything I can dredge up."

He stared at me with his cold, clear eyes. "Please remain in Colorado until we settle this matter."

"Yes, sir."

With that he stood up, strolled to the door and let himself out.

THAT AFTERNOON, I prepared for my outing to the Centennial Community Center, and Jennifer agreed to walk over with me before her tennis lesson.

She came bouncing up to me wearing white tennis shorts, a T-shirt that said "Wham!" and purple tennis shoes.

"Where's your tennis racquet?" I asked.

"I have a locker at the club. I keep one racquet there and one at home. That way I don't have to carry it back and forth."

"And how's your tennis game?"

"The pro says I whack the ball pretty good. But I need to develop more control."

Two blocks from Denny's house, we passed a building next to a park.

"That's my school, Grandpa."

"Speaking of which, why aren't you in it?"

"Oh, Grandpa. It's Sunday. But we have less than a month left before summer vacation."

"I bet you'll be glad when the school year's over."

"I like summer, but school's okay too. I have my swim and tennis friends during the summer and my school friends during the rest of the year."

"Yeah, I would have Hawaii friends and Boulder friends if I could remember where I left my brain cells."

"You talk funny, Grandpa. Maybe you'll make some new friends at the Community Center."

We arrived in front of a building in the shape of the letter W. Two wings flared out to each side of a lobby that stuck out in the middle. The structure contained large windows rimmed with white, surrounded by brown and reddish brick, leading to a green tile roof topped with a glass-encased square tower. I spotted a sign to the right that indicated "Senior Center." Above the doorway appeared pink cement and in the ground to the side stretched a small garden with a placard thanking the Boulder Garden Club. We entered a well-lit entryway containing bridge tables, a magazine rack with literature and two computers. In front of a large meeting room, I spotted a sign for Colorado Mountain Retirement Properties.

"I can get back home on my own," I told Jennifer.

"Okey dokey," she replied. "I'm going to walk over to the tennis club."

Once I entered the meeting room, a man in his thirties with bright white teeth, a puckered face and thin glasses greeted me. He smelled of cigarette smoke and beer. I wondered if he had just escaped from a sports bar. "Hello, I'm Randall Swathers. Please take a seat." He indicated a half-filled collection of folding chairs and handed me a business card. Color picture of a smirking salesman. "Please sign the sheet on the table and help yourself to a brochure."

I ambled over and added my signature to the list of eight

other names. I grabbed a color pamphlet, sat down in the back row and studied a pond visible through the large windows to the right side of the room.

Other old fogies limped in. Crap. Old people surrounded me.

I leaned over toward a woman two chairs away. "You have these kinds of events very often?"

"We have an active senior group here at the Community Center." She smiled at me. "You're new."

"Yeah," I replied. "I just moved to Boulder. Living with my son and his family."

"I'm doing the same," she said. "Came here from Chicago."

I regarded her more closely. An attractive woman with gray hair. She'd obviously kept herself in good shape. Her perfume made me think of gentle ocean breezes and Hawaiian flowers. She gave me a smile revealing her own teeth, and then with a twinkle in her eyes said, "Why are you looking into Colorado Mountain Retirement Properties?"

"I received some information when I flew here from Honolulu. Thought I'd check it out. And you?"

She wrinkled her brow. "I don't want to overstay my welcome with my daughter. I've been here six months, and it's time to look into some other alternatives."

"So are you familiar with this outfit?" I asked.

"Not really. Originally I picked up a brochure here at the Senior Center. Then when I heard of this presentation, I decided to find out more."

"Any idea how reputable these people are?"

"I don't know," she said with a shrug. "I haven't met anyone in person."

Randall Swathers, the man who had welcomed us at the door, came to the front of the room.

"Let's get started," he said, giving us an insincere smile.

"I'm glad you're able to join us today to hear the newest and most exciting concept in retirement living."

Swathers paused and took a sip from a paper cup.

"As you know, the challenge is finding a mixture of independent living combined with necessary care as required in an affordable package and located where you can enjoy a high quality of life. With that in mind, Colorado Mountain Retirement Properties has begun development of your new home in the foothills northwest of Buena Vista."

He clicked a button, and a computer-controlled projector flashed a picture of snow-capped peaks on the wall.

"Within sight of the Collegiate Peaks, fourteen-thousand-foot Mount Princeton, Mount Yale and Mount Harvard, your beautiful and affordable cottage offers both the independence of your own house and the central amenities of a five-star hotel. Each cottage has a panoramic view of the mountains with independent outside access, while being connected by a temperature-controlled corridor to the central building where dining, health care, indoor swimming pool, Jacuzzi and a complete business center reside."

A picture of an attractive two-bedroom house appeared, followed by an artist's rendition of a well-lit indoor swimming area.

"This ideal location provides Colorado's most attractive retirement option," Swathers said. "And now the best part. Each of you has an opportunity of being a founding owner. For the small amount of two hundred thousand dollars, you can reserve your own cottage. This will cover the purchase price and the first year of meal and maintenance services."

Heads nodded in front of me, and the corners of Swathers's mouth turned up. I couldn't tell if the expression resembled an attempted smile or a dog baring its teeth.

I raised my hand. "How far along is the construction?" I asked.

Swathers cleared his throat. "Construction has begun and will be completed next year."

"Any pictures of how far along the construction is?"

Two women turned around and gave me questioning stares.

"I don't have any in this presentation," Swathers replied. "Now let me show you an artist's drawing of the dining area."

Up flashed a colored sketch of a large room with plate glass windows, snow-covered peaks in the background and deer grazing in the foreground. A collective sigh went up from a number of women in the room.

"What about road access?" I asked.

"A paved driveway will be provided from Highway 24. The property resides a mile off that main thoroughfare. Close enough for easy access when your relatives visit, but far enough from the highway for quiet and seclusion."

After the presentation, the woman I had spoken to before the program leaned over and said, "Seems too good to be true, doesn't it?"

"That's what I'm afraid of," I said. "Something doesn't seem quite right."

"I'm looking into a number of retirement facilities, but this is the best one I've found so far."

"Have you spoken with anyone who's visited the location?" I asked.

"No."

"I'd want to take a look at it before plopping down that kind of money."

"I can't drive that far, and most of the people here have the same problem," she said.

"I think I'll get my family to take me on a little trip to check it out. I'll let you know."

She smiled at me. "That would be very helpful."

"So how do I get in touch with you?"

She took a pad of paper out of her purse, wrote on it, tore off the top sheet and handed it to me.

I read the name. Helen Gleason.

"Helen, it's a pleasure meeting you." I held out my hand, and she took it. I felt a pleasant warmth. "I'll give you a call after I visit the place."

She gave me a parting smile as she turned and left the room.

I waited until all the people had departed and approached the salesman.

"Swathers, what kind of scam are you trying to pull off here?" I said.

"What do you mean?" Beads of sweat formed on his forehead.

"Up-front payments for property in a questionable state of development. Come on."

"I'll have pictures soon," he said with a gulp.

I looked him in the eyes, and he averted my gaze.

"How do you live with yourself deluding all these old people?" I said.

"I...uh..."

"I should report you to the Better Business Bureau."

He swallowed. "Please, don't say anything. My boss will take it out on me."

"Did you know Daniel Reynolds?" I asked.

"Yes."

"Do you know what happened to him?"

"Heart attack, I think," Swathers said.

"Someone murdered him," I said. "Maybe he got crosswise with the ringleaders of this crooked development."

The man's eyes opened wide.

"You could be next," I said.

I felt a tap on my shoulder. A woman I hadn't noticed glared at me. She had a tight-lipped expression as if she had been sucking a lemon. "You need to vacate this room," she said. "We have another meeting starting in five minutes."

"Yes, ma'am," I said with a salute and turned toward the door.

I decided to explore the Community Center before heading back to the ranch. Ahead of me appeared a large swimming area with a lap pool and play pond where kids slid down a twisting slide into the water. I shivered. I might not have been able to remember anything from the day before, but I knew I hated the water. Pools and I coexisted like beer and rocks. If you dropped a rock in a beer, it would sink immediately. Put me in water, and I did the same.

A quick tour revealed a locker room, a gym with young men thumping basketballs and a weight room. I strolled through an exercise area and came to an artificial climbing wall. Down in a sunken pit, a man was helping a young boy into a harness while a woman held a rope for a girl who had scaled twenty feet up. I watched as the girl moved her right hand to grab a red handhold and then moved her left foot up to another indentation in the wall. Amazing. You didn't even need to go up into the mountains anymore to climb.

With my curiosity satisfied, I ambled back to the lobby and eyed two vending machines. Swathers's talk had made me hungry. One machine had healthy snacks including a tuna salad and milk; the other contained the usual contingent of junk food from the sugar and salt food groups.

I decided to wait to eat until I returned home. A large fish tank contained bluegills, a yellow perch, a channel catfish and a green sunfish. At least no sharks or piranha. Deciding I needed to escape the chlorine-filled air, I strolled outside. From the parking lot I could see the rock formations along the foothills and barely make out the peaks of the Continental Divide. I looked at the brochure from the presentation. Nice mountains there as well. I wondered how much substance existed behind this development.

I angled across the parking lot and noticed an arm dangling at an awkward angle from the driver's-side open window of a white Honda Accord. I put my hands on the side of the car and bent down to look inside. There sat the sleazy salesman Randall Swathers. His head lolled to the side at an unnatural angle, his glasses were broken and he had thrown up on himself.

FIVE

I TWISTED MY HEAD BACK and forth like at a ping-pong match. No one else in the parking lot. Why didn't someone with an annoying cell phone appear when you wanted one?

I jogged back into the building as fast as my old legs would carry me and leaned on the reception desk, panting.

A young woman sat there, filing her nails.

"Call 9-1-1," I shouted between gasping breaths.

She jumped.

"There's an injured man in the parking lot," I said, knowing I now had her attention.

Her eyes expanded to the size of silver dollars.

A man who had been standing on my side of the counter punched in numbers on his cell phone. "I'm calling for you." He started speaking on the phone, describing his location and explaining that someone required medical attention.

I asked the gal behind the desk, "Do you have any trained medical personnel on site?"

"Just the lifeguard."

"Well, get him."

"We'll have to close the pool."

"Why don't you watch the pool while he checks on the injured man?"

"Then who will take care of the front desk?" she asked.

I contemplated homicide. "There's a guy in a car outside who may be dying. Get the damn lifeguard!"

She finally got the message and dashed into the pool area. Moments later, a tall, muscular young man in a skimpy swimsuit appeared. He looked like he needed a vine to swing on and a friend named Jane.

"I hear there's a problem," he said.

"Yeah. Come with me." I burst through the door with him trailing behind. I turned back and saw him limping over the asphalt in his bare feet. You'd have thought he was the old fart.

I reached the car and turned around to signal to the lifeguard, who kept high-stepping like he was walking on live coals. "Get a move on. Over here!"

He finally arrived and bent down to look inside the car.

I heard a gurgling sound.

The next thing I knew, the lifeguard spewed his lunch all over the parking lot.

Kids. They didn't have the stomach for this kind of thing.

Fortunately, the scream of a siren overwhelmed the sound of heaving, and two paramedics jumped out of a white ambulance van. They opened the car door and began ministering to Randall Swathers before the lifeguard could empty his stomach again.

"How's he doing?" I asked.

"We're too late," one of the paramedics replied. "He's dead."

Within half an hour the police had arrived. Two officers cordoned off an area around the car. With all the commotion, a crowd had gathered outside the yellow ribbon.

A photographer took pictures of Randall Swathers from various angles, and then a man with latex gloves poked at the body before two attendants removed it on a stretcher. Finally, a woman arrived who began dusting the car for fingerprints.

I noticed a tall, skinny man in a gray suit speaking with the lifeguard. The lifeguard pointed toward me, and I waved back.

Moments later the skinny guy came over to me. He had a large nose and piercing gray eyes.

"I'm Detective Lavino," he said. "Let's get out of the crowd. I need to speak with you."

We walked into the building and found an unused room in the Senior Center.

"I understand you reported finding the victim in the parking lot."

"That's correct."

"May I see some identification?"

I reached in my wallet and pulled out my ID card.

"Mr. Jacobson. This shows you're a resident of Hawaii."

"Not right now. I'm living with my son and his family here in Boulder."

"And you indicated finding the victim in his car in the parking lot."

"That's correct. I was heading back to my son's house and saw an arm dangling out of the car."

"And do you know the victim?"

"I wouldn't say he's my best buddy, but I met him earlier. He gave a pitch for Colorado Mountain Retirement Properties. Speaking of which, there's something fishy. If I were you, Detective, I'd look into that outfit."

"Why's that?"

"I think they're selling fraudulent property."

He jotted a note on his pad. "I'll look into that. I also need to get the address of where you're staying in Boulder."

"Sure. I should have it written down in my wallet." I rummaged through and found a slip of paper with my son Denny's name, address and phone number.

While he wrote in a notepad, I noticed that his fingernails were chewed to the quick. He returned the notepad to his jacket pocket and said, "Please don't leave Boulder for the next few days. I may have some additional questions."

"I have no grand tour plans. You know where to find me. And, Detective, it's not a good idea to chew your fingernails."

Having had enough of retirement home scams, the police and upchucking lifeguards, I moseyed back to Denny's house.

Along the way I assessed my situation. I felt the confusion

of again being connected to a murder, the victims working for the same slimy outfit. Something was going on with this retirement property company that didn't make sense. I'd have to think this through carefully and watch my back.

THE NEXT MORNING I woke up wondering where the hell I was but caught sight of a note that read: "Read this before you wander off, you old coot." It was in my handwriting. I'd learned to follow my own directions, so I read my diary entry describing all the fun and games at the Community Center the day before.

Later that morning I was preparing for a day of quiet when the doorbell rang. Allison greeted a tall, skinny guy in a suit. I wondered if he was proselytizing for some religious group.

"I need to speak with Mr. Paul Jacobson," he said to Allison.

I heard the remark and approached the door.

"Mr. Jacobson, I need to follow up on our conversation from yesterday," the man said.

"But I don't remember speaking with you."

"I'm Detective Lavino. We discussed the murder at the Centennial Community Center."

Allison stepped forward. "Paul has short-term memory loss, Detective. He remembers things fine during the day, but completely forgets the recent past overnight."

"But I have a photographic memory except for that one little flaw." I said.

Lavino looked puzzled.

"It's like this. I can answer anything you want before the year 2000, but this century remains blank."

"I do need to ask you further questions regarding the events of yesterday."

"Let's sit down," I suggested. "I'll try to help any way I can within the limitations of my crappy memory."

I plopped down on the comfortable brown and white

couch, and Lavino pulled up a gold-padded chair with a wicker back. Allison offered coffee, but the detective declined.

"Mr. Jacobson. I'm very curious on several points. You reported finding the body of Randall Swathers in the parking lot. Tell me the particulars once more."

"Well, Detective, I don't remember it directly, but I keep a journal. From what I read this morning, it seems pretty simple. I was walking home, saw an arm dangling out of a car window, looked inside, saw Swathers unconscious and reported it to the receptionist inside the Community Center."

He looked at his notepad. "A witness claims that you threatened the victim shortly before you reported finding his body."

"Sure. I was heated. The guy tried to scam all these little old ladies."

"You were overheard saying, 'You could be next.' Interesting statement just before he's murdered." He now stared intently at me. "And in checking you out, I found your name linked to another recent murder. Two days ago, you were questioned in regards to the death of Daniel Reynolds. Ring any bells?"

"Again, I don't remember. But what I read says he sat next to me on the flight from Honolulu to Denver."

"Now what's disconcerting is your proximity to two murders, both victims working for the same company. Any explanations?"

"You probably should start with people working for that company. In fact the first victim's boss was reported to be traveling with him."

"Yes, we've spoken with him. But we verified he wasn't in the vicinity of the second victim yesterday. Do you have any other information to share?"

I shrugged. "I obviously was near someone who doesn't like real estate peddlers."

"Like yourself?"

Allison gasped. "Is Paul a suspect, Detective?"

"I wouldn't go that far. Let's say that he's a person of interest in two unsolved murders."

"We better find you a lawyer, Paul," Allison said.

"I hate lawyers," I replied. "I can handle this on my own."

"I still find it very interesting that you, Mr. Jacobson, happened to be in proximity to both murders," Detective Lavino continued. "Why were you at the Community Center in the first place?"

"I went to hear the sales presentation from that so-called Colorado Mountain Retirement Properties outfit."

"And can you account for what you did between the time the presentation ended and the time you reported finding the victim in the parking lot?"

"Again, Detective, I'll help you as much as I can. With my faulty memory I don't remember specifically, but from what I wrote down it appears I wandered around the Community Center before going outside."

He stared at me again, his eyes boring in on my eyes like he was trying to see into my defective brain cells.

"One other piece of information," Lavino said. "I tracked down a copy of your fingerprints from Hawaii. Apparently the police had files on you in regard to several crimes."

"All that was cleared up," Allison said. "Actually, Paul helped solve a murder and a theft."

Lavino looked toward the ceiling. "Great. That's all I need. An amateur involved who messes things up."

"I'll be happy to help you any way I can, Detective," I added with my most sincere smile.

Lavino looked back at me. "Your fingerprints matched exactly with a set of prints lifted from the side of the victim's car. Care to venture a guess on how they ended up there?"

"It's pretty obvious. When I saw the dangling arm protruding from the car's window, I bent down, put my hands on the car door while I peeked inside."

"Are you trained in the martial arts?"

"No, I never learned how to give Karate chops."

"That may have been what killed the victim. Any other comments, Mr. Jacobson?"

I flinched. "Yes, you should check up on Colorado Mountain Retirement Properties. I think they're running some kind of scam."

"Why do you suspect that?" Lavino asked.

"Just my geezer intuition. They seem to pitch pretty hard to old ladies."

"As I told you yesterday, we'll be investigating all aspects of this case." He placed his hands on the end table between us and leaned toward me. I noticed his fingernails were bit to the quick. "We'll be talking again, Mr. Jacobson."

"Fine by me. I'd suggest that you quit chewing your nails, Detective. You'll want to keep your fingers looking nice for snapping handcuffs on real criminals."

He gave me one of those looks where cartoon characters shoot daggers at someone.

After he left, Allison said, "What are you going to do, Paul?"

"First I'm going to find out more about Colorado Mountain Retirement Properties. Something strange is going on with that organization."

"I think you need some legal advice. When Denny gets home we can ask him the names of any attorneys he knows."

"No way. I'm not getting involved with any blood-sucking lawyers."

"Why do you hold the legal profession in such low regard?" Allison asked. "Your good friend in Hawaii, Meyer Ohana, was a lawyer."

"I'm sure Meyer is the exception to the rule, but I had a bad experience many years ago when I ran my auto parts business in L.A. Lawyers do more harm than good."

I went into my room and looked in all the drawers until I found the business card from the dead guy on the plane. Then I placed a call.

"I'm a prospective buyer of one of your properties, and I'd like to speak with Randall Swathers, please," I said to the woman who answered the phone.

"I'm sorry, he's not around today," she replied in a syrupy voice.

If she only knew how much he really wasn't around.

"May I ask the nature of your call?" she continued.

"You may."

I waited.

"And what is the nature of your call?" she finally asked.

"I'm interested in retirement property for yours truly. Why don't you put me in touch with Gary Previn."

"Oh, I'm sorry. He doesn't take calls from individual prospects. Those go to one of his sales people."

"Too much of a high muckety-muck?"

The woman cleared her throat. "He gave me those instructions."

"How does someone like little old me get information so I can buy property? I'd try Daniel Reynolds, but he's not around either because he's dead."

"I can have another sales person or Randall Swathers call you," she said in a clipped tone.

"Right. I'll tell you a little secret. I saw Randall in Boulder yesterday, and he's as dead as Daniel Reynolds. There seems to be a contagious epidemic of murders in your sales force."

She gasped.

"How does it feel to work at a place where people keep dropping like flies?" I asked.

"That's terrible," she said. "Gary Previn was supposed to be with Randall yesterday."

"You mean the big cheese lowered himself to go with one of his salesmen?"

"He lives in Boulder and planned to meet Randall at the Centennial Community Center in the afternoon."

"That's interesting. I didn't see anyone with Randall either before or after he died."

"Well, I'm sure Mr. Previn intended to meet Randall."

"This guy Previn sounds like someone I should talk to. Even though this may be beneath him, I think it would be advisable for him to call me." I gave her Denny's home phone number.

Leaving the receptionist to unravel the problem of a quickly depleting sales organization, I opened a Boulder phone directory and thumbed through the pages. I found two Gary Previns listed, one on Fourteenth Street and one on Darley. I picked the one on Darley and called. Heard a voice-mail that gave no hint of being the right person. When I tried the other number, a woman answered.

"Is this the home of the Gary Previn who works for Colorado Mountain Retirement Properties?" I asked.

"No. You must have the wrong number."

I apologized and hung up. By the process of elimination, I would call what I hoped was the right phone number again later.

That afternoon when the mail arrived, Allison handed me an envelope. Inside, I found a check made out to the Paul Jacobson Living Trust from my municipal bond fund.

"I need to set up a checking account here in Boulder," I told Allison.

"I can drop you off at the bank in a few minutes. I need to run some errands."

I sloughed off my slippers and put on my dancing shoes to be presentable.

AT THE BOULDER Central Bank I waited for ten minutes, and then the receptionist pointed me to a desk where a young whippersnapper in his forties sat peering at a stack of forms.

He wore a dark blue suit, white shirt and red tie. His neatly trimmed hair held a hint of gray at the temples.

He stared at me over the top of the glasses that sat low on his nose. "I'm Gilbert Kraus. How may I help you?"

I dropped down into an institutional chair. "I need to open a checking account at your fine bank."

He smiled. "Of course. Please fill out this form." He extracted a sheet of paper from the stack on his desk like a jukebox selecting a phonograph record, and I proceeded to fill in everything with the help of the crib sheet in my wallet. I could still remember my social security number, but I had to check on Denny's address.

Once I completed the paperwork, he went off to probably execute some secret handshake with a guy who wore a green eyeshade in a locked back room. When he returned, he handed me a booklet of temporary checks. "Now I can order permanent checks for you. It's a matter of what picture you want."

"Picture?"

"Of course." He extracted a sheet from the pile of papers on his desk and slid it toward me.

I squinted at color pictures of thirty different scenes: the mountains, ocean, a moose, clouds. "What do you have in the way of plain old checks?"

He touched his glasses. "No such thing. You have to choose from one of these pictures." He tapped his pen on the sheet.

"What if I don't want one of your god-awful pictures?"

He puckered up like an engine ready to blow a gasket. "Now don't be difficult, sir. Please make a selection."

I let out a deep sigh. "If you had a picture of someone walking out with a bag of money, I'd choose that one."

"That's not funny." He tapped his fingers on his desk. "Select one."

I regarded the pictures again. "I'll take the one of this big oak tree. It reminds me of you. No flexibility."

He glared at me. "Now, as for the initial deposit."

"Yeah. Here's some money you can put into my new account."

I handed him the check made out to the Paul Jacobson Living Trust from my municipal bond fund.

He eyed it like a hairball coughed up by a cat.

"I can't deposit this check in your account," he said.

"Why not?"

"It's made out to the Paul Jacobson Living Trust. The checking account is in the name of Paul Jacobson."

"What the hell difference does that make? I'm Paul Jacobson. I'm also the trustee of the Paul Jacobson Living Trust."

"I'm sorry. These are two entirely different legal entities. I can only deposit the check in an account that has been set up for the Paul Jacobson Living Trust."

"This is the stupidest, most petty, bureaucratic piss-pot I've ever heard of!" I shouted.

Heads turned throughout the bank.

"Mr. Jacobson. We have rules to follow."

The security guard strolled over. "Is there a problem, Mr. Kraus?"

Kraus eyed me warily. "I don't think so. Now, Mr. Jacobson. You either need to change the name on the account or deposit something that is made out to the name on the account."

"I don't care about your idiotic rules. This is plain bull pucky."

I grabbed my check and stomped away.

"Mr. Jacobson. You need to make an initial deposit in your account."

"You know where you can stuff your account," I yelled as I pushed through the swinging door.

I had only stood on the sidewalk for a moment, when a man burst through the door of the bank. He ran across the parking lot and vaulted onto the top of a retaining wall. Something white fell into a bush just before he disappeared onto the other side.

SIX

BEING A NOSY CODGER, I moseyed over to see what fell when the man jumped over the wall. I pushed aside part of the bush and found a small bag. Picking it up, I saw the logo of the Boulder Central Bank. I undid a tie string to find a collection of twenty-dollar bills. Uh-oh.

I needed to get this back to the bank. I hurried across the parking lot but, halfway there, two police squad cars screeched to a halt in front of the building. One large policeman raced inside the bank with his gun drawn. One other officer, a short skinny guy, saw me holding the bag, so to speak.

"Stop right there," he commanded.

"Yes, sir. Here's something I found in the bushes." I pointed toward where the bag of money had fallen and then handed him the packet of money.

"And when did you find this?" the thin policeman asked.

"Moments ago."

"Please stay here, sir. One of the detectives will want to speak with you."

I shrugged. "I don't have anything better to do until my daughter-in-law picks me up."

The large policeman came out of the bank, and the two of them conferred out of my hearing range. Finally, the one that had taken the money approached me again. "We'd like you to come down to the police station to make a statement about what you saw."

"Okay by me. You mean I'll get an all-expense-paid trip in your squad car?"

In spite of the situation, I guess he had a sense of humor as he gave me a smile and said, "You could look at it that way."

Just then, Allison drove up. Her window went down, and she said, "Are you ready, Paul?"

"No. I need to take a little trip with the police."

A frown crossed her face. "Are you in some kind of trouble?"

"I don't think so. I witnessed the tail end of a bank robbery, and they want to question me."

"Do you want me to come with you?"

"Nah. I can handle this on my own."

"Are you sure?"

"Go run some errands, and I'll call you at home later."

"I need to pick up Jennifer at school. She has a half day, and we were going to meet Denny for lunch. Instead, we'll all come retrieve you at the police station."

She reluctantly drove away, and I waited for my escort.

My new buddy, the skinny police officer, asked me to get in his car.

"I assume you're not going to lock me in the back," I said.

"It's not very comfortable back there. You can sit in the front with me."

After a short drive, we arrived at the City of Boulder Public Safety Center. It didn't make me feel safe at all. The sign read: Police—Fire—Communications. I wondered what needed to be communicated.

I scanned the building—an institutional structure with three shades of brick: gray, gray-white and gray-brown. A steel beam (gray) connected three gray pillars to the left of the door, and to the right of the lobby stood another pillar attached to a gray beam. The United States and state of Colorado flags hung limply on tall gray poles. Above the flat roof of the building appeared a jumble of antennas. That must have been for the communications.

We pulled into a parking lot on the side of the building, waited for a guard bar to rise and proceeded to the back of the building. My companion police officer escorted me to my own private waiting room that was the size of a closet and consisted of a table, two chairs and a camera mounted in one corner. Ah, the wonders of crime investigation.

I thought how nice it would be to take a nap, but reconsidered, knowing my memory would reset and then I'd be in deep trouble.

Closing my eyes, I tried to imagine beautiful places I had visited, but instead my mind dredged up the image of the stockroom in the store I'd run in Los Angeles many years ago where a prankster had locked me in.

My musings were interrupted by the arrival of Detective Lavino.

"Mr. Jacobson. We meet again."

"You never know who you're going to run into."

"Would you care to tell me about the bag of money you had in your hand in the parking lot of the Boulder Central Bank?"

"It's simple, Detective. When I left the bank, I noticed this guy charging across the parking lot. He leaped up on a retaining wall and, before he disappeared on the other side, something fell into the bushes. I went over to investigate, being a duty-minded citizen. Voila. I found a bag. You can imagine my surprise when I opened it up and saw twenty-dollar bills. I started back to return it to the bank when one of your officers intercepted me."

"You certainly have a way of being right nearby when crimes are committed. One of the bank officers, Mr. Kraus, had something interesting to say concerning you."

"Oh, and I have something interesting to say about him,

Detective. He wasn't very helpful. If you're looking for a bank, I'd suggest you try elsewhere."

Lavino thumbed through his notepad. "He states you caused considerable commotion in the bank. Yelling and calling attention to yourself."

"I merely voiced my displeasure over the stupidity of the banking system."

Lavino smiled. "I know what you mean. I've run into some strange banking rules a few times myself. But you should know that Mr. Kraus thinks you caused a disturbance to distract the bank personnel while the robbery took place. He even suspected you were working with the robber."

I flinched. "An old coot like me? There was nothing planned on my part, just a spontaneous reaction to Mr. Kraus and his silly regulations."

Lavino nodded. "Okay. Did you recognize the bank robber?"

"I have no idea who he is. I saw the back of a man running, that's all."

"Describe what you saw."

"A man in jeans, a dark sweatshirt and tennis shoes, who seemed athletic. Caucasian with brown hair, poking out from under a black baseball cap. I didn't see his face."

"Pretty good description for someone with memory problems."

"My memory blanks out when I go to sleep, but I have a darn good memory when I'm awake. I could repeat our conversation word for word if you like."

"Go ahead. Show me."

I proceeded to do so.

I detected a hint of surprise in his eyes.

"I could also do the same for when we spoke earlier today. But I remember nothing regarding yesterday."

"You have quite a selective memory, Mr. Jacobson."

"Just the way my defective brain works, Detective. I have to live with the hand I've been dealt. Unless you have any more questions for me, I'd like to return to my family."

He shook his head and moved to the door. "Come on. I'll escort you up front."

Denny, Allison and Jennifer were sitting in the lobby, and they all jumped up when I appeared.

Jennifer raced up to Detective Lavino and wagged her finger at him. "You let my Grandpa go. He's innocent."

Lavino looked down at her and laughed. "You're as feisty as the old man. He's not accused of anything today. He's just a witness to a bank robbery."

She put her hands on her hips. "I'm going to be a lawyer when I grow up."

He nodded his head. "I'm sure you will." He turned toward me. "You're free to go home, Mr. Jacobson. With all the things you've witnessed lately, just don't leave the state."

"Okay. I'll put off my trip to Bogotá."

Lavino looked at me askance. "Get out of here."

"Yes, sir," I said and saluted.

As we headed out of the building, Jennifer said, "A man from a bank came to speak at our school this year. Do you know what happens when bags of money are stolen?"

"Other than a robber jumping over a wall to escape?"

"Not that, Grandpa. They have red dye that explodes in some of the bags of stolen money."

I looked at my hands. "Obviously not the bag I found."

Jennifer bounced along the parking lot. "That was so cool, Grandpa. The police questioned you again."

"Again?" I said.

"Yes, when we visited you in Hawaii, the police took you in for questioning."

"What are you referring to?" Denny asked.

"You remember," Jennifer said. "Grandpa was sitting in a reported stolen car."

Denny looked as blank as me.

"Uh-oh," I said. "Denny, I think your memory may be starting to act like mine."

Denny's brow furrowed. "Do you notice me forgetting things, Allison?"

"No worse than any of us at our age," Allison said, patting Denny on the arm.

"But he may have inherited my memory," I said, helpfully.

Now Denny looked worried. "That would be terrible."

"Although to be honest," I said, "I can't remember for sure if we adopted you or not. If adopted, there would be no risk, unless it's contagious."

Denny cracked a faint smile to acknowledge my joshing him.

"Don't worry, Dad," Jennifer said. "I have a good memory. I'll remind you if you start forgetting like I do with Grandpa. Besides, you can always keep a journal." She gave Denny a big hug, and he seemed to relax. "And Grandpa remembers fine from the past. I'm even going to have him help me with a school project tonight."

"What's that?" I asked.

"I'm supposed to give a report covering something during World War II. I thought I'd base it on your experiences."

"I should be able to dredge up something of value from this soggy old brain of mine. Thank you all for rescuing me from the inquisition. And me such a law-abiding citizen."

Allison smiled at me. "Some men are chick magnets. I guess you're a crime magnet."

"Anything I can do to bring a little excitement into your lives," I said.

"Why not simply avoid these little incidents?" Denny said.

"Nah. You'd be too bored."

BACK AT THE OLD homestead before dinner, Allison reminded me to take my pills.

"Your mom is a slave driver," I told Jennifer.

"She wants you to stay healthy." Jennifer crossed her arms. "Now take your medicine."

"You're both turning against me," I said. "Denny, protect me from these overzealous women."

"I'm on their side," he said. "Take your pills."

"Three against one," I said. "I don't like those odds." I managed to gulp down the three rocks disguised as pills without choking to death.

Allison retrieved the mail and handed me two letters. "Some people from your fan club, Paul?"

"Who'd be writing to me?" I read the return address on the first letter out loud. "Meyer Ohana from Kaneohe, Hawaii."

"It's your friend who you ate meals with at the retirement home," Jennifer said, jumping up and down. "Open it so we can find out how he's doing."

"The letter is addressed to me, young lady."

"Meyer's my friend too," Jennifer said. "He described being a judge in Hawaii. That's why I want to be a lawyer when I grow up."

"I'll disinherit you if you go over to the dark side and become a flesh-eating attorney."

"Oh, Grandpa. You say the funniest things." She gave me a hug. How could you argue with that? She'd probably be a good lawyer and win cases by giving the judge and jury hugs.

I read the letter out loud to Jennifer. Meyer described living in a care home and said that his macular degeneration had stabilized. He had taken up watercolor painting and could see shapes well enough to do abstract pictures. The letter ended with: "But, Paul, without you here things are definitely too calm." He included his address and phone number.

The second letter had a return address in California. I opened it to find the name Marion Aumiller.

"It's your girlfriend who used to live in Hawaii," Jennifer said.

"How do you know so much about me?"

She clucked at me. "Grandpa, I met all your friends in Hawaii last year."

I adjourned to my room to read this letter in private. Marion said she missed me and had obtained my address from Meyer. She indicated she would be passing through Colorado with her daughter next week and wanted to let me know so we could get together. It included a phone number.

I called Jennifer into my room.

"Marion says she might be coming to visit," I said. "I don't even remember what she looks like."

"You used to have a picture of her on your dresser in Hawaii. Maybe you brought it with you."

I still had one bag I hadn't unpacked. We rummaged through it, and Jennifer extracted a framed picture.

"Here it is," she said, bouncing up and down.

I placed it on my new dresser. Not a bad-looking old broad.

"What's Marion like?" I asked Jennifer.

"She's really nice. She's the one who helped pick out the Hawaiian stuffed animals you gave me."

"From her letters it seems we were…uh…pretty intimate."

"That's right, Grandpa. You were lovers."

"What! You shouldn't know these things."

"Well, I am twelve. But I also read the diary you kept when you lived in Hawaii. But don't worry. I promised to keep it a secret between just you and me… Grandpa, what happened to the journal you kept in Hawaii?"

"I have no idea."

"I'm sure you would have brought it with you. Let's check some more in the bag where we found Marion's picture."

We both sorted through everything. No journal.

"Grandpa, when you arrived at the Denver airport, you didn't have any carry-on bag with you. You may have left it on the plane. That could be where your Hawaiian diary is."

"It's probably long gone if that's the case."

"You never know, Grandpa. Maybe someone found it and turned it in to the lost and found. You should call them."

So at Jennifer's assistance, I called the airline. After listening to music for ten minutes, being placed on hold twice, and listening to the damn music again, a human being answered.

"I may have left a bag on a flight from Honolulu a few days ago."

"Flight number and date?"

"Hell, I don't remember. Just a minute."

"Jennifer," I bellowed. "What date did I arrive?"

She shouted the information back to me.

"And the flight number?"

Allison walked up to me and handed me a folder that had my ticket receipt. I thumbed through it and gave the man on the phone the flight number.

"Your name and a phone number where you can be reached?" the man asked in a clipped tone.

"Paul Jacobson and here's the phone number." I read it to him.

"Description of the lost item."

"Crap, I don't know."

"Sir, how can we be expected to find a lost item if you can't describe it?"

"That's a damn good question. See if you can find some sort of carry-on bag."

"Sir, we handle thousands of misplaced items a day."

"Don't take very good care of people's stuff, do you?"

"Sir, I wasn't the one who left something on the plane."

"Just see if you can find a bag with my name on it."

I hung up, then decided to call the phone number in Marion's letter.

"Paul, it's so nice to hear your voice."

"I received your letter and wanted to call to say hi."

"I'll be passing through Boulder next Tuesday."

"Then I'll plan something for us to do." I gave her Denny's phone number.

We chitchatted and then parted.

I returned to my room and admired the picture on my dresser. I'll be damned. She seemed to like me. I pressed my palms against my forehead, trying to squeeze out some memory of Marion. I could remember squat concerning her.

After dinner I called Gary Previn's number and listened to the recorded message again, but no human answered. Jennifer left for her room to start her homework, and Denny departed for the garage to tinker with an end table. I looked over Allison's shoulder as she sat at the dining room table. "What are you working on?" I asked.

"A Sudoku puzzle, Paul. Do you want to try one?"

"Never heard of it," I said.

"Sit in the chair."

I obeyed and she handed me a booklet that had a bunch of squares with a random mix of numbers spread around.

"Looks like an incomplete set of social security numbers," I said.

"No, it's the latest craze and a good way to keep your brain in shape."

"A little late for me, but you may want Denny to give his gray matter a workout."

"As long as he stays active with his woodworking projects, he'll be fine. Now here's a pencil and some scratch paper, and I'll point out an easy puzzle to start with. You need to fill each square of nine boxes with the digits one through nine in such a way that every complete row and every complete column also have the digits one through nine. No duplications in either the boxes or the complete rows and columns."

"Looks complicated," I said.

"The puzzles can be easy to extremely difficult. Let me give you a hint. Work each square first. With the pencil fill in the possibilities in each individual box. By looking at what digits are already in the square, the row and the column you can eliminate digits. You have to be diligent not to make mistakes or you have to start over."

"Kind of like my brain every morning."

She smiled and patted me on the arm. "You have a good brain during the day. Give the puzzle a try."

I felt like I was back in school again. I licked the pencil, flexed my arms and dove in. At first nothing seemed to get eliminated. Every box had multiple alternatives penciled in. Then in one little square the alternatives dwindled to being only one digit. I circled it. A minor victory. Whenever I circled one, it eliminated other alternatives in other boxes. By a slow process of elimination, I began to fill in the puzzle. Then suddenly, like winning at solitaire, the digits cascaded into a completed puzzle. Damn. I had done it!

I felt like a kid who had managed to navigate his two-wheeler for the first time.

"You can try a harder one now, Paul, if you like."

"I think I'll quit while I'm ahead. And just think, I can redo that same puzzle tomorrow because it'll be all new to me."

Allison laughed. "No need to invest in more puzzle booklets for you."

"I'm supposed to talk to Jennifer regarding World War II for her school project. I'll mosey into her room and see if she's ready."

I sauntered upstairs and entered Jennifer's room. On the walls she had pictures of Perry Mason, F. Lee Bailey, the Justices of the Supreme Court, and Bart Simpson. Seemed like birds of a feather to me.

"Hi, Grandpa." Jennifer stopped pounding away on the keyboard of her computer. "You ready to help me with my report?"

"I sure am. What have you found so far?"

"I've done some reading on the European Theater of World War II and checked some web sites. There's so much material."

"It was a big war. You need to pick one part of it."

"Tell me what you did."

"I participated in Operation Overlord. My job was logistics—getting supplies from England to the troops who landed in Normandy."

"Wow, you were right there."

"But not in the fighting itself." I related my experiences and Jennifer typed into her computer.

"That's good, Grandpa. How'd you like to come to class with me tomorrow? History's right at the end of the day. You could meet me at school. That way when I give my report, you can be my expert witness."

"You're starting to sound like one of those blood-sucking attorneys."

She scrunched up her face. "Oh, don't be so down on lawyers. Your friend Meyer was one."

"Yeah, but most of them are useless or worse than useless."

"You'll like lawyers more when I become one."

"You can defend me if I ever need it. Did you know that the bank officer I met with made a comment to the police that he thinks I was in cahoots with the bank robber?"

Jennifer regarded me thoughtfully. "Once they catch the bank robber they'll find you had nothing to do with it, Grandpa. I have an idea."

"I can always use good ideas."

"There is probably red dye on some of the stolen money. If we can find some of that, it should lead to the robber."

"I'm sure the police are looking."

Jennifer's eyes lit up. "But we can help. I'll tell a bunch of my friends to look around for money with red on it."

I shrugged. "Whatever you can do to keep detectives and bank managers from breathing down my neck."

"Now that you've helped me with my school project, I want to show you how to search on the Internet."

"Why would I want to do that?"

She sighed. "Really, Grandpa, I don't know what I'm going to do with you. You need to learn to surf the Internet."

"I don't even want to surf in the ocean, much less the Internet."

"It's easy and together we can gather information that will help clear you in the murder investigation."

"If you can find some way to get Detective Lavino off my back, I would appreciate it."

"Let's start by finding out more concerning the company the murder victims worked for. Here…"

She started clicking away.

"How'd you learn to type so fast?" I asked.

"I've been using a computer for years, but I took a typing class in the sixth grade."

"I never learned to type until I entered the Navy. Had to fill out all those requisition forms."

"Here's the home page for Colorado Mountain Retirement Properties," Jennifer said, pointing.

I looked at the screen and read words describing the wonders of owning my own property in the beautiful Colorado mountains. All units connected to a main commons area so when it snowed, I wouldn't get my feet wet. Indoor swimming pool, Jacuzzi, exercise room, library, gourmet food. What more could I want? Except I hated going in swimming pools. Water over my head scared the crap out of me.

"See if you can find something on Gary Previn," I said.

Jennifer raised herself up from her chair. "Here. You try it."

"Me?"

"Yes. Now you sit right there, Grandpa, and I'll show you. You need to learn by trying it yourself."

"But I've never used a computer."

"Then it's about time. There's nothing scary. You can't break anything. See that box that says 'Search'? Type in 'Gary Previn' and hit the enter key."

I started sweating. This was as strange as doing one of those Sudoku puzzles. The modern world wouldn't leave me alone.

I followed the instructions of my Drill Sergeant, and in seconds a set of pictures and words popped up in front of me describing the two officers of the Colorado Mountain Retirement Properties Corporation. I stared at the serious face of Gary Previn—clean-shaven, short haircut, square jaw and steely eyes. The description read that he held the position of Vice-President of Sales and Marketing, with a previous twenty years of corporate sales and marketing experience. He had worked in another company with Peter Kingston, the current President of the corporation, and they had met each other while serving in the Special Forces.

Interesting. My attention focused next on the picture of Peter Kingston III. He looked like a younger version of Uncle Sam in that poster where he pointed a finger and said, "I Want You." I felt distinctly like he wanted to reach in my pocket and take my wallet. Kingston's background bio confirmed my concern. After retiring from the military, he received a law degree from the University of Colorado before serving as corporate counsel for an investment-banking firm. Now he held the position of CEO of this scam. He and Previn made quite a pair.

"Can I print this page?" I asked Jennifer.

"Sure. See that icon third from the left on the top of the screen? Now click on it."

I squinted at it and snapped my fingers. Nothing happened.

"Grandpa, you need to use the mouse."

"I don't know the mouse from the cat or dog."

She exhaled as if trying to expel some unhealthy air. "Put your hand on the black object next to the keyboard."

"Oh."

"Now wiggle it around and look at the screen."

I picked it up and shook it. Nothing happened.

"Grandpa, keep it on the mouse pad."

I looked at the bottom of the object expecting to see mice feet.

"Put it down on the felt pad and move it like ironing a shirt."

"Now I get it." I followed her instructions and saw a tiny vertical arrow bounce around on the screen.

"Now position the arrow on the printer icon."

"You mean that little box?"

"That's the one."

I flew the arrow around until I got it centered.

"Now push the left button on the mouse."

I did so, and moments later I heard a whirring sound and a piece of paper spewed out of a box sitting next to the computer. I extracted it and found a nice color copy of my two new buddies, Previn and Kingston III. I felt so computer literate, I couldn't stand it.

"Well here are two nice scumbags," I said. "I vote for the lawyer as the one who did it."

"Oh, Grandpa. We don't know yet. We have further investigating to do."

"You're right. I need to track down Previn and talk to him. Here, I'll let you drive the computer now. The excitement exceeds what my old body can stand."

Jennifer took over and started searching to find out more information on Colorado Mountain Retirement Properties.

"Cool. Look, Grandpa, they're sponsoring a team for the Kinetic Conveyance Race."

"What the hell is that?"

"Please, Grandpa, watch your language. You're with a child."

I opened my mouth to say something but thought better of it.

She gave me the most angelic smile. "I'm kidding. I hear much worse than that near the lockers at school. You can speak any way you want."

"I'll be damned."

"To answer your question," Jennifer said in her most professorial voice, "every May there's a big race at the Boulder Reservoir. Teams dress up in crazy outfits and race contraptions that need to both float and move through the mud flats. Teams are judged on both speed and style. It's a big party and lots of fun. And it says right here that Gary Previn heads the team."

"So if I can't track him down before then…"

"Right, Grandpa. We'll go to the race in two weeks and question him."

"You're planning to show up at this thing?"

"Of course. We go every year. But this time, you get to come with us."

"Just as long as I don't have to go in the reservoir. I hate bodies of water."

"You're funny, Grandpa. You hate so many things: pills, lawyers and water. But what do you like?"

"I like you. Now get back to your homework."

"First I have a web site to show you." She hit some keys and a fill-in form appeared on the screen. "You can write a message to yourself or someone else and put a future date for when it will be sent. You could use this to send yourself a message to remember what you've forgotten."

"Thanks, but I'll stick with my handwritten journal, although I could send myself a message each day to ask if I'm still alive. That might help with the green banana syndrome."

Jennifer looked at me and wrinkled up her nose. "What's that?"

"People my age aren't supposed to buy green bananas because we might not be around long enough to eat them."

"Oh, Grandpa, you're going to be around for a long time. You have to come see me graduate from law school in twelve years."

"I don't think my green bananas will last that long."

SEVEN

THAT NIGHT I SAT ON my bed pondering the events of the day. I felt overwhelmed. Witnessing a bank robbery, the experience at the police station, the world of Sudoku puzzles and using a computer put too much stress on my shoddy brain. I sat there holding my head in my hands. I'd have to control my life better if I intended to stay out of the clutches of Detectives Lavino and Hamilton. Then I thought how my friend Meyer who had written me the letter knew the intricacies of the legal system. I wondered if he had any contacts in Denver who might be able to help me understand the circumstances of the mysterious death on the plane when I arrived from Honolulu. I'd have to pursue that in the morning.

THE NEXT MORNING when I woke up in my usual confused state, I found a note on top of a notebook that read: "Welcome to the computer world, you old fart. Read this before you do anything stupid, and it will remind you to call Meyer today."

At breakfast Jennifer told me that I needed to come to her school in the afternoon. "Do you have any medals from World War II that you could wear?" she asked.

"No, but I could stick on some Presidential campaign buttons."

"What are those?" she asked.

"You don't see them around much anymore, but in my sprightly youth, we wore metal buttons that promoted our favorite candidates during a campaign. I may still have one kicking around somewhere that says, 'I like Ike.'"

"Never heard of him," Jennifer said.

"Yes you have. You studied him. He commanded the Normandy invasion. Dwight D. Eisenhower's nickname was Ike when he later ran for President."

"See, that's why I need to take you to school today. You're a walking encyclopedia."

"More a limping who-done-it with a few pages missing."

After Jennifer left for school and Denny for work, I asked Allison if I could make a phone call. I wanted to call Meyer to ask his advice concerning the murder on the flight from Honolulu to Denver. I located the letter and punched in the phone number written there.

After five rings a sleepy voice answered, "Hale Pohai Care Home."

"I need to speak to Meyer Ohana," I said.

"At four in the morning?"

"Damn, I got the time zones all confused. I'll call back later." I slammed down the phone.

I waited until after lunch and then called Meyer again.

"Paul, it's great to hear from you."

"Thanks for the letter. My granddaughter Jennifer helped me remember you."

"Colorado mountain air hasn't rejuvenated your memory?"

"No, but Jennifer has me keeping a journal so I can review things from recent days."

"That's like you used to do in the retirement home. You may not remember Henry Palmer, but he sat with us at meals. He's here with me in the care home recuperating from a heart attack. He still recites baseball statistics and insults everyone. We both miss you."

"I'm sure I'd miss you if I could remember you. Say, I have a favor to ask."

"Fire away."

"I sat next to a guy on the plane coming here who died under strange circumstances…"

"Getting involved in murders again?"

"Let's just say I happened to be in the wrong place at the wrong time."

Meyer chuckled. "Same old Paul."

"Old being the operative word. Since I'm a curious geezer, would you have any contacts in Denver who might be able to shed some light on what happened?"

"I have a friend from law school whose son works in the Denver District Attorney's office. I could check with him."

"That would be great. The dead guy's name is Daniel Reynolds. See what you can find out." I told him to phone me back at Denny's number.

"I'll call you as soon as I track down any information," Meyer said.

"How are you doing?"

"My eyesight isn't getting any worse. I can still make out shapes pretty well. You probably don't remember, Paul, but you used to read to me. Now I have a nice girl who comes twice a week to do that."

"Sounds like you may have a girlfriend."

"Unfortunately, I'm sixty years too old for her. You're the one with the girlfriend. How's Marion?"

"I'll find out pretty soon. She's coming to visit.'

"You sly dog."

"We'll see. This will be a whole new experience for me."

"Not new, but with your interesting existence, your experiences are always fresh. Say hi to Marion and Jennifer for me."

That afternoon, after Allison pointed me in the right direction, I strolled over to Jennifer's school, enjoying the warm spring day. I could see shadows forming on the Flatirons, the rock formations that dominated the foothills above Boulder, and in the distance, white from the caps of North Arapahoe Peak and Mount Audubon caressed the blue sky.

I arrived at Marshall Middle School and made my way into

a building full of emerging hormones and misdirected energy, reminding me of two hundred Jennifers on steroids.

I pulled out the note Jennifer had given me and asked the first adult I encountered where to find Mrs. McConnell's room. This man with rumpled hair and darting eyes looked like a refugee from a prisoner-of-war camp. I guessed when you're around a school full of pre-teens, that's the way you ended up. He directed me down a hallway lined with lockers.

Marching in the direction he pointed, I expected live creatures to be rattling around in the rusty, dented lockers while green ooze emerged from the vents.

Nothing attacked me, and I navigated my way into Mrs. McConnell's class. With her short blond hair and no makeup, she didn't look much older than some of the girls who appeared more like twenty-year-olds than pre-teens.

I spotted Jennifer.

She waved to me.

I found an empty seat in the back and squeezed my aging frame into a little chair with attached desktop. I felt that school-day excitement and dread from ages ago when I was a mere emerging human being.

I listened to a boy give a report describing how the atomic bomb interrupted over a hundred thousand lives in Hiroshima, a bubbly girl spoke on the role of WACS and WAVES in World War II, and then Jennifer stood up.

She did a commendable job explaining Operation Overlord. "And my Grandpa, sitting in the back of the room, helped move supplies from England to Ohio Beach in Normandy. He wanted to be in the fighting, but had a different job to do."

Mrs. McConnell cleared her throat. "That's a nice report, Jennifer, but I can't imagine anyone wanting to be in the fighting if they didn't have to."

I raised my hand, and the teacher nodded to me.

"Not to disagree, ma'am, but the times were different in

World War II than in the Vietnam War or these other recent conflicts. We had to shut down an evil machine, intent on taking over the world. My granddaughter means that my generation was united in support of the war effort—everyone wanted to fight. We were committed to doing whatever it took to stop Hitler, even if it meant killing a bunch of Nazis." My voice rose with vehemence. "I still feel that way."

Several of the kids gasped, and the bell rang. In the ensuing pandemonium, I didn't know if I had helped or hurt Jennifer's grade, but after class she came bouncing up to me. "Thanks, Grandpa. That was great."

"I hope speaking my mind didn't upset things."

"No, you clarified the issue." Jennifer grabbed my hand and led me toward another classroom. "Come on. I have some people I want you to meet."

A woman and a girl Jennifer's age sat at a table covered by a variety of plants.

"Meet my science teacher, Mrs. Evans, and my best friend, Katherine," Jennifer said. "Everyone, this is my grandpa."

I waved to both of them. Mrs. Evans was a perky young woman with long, flowing, streaked blond hair, and Katherine resembled Jennifer, but with her hair held back in a clip rather than in a ponytail.

"We've been classifying plants," Katherine said as she looked up through her glasses and gave Jennifer a smile. "But I need to get home. Thanks, Mrs. Evans."

"We'll walk you home, Katherine. Is that okay, Grandpa?"

"Sure. I like walking, and my old legs could use the exercise."

After the girls visited their lockers, threw some things inside and grabbed a few books, we left school with the two of them yakking about the end of the school year.

"We're having a game night next week, Grandpa. You'll have to come."

"I'm game," I said.

"Oh, Grandpa, don't start making dumb jokes like my dad does."

"Where do you think he learned all his dumb jokes?" I said.

As we ambled along Jennifer said, "I spoke to all my friends today and asked them to look for money with red dye on it."

"That will be fun to check on," Katherine said. "It will give us an excuse to go in stores all over town."

Jennifer nodded her head. "If anyone sees anything, they're supposed to let me know right away."

"I'll mention it to my mom as well," Katherine said. "She's a lawyer and might have some further ideas."

I grimaced. "How come there are so many lawyers these days?"

"It's a noble profession, Grandpa."

After a pleasant stroll we arrived in front of a white two-story house with a neat row of white and blue irises planted in front. A black Mercedes was parked in the driveway.

"Daddy," Katherine shouted and ran toward the car.

A man in slacks and a blue pullover sweater extracted himself from the car and gave Katherine a hug.

"Everything okay?" I asked Katherine.

"Sure. I'll see you at school tomorrow, Jennifer. Nice meeting you, Mr. Jacobson."

As we headed home I said to Jennifer, "She seems like a nice girl."

"Yes. We've been best friends all year. But Katherine has been through a tough year. Her parents recently divorced."

"Maybe her dad found it hard to be married to a lawyer."

"Oh, Grandpa. It wasn't that at all. They simply couldn't resolve their differences."

"Was that her mom or dad's house we just stopped at?"

"That's her mom's house."

"I wonder what Katherine's father was doing there today."

Jennifer shrugged. "Probably one of his regular visits to

pick her up. Although I'm going to be a lawyer, I don't think I'll practice divorce law. Divorces can be tough on kids."

"I'm glad your parents aren't going through something like that."

"Me too. But if they did, I'd sit them down and tell them to work things out like adults."

"I'm sure you would."

Jennifer turned her head toward me. "When I visited you in Hawaii, I read some letters from your dad to your mom. What do you remember about your parents?"

I scratched my head. "That was a long time ago."

"But I know you remember things fine from the distant past."

I sighed. "Let's see. My mom took good care of me, and my dad worked hard as a salesman, but he died young. He provided for us and seemed proud of me, but he never shared his feelings—not the type to give me a hug. I inherited that, I guess. I never hugged your dad either."

"But I've cured that." Jennifer reached over and put her arms around me.

"You certainly have."

"What of your grandparents?"

"I never met my mother's folks, but my dad's parents came from the old country. They spoke Polish, lived on a farm in Minnesota and we visited them once a year or so."

"I have relatives from Poland?"

"Yes. The family name originated as something like Jaku-bowski and must have been changed to Jacobson by some lazy immigration official."

"Have you ever researched the history of our family, Grandpa?"

"No. I never had an interest in genealogy."

"But what if we have kings or murderers in our past?" Jennifer asked, her eyes widening.

"I'm sure every family has some of each, sometimes in the

same person. I'm perfectly content to know all of you. You're the relatives who matter to me."

"I have cousins on Mom's side, but with you and Dad being only-children, I don't have any uncles, aunts or cousins on your side of the family."

"That's right. You're the third generation of spoiled kids."

She stopped and stomped her foot. "I am not spoiled." Then she grinned. "Maybe a little rotten."

"People raised large families back then. My dad shared a house with six siblings."

Jennifer grabbed my arm. "Sometimes I wish I had brothers and sisters, but I have lots of friends to make up for it."

"That's good. I felt the same way and your dad probably did as well."

"Yes. I've talked to him. He says being an only-child caused him to learn things on his own."

"I guess that's true."

THAT EVENING the doorbell rang, setting off Max woofing and scurrying into the entryway. I happened to be closest, so I opened the door to find a skinny man in a dark suit. "I'm sorry, we already donated," I said.

"Very funny, Mr. Jacobson. We need to speak."

I looked at him carefully. "You know my name, but who are you?"

He gave a resigned sigh and pulled out a badge. "I'm Detective Lavino. Your memory problem again?"

"Yeah. Have you closed down that retirement community scam yet?"

"No, but I have some further questions to ask you."

"And I have some questions to ask you, too. What do you know regarding Gary Previn and Peter Kingston?"

"Mr. Jacobson, we have a more pressing matter at hand. A

Mrs. Evans at Marshall Middle School told us you left school today with a girl named Katherine Milo."

"My granddaughter has a friend named Katherine. We walked her home."

"Her mother came home and found no sign of her. She called to report a kidnapping."

"What?"

"And since you were the last person seen with her—"

"The last I saw of Katherine, she was giving her father a hug in the driveway."

"That puts a whole new light on the situation. Mrs. Milo has custody of Katherine. It looks like her ex-husband may have abducted Katherine."

"I didn't realize he was doing anything wrong. Katherine seemed happy to see him."

"These things get kind of messy sometimes. I'd like to speak with your granddaughter as well. I need to ask you to leave the room while I speak with her."

Allison called Jennifer, who came bouncing down the stairs.

I went to my room to ponder my strange life in Boulder while Detective Lavino gave Jennifer the third degree. I felt overwhelmed by everything happening so quickly. I didn't seem to be able to stay in front of being around crimes. Here I was a law-abiding citizen and, whammo, I'm interrogated regarding murder, robbery and now a domestic kidnapping. I felt like I had been punched in the gut.

Later Allison came to retrieve me, saying the detective wanted to speak with me again.

"Your granddaughter corroborated your statement," Lavino said.

"I would have expected as much. Now we need to discuss Previn and Kingston."

"Another time, Mr. Jacobson. I have this reported kidnapping to attend to. I need to get back to Mrs. Milo with this new information."

"Have it your own way, Detective."

"We'll be speaking, Mr. Jacobson."

After the detective left, Denny said, "You seem to keep witnessing crimes. Do we need to find you a lawyer, Dad?"

"I don't need any stinking attorney. I can handle this myself. Jennifer, I'm sorry things have become problematic for your friend Katherine."

"In spite of the problems between Mr. and Mrs. Milo, Katherine loves her dad, and he's always treated her well. I also told that to the detective."

An hour later the phone rang. "It's for you, Paul," Allison said.

I picked it up.

"This is LeAnn Milo. Why did you let my asshole ex-husband take my daughter away?"

"And hello to you too, Mrs. Milo," I said. "I'm sorry to hear of your daughter's disappearance."

"The detective said you walked her home and allowed my ex-husband to take her away."

"I didn't allow anything. Jennifer only told me later that you were divorced."

"If I find you had anything to do with my daughter's abduction, I'm going to make your life so unpleasant you'll wish you never set eyes on me."

"I'm wishing that already, and I've never even met you."

"Don't be a smartass."

"Look, I'm just an old codger and haven't done anything wrong. Let me put my lawyer on the phone to explain."

I cupped the phone and called to Jennifer. "Come describe to Katherine's lunatic mother what happened today."

Jennifer grabbed the phone. "Hello, Mrs. Milo… Yes, ma'am… No, my grandpa and I left right after Katherine hugged her dad… No, ma'am… Yes, I'll let you know if I hear from her, and my grandpa didn't do anything wrong… Okay."

"What did Mrs. Dracula have to say?" I asked.

"Oh, Grandpa, she isn't so bad. She's only worried. I tried to explain to her that I think Katherine is safe with Mr. Milo. Mrs. Milo has this wild idea in her head that you're at fault for the kidnapping. I told her that wasn't the case."

"That's me. The hired gun"

Jennifer pursed her lips. "She's pretty upset."

"Great. That's all I need. In addition to Detective Lavino breathing down my neck, there's a misguided lawyer disguised as a mother after me."

"With all the things happening to you, get a lawyer, Dad," Denny added from his easy chair.

"I don't need one. I have enough trouble with the ones around me. I'll let Jennifer represent me. She'd be better than any scumbag I could hire."

"Cool. My first case."

EIGHT

DURING THE REST OF the week no one showed up to throw me to a pack of hungry lawyers, so on Saturday we prepared for a family outing into the mountains to check out the real estate touted by Colorado Mountain Retirement Properties.

We all piled into the family van with Max perched on Jennifer's lap, nose pressed against the window.

Jennifer let out a loud hiccup.

"Where'd that come from?" I asked.

Jennifer scowled. "Uh-oh. When these start, they sometimes last for hours."

"Hold your breath."

"No. That doesn't work for me. I've tried that, putting a bag over my head, standing upside down, drinking water. Nothing helps. After awhile they seem to stop."

"Why the interest in seeing this place?" Denny asked as we left I-470 and merged onto Highway 285.

"Hic…sorry."

"I can't mooch off you forever," I said. "But more to the point, I'm suspicious of this outfit. With two of their salespeople flopping over dead practically on top of me, I need to check out their operation."

"Grandpa and I will get to the bottom of this," my backseat companion piped in, and then she hiccupped.

"Jennifer has been helping me with research on the computer, but I want to see for myself this property they're trying to railroad people into buying."

We continued our journey with the backseat jiggling every minute or so from the cacophony of hiccups.

An idea occurred to me. "I have a puzzle for all of you."

"I love puzzles…hic…Grandpa."

"And I know your mom likes puzzles. Are you all game?"

"Sure," Allison replied.

"I'll concentrate on driving but will listen," Denny said.

"All right. Pay attention. A man walks into a bar and asks for a drink. The bartender points a gun at him. The man says 'Thank you,' and leaves the bar. You can ask any question that can be answered 'yes' or 'no.' What happened?"

"You're sure you remember the answer, Dad?" Denny asked.

"Yes. I learned this before my memory went on the fritz."

"I'll start, Grandpa. Was the gun loaded?"

"Doesn't matter."

"Did the two men know each other?" Allison asked.

"No."

Jennifer bounced up and down. "Does it matter what the man asked to drink?"

"Good question. Yes."

"Booze?" Denny chimed in.

"No."

"Soft drink?"

"No."

"Hummm." Jennifer put her finger to her chin. "Could it be water?"

"Bingo."

"He asked for water and the bartender pointed a gun at him…"

"I notice your hiccups have stopped," I said to Jennifer.

A big smile crept over her face. "You're right. I was so involved in the puzzle that I forgot about them, and they went away."

"Does the man's occupation matter?" Allison asked.

"No."

A Cheshire cat grin spread across Jennifer's face. "I think I have it, Grandpa."

"Whisper in my ear. If you're right we can let your folks keep guessing."

She cupped her hand and in a soft voice said, "It's something I was just suffering from."

"You're right."

So Denny and Allison kept guessing, and Jennifer ricocheted around the backseat like a pinball shouting "yes," or "no."

Finally, Allison snapped her fingers. "Of course. A man walks a bar and asks for a glass of water because he has hiccups. The bartender points a gun at him, scaring the hiccups away. The grateful man thanks the bartender for helping rid him of the hiccups and walks out."

"Yes, Mom. That's it!"

"Too bad someone couldn't point a gun at me and scare my memory back," I said.

We stopped for a snack in Buena Vista with Max whining when left by himself in the car. A friendly waitress took our order.

"Do you know anything about a retirement community being built just north of here off Highway 24?" I asked.

She gave me a pleasant smile. "Nope. Nothing I've heard of."

"How did the town get its name?" Jennifer asked.

The waitress placed a finger on her chin. "The original name was Cottonwood because of all the cottonwood trees growing here along the upper Arkansas River. Then the name changed to Mahonville after a local rancher. But in 1879 it became Buena Vista because of the beautiful view."

When we left the restaurant, I admired the fourteen thousand foot peaks off in the distance, agreeing with the name of the town and wondering what the retirement property would actually look like.

Back on the road, we followed the directions from the brochure and came to a dirt access road off Highway 24.

"Pretty place," Allison said.

"Yeah, I wonder how much of the development they've completed. The property should be a mile up this road."

And after that, the dirt road simply ended; no signs, only sage and tumbleweeds.

We jumped out of the car to wander around. I scanned in all directions like an Indian scout checking for buffalo. Nothing.

Max shot off after a prairie dog that had taunted him before disappearing into a hole.

"There's a sign on the ground over there," Jennifer said and pointed.

We moseyed over, and Denny picked it up. It read: "Future home of Colorado Mountain Retirement Properties."

"Future as in another century," I said. "They haven't even broken ground yet. No sign of a bulldozer or even a shovel having been put in this ground."

"Let's divide up and check it out," Jennifer said. "Mom and I will go this way."

Denny and I strolled in the opposite direction. We found no evidence of construction other than the mounds from the colony of prairie dogs and several anthills.

"Dad, I've been wanting to ask you. When did you first start noticing your memory loss?"

I stopped and looked at Denny. "I can't remember. That's the doggone trouble with this rotten memory business."

"I'm worried that I'm starting to have the same problem."

"Well, if you end up like me, you'll be an old codger in good shape except for your memory." I patted my stomach. "With walking and excitement from the law, I stay fit."

"But I'm too young to be experiencing memory problems."

"Most people over fifty start forgetting things. Have you been to a doctor?"

"No. I'm afraid of what I'll hear."

"Go get a checkup. No sense worrying."

"I guess you're right."

We turned around and hooked up with the girls back at the car.

"Any luck?" I asked Jennifer and Allison.

"I found a cool arrowhead," Jennifer said, holding it up for me to see.

I inspected it. "Looks kind of old. Maybe this used to be a Native American retirement community. Certainly no sign of any current construction."

I scanned the mountain backdrop. I had to admit that the view was spectacular, but living here in a pup tent and snuggling with prairie dogs wouldn't be my idea of retirement luxury.

We headed back to civilization with Max sleeping on the backseat floor, no doubt dreaming of actually catching prairie dogs.

I whispered to Jennifer next to me in the backseat, "I need to speak with Gary Previn."

"You can see him next Saturday at the Kinetic Conveyance Race," she whispered back.

"What are you two plotting?" Allison asked from the front seat.

"I'm telling her to stay on her side of the seat," I replied and gave Jennifer a wink.

WHEN WE RETURNED home, Denny went off to finish one of his woodworking projects in the garage and Jennifer said she had plans to meet a friend at the club for a quick game of tennis.

"Paul, I'm worried about Denny," Allison said. "He's starting to forget things but seems overly concerned that he will seriously lose his memory."

"I know," I replied. "He talked to me while we scoured that empty field today. He's afraid he'll end up like me. I'm not exactly the role model for the memory branch of Mensa. I told him to go get a checkup rather than worry."

"That's probably best. I'll call our family doctor and see what he recommends."

"Now I need your advice on something. I may be taking a young lady out to dinner. Do you have a restaurant recommendation?"

"Do you already have a girlfriend here in Boulder?" Allison asked with a smile.

"I did meet a woman when I went to the Community Center last weekend. I promised to tell her what I found out when we visited that so-called retirement property. I thought I'd invite her out for some vittles."

Allison thought for a moment. "The Red Lion Inn up Boulder Canyon offers a good meal and overlooks Boulder Creek. They even have an early bird special before six P.M."

"Sounds perfect for a pair of old birds. Now I need to use the phone."

I retrieved two phone numbers from my room. First, I tried Gary Previn. The same damned recording. Then I called the number given me by Helen Gleason.

"Helen, this is Paul Jacobson. We met at the Centennial Community Center during the presentation from that Colorado Mountain Retirement Properties outfit."

"Yes, Paul, it's nice to hear from you."

"I went with my family to check out the real estate, and I promised to tell you what I discovered."

"What did you find?"

"Well, it's a long tale. Would you be interested in accompanying me out to dinner tomorrow night, and I'll relate the whole sordid story?"

She laughed. "That would be wonderful."

"My daughter-in-law recommended the Red Lion Inn. I'll get a cab and be by around five-thirty."

"I'm still driving. I could borrow my daughter's car and pick you up."

"Fine. You provide the wheels, and I'll bankroll dinner."

After giving her my address and hanging up, I sat down with Allison. "I have a date. I wonder what she looks like."

"Paul, what an adventurous life you live."

"It's a shame I have to waste such good health and fitness on a defective brain."

"It seems to always be something. Before she died, my mom suffered from MS. Such an awful degenerative disease."

"So's life," I said.

THE NEXT AFTERNOON I showered, patted a little aftershave lotion on my baby-soft cheeks, put on my party shoes and loped into the living room, ready for my date.

When Helen arrived, imagine my pleasant surprise to see that she was an attractive young chick probably still in her seventies.

Jennifer came bounding down the stairs.

"You look the same age as my granddaughter," Helen said. "She's in seventh grade at Casey Middle School."

"Cool. Does she play tennis? I'm still learning."

"Yes she does. You two will have to get together."

"That would be great. I'm always looking for new people to play. That's the best way to improve your game. Now remember, Grandpa, don't be too late."

"I'll be on my best behavior," I said and gave Jennifer a hug.

"Quite a young lady," Helen said as we walked to the car.

"Darn right. She has more energy than any dozen adults."

Helen drove us to the restaurant, and we were seated at a table next to a large plate glass window overlooking the stream. Aspen leaves quivered in the evening breeze, and I could see two boys with fishing poles along the creek. I thought back to when I had gone fishing with my dad when I was their age. Now I was the fish with Detective Lavino trying to yank me out of my safe habitat.

We scanned the eclectic menu and ordered a game platter for hors d'oeuvres to go with steak and lobster.

"I've been fortunate," I said. "I can still eat anything."

"That goes for me too," Helen replied. "I walk every day and that seems to keep me in shape and my appetite healthy."

I admired her shape. Not bad.

"Now regarding Colorado Mountain Retirement Properties," I said. "I recommend that you don't put a dime into that outfit."

"Why's that?"

"After that big spiel, there's nothing to show for it but an empty field full of weeds and prairie dog mounds."

"Maybe they're running behind on the development."

"I'm convinced it's a scam. They stated that the development had started, but we didn't find a lick of evidence that they had done anything. I think they're trying to get people's money up-front and then will declare bankruptcy, having run off with the funds."

"Well, thanks for the warning. I'll keep looking."

We had a pleasant dinner, discussing our backgrounds.

Over a serving of crème brulé that we shared, Helen asked, "Do you have any hobbies?"

I thought of saying that I collected murders, but restrained myself. "Nothing much anymore. I read short stories and do whatever I can to irritate my son. And you?"

She sighed. "I love gardening. Give me a spot of dirt and a trowel and I can while away the day."

"Gardening and I never saw eye to eye. When I planted seeds, only rocks came up."

"Come now, Paul. You couldn't have been that bad."

"You're right. I did have a knack for growing weeds."

She whacked me on the arm.

Afterward, Helen said, "It's such a warm spring evening, let's take a little walk. Have you been to the Pearl Street Mall?"

"No, I haven't explored much of this town yet."

"We'll be able to see street performers this time of year."

"I'm always game for a performing street."

Helen drove us down the canyon and found a parking spot in town. We walked several blocks and came to a street lined with trees and a walkway. Helen grabbed my hand and gave it a squeeze. I felt like a teenager on his first date.

"Oh, look," Helen said. "There's the Zip Code Man."

"What the hell is a zip code man?"

She laughed. "He knows all the zip codes in the country. Come watch."

A crowd of people stood around a man who had placed a long chain on the ground in the shape of the United States. He asked people to shout out their zip codes, and he placed them around the map of the country. Then he told a story how Mary from Seattle took a trip across country and met Fred in Salt Lake City and then Ralph in Des Moines.

"I'll be damned," I said. "He really knows all the zip codes. He must have as good a memory as mine."

Helen looked at me. "You have a good memory?"

"Actually, I don't. I suffer from short-term memory loss."

"Really, I hadn't noticed anything."

"I'm good at covering. I don't even remember you from the Community Center."

"You mean you won't remember me the next time we meet?"

"You're someone I definitely want to remember, but unfortunately my soggy brain resets overnight."

"We're going to have to remedy that," Helen said and gave me a kiss on the cheek.

This was getting interesting.

"Before I drop you back at your place, we're going to stop at my daughter's house. I have a present for you."

We arrived in front of a new two-story house in North Boulder, and Helen went inside. Moments later she returned and handed me a framed picture.

"Here's my picture, so that you can remember who I am."

"Thanks." I gave her hand a squeeze.

We chatted for awhile and then decided we should head back to my stomping grounds.

"Would you like to come in?" I asked Helen when we arrived in front of Denny's house.

"Sure."

I opened the door with the key Allison had given me. Having the downstairs to ourselves, we sat on the couch and talked. At this moment Jennifer came bouncing down the stairs.

"My chaperone has arrived," I said.

"Don't let me interrupt anything," Jennifer said. She ran into the kitchen for a moment and then dashed upstairs again.

"I better be heading home anyway," Helen said. "There's an event at the Senior Center you might want to attend on Tuesday night."

"What's that?"

"Once a month they hold a poker night."

"I used to play some poker."

"I can't make it this time. My granddaughter has a school concert."

"Rain check then. I'll give you a call, and we can get together on another occasion."

"I'd like that, Paul."

I escorted her to her car, and she gave me a kiss on the cheek. She drove off as we waved to each other.

Back in the house, Jennifer stood, waiting for me. "Do you have a new girlfriend?" she said, bouncing up and down.

"No, but we are friends. She gave me a picture."

"Now you'll have a second picture to go with your other girlfriend Marion. You'll have to be careful which picture you put up."

"You're right. Women don't appreciate a man keeping someone else's picture on his dresser."

I MANAGED NOT to get into any trouble in the next two days. Denny went in to see a specialist and had a whole series of tests run. On Tuesday afternoon I received a call from Marion.

"My daughter and I are staying at the Days Inn," she said.

"Say. There's a poker night at the Senior Center. You up for a little excitement?"

"I used to play a pretty mean game of poker. You're on."

"I'll get a cab, pick you up at six. We'll have a nice meal and then take all the locals at the poker table."

"Sounds good. See you then."

Later I checked the two pictures on my dresser and couldn't remember which one was Marion.

"Jennifer, I need your assistance," I shouted.

She came bopping into my room.

"Point out the picture of Marion."

She clicked her tongue. "Grandpa, I warned you. Marion is the one on the left."

I looked carefully at the smiling woman with an attractive nose and fetching lips. "Okay, I think I'm ready now."

MARION STOOD in front of the motel when I pulled up in the chariot driven by a talkative young man named James who had explained that he was paying his way through a PhD program in biology at the University of Colorado.

I scrambled out and gave Marion a hug. She reached up, turned my face toward hers and planted a juicy kiss on my smacker. This was getting interesting. I felt something come alive in my pants that I didn't know existed anymore.

I heard a clapping sound. I turned toward the cab and

James gave me a thumbs up sign. I opened the door for Marion, and we slid into the backseat.

"To the Greenbriar restaurant, James," I said.

"You got it."

We raced away with Marion snuggled up against my shoulder. We caught up on old times although I could remember zip regarding being together in Hawaii. When we arrived at the restaurant, I paid James. "If you want a return fare, be here in ninety minutes," I said.

"You got it."

After we took our seats at a table near the windows, Marion gave me a wide smile. "It's so nice to be with you again, Paul. I've missed you."

I reached across the table and held her hands in mine. "I'm delighted to see you too, Marion." Something in the back of my foggy brain made a connection. "I try to remember people I care about."

She frowned. "I've been thinking a lot. When I left Hawaii, I told you I wasn't sure I wanted to be with someone who would forget me overnight."

"I wish my strange brain worked differently, but that's the crap shoot of yours truly."

"Do you remember anything from our time together before? Any of the details of our intimacy?"

I thought how easy it would be to lie, but I couldn't do that to Marion. "Unfortunately, I don't. I have your picture, and Jennifer was quite taken with you, so she talks to me about you."

Marion giggled. "The source of memory. Through your granddaughter."

"She's my best memory device. Sharp as a tack."

A twinkle appeared in her eyes. "Maybe I could convince you to come visit me in California."

"I'd like that. After my family gets sick of me, I could come see you."

Marion's eyes sparkled. "You know, I have a separate apartment above my daughter and son-in-law's garage. It could accommodate two people."

"That's tempting, but I think you'd get tired of an old poop who couldn't remember you every morning when he woke up."

"But I'd remember you, Paul."

"You probably told me this before, but I don't recall. What happened to your husband?"

She let out a deep sigh. "Carl died of prostate cancer. He refused to go in for checkups, and by the time he recognized the symptoms, the disease had progressed too far."

"I'm sorry." I reached over and held her hands. "I lost my wife Rhonda to the big C as well. Seems like you and I are survivors."

We chatted on while eating our meal. Marion related more stories of our time in Hawaii, reminding me of my table-mates, Meyer Ohana and Henry Palmer, at the Kina Nani retirement home. For me, it was like hearing it all for the first time.

"We must have been quite a couple," I said.

She squeezed my hand. "The best."

I sighed. "If I didn't have such a crappy memory, I'm sure I would have married you."

"Let's not overdo things, Paul. But we did discuss living together."

"If we did that, you'd be able to determine how much of me you could put up with."

"We'll keep that idea in mind. Right now I have you all to myself for an evening, and then the day after tomorrow my daughter and I have a road trip to complete."

"Will I see you on your return journey?"

"That could be arranged. I could stop back for a short time on our way back to California."

"I'd like that."

What a woman! I felt like I'd known her for ages, yet I couldn't remember her before tonight. Could I have a relationship with someone on that basis? It didn't seem fair to her.

After dinner we found our man James waiting for us. He opened the door for Marion with a flourish, then dashed around to hop in for the drive to the Centennial Community Center.

As I paid him, I said. "Thanks for the magic carpet ride. We have an evening of gambling ahead of us."

"Don't get busted," he said as he returned to his taxi.

At the entrance to the Senior Center a woman sat at a table, collecting money. "Ten dollars for each carton of chips," she said.

I gave her a twenty-dollar bill to stake both Marion and me.

"You can leave your coats in the closet over there," the woman said, pointing

I collected Marion's wrap, took off my jacket, entered a large walk-in closet and hung everything up.

Marion grabbed my hand and led me to a table with several other aging gamesters. We settled in for a game of Texas Hold'em.

"I didn't think you could legally collect money for a poker game," I said.

"I'm sure it's to pay the dealers," Marion replied and squeezed my arm.

The dealer delivered me a series of crapola hands, and my stack of chips dwindled as Marion's grew.

I hit a winning streak, finally, and replenished my chips.

"I need to visit the powder room," Marion said, standing up and stretching her arms.

"I'll hit the head as well," I said.

We visited the accommodations, and I waited for Marion outside the women's restroom. When she emerged, all powdered, she grabbed my arm and snuggled up against me as we walked back into the den of iniquity.

At that moment a whistle blew and a throng of policemen stormed through the door.

"It's a raid!" Marion shouted.

I looked around, trying to find an escape route and spied the coat closet.

"In there," I said and pushed Marion into the closet in front of me. The door clicked shut.

We heard shouts, the sound of furniture capsizing and a male voice commanding, "Line up against the wall."

Things quieted down, and I didn't hear anything again until the same male voice said, "Move outside. Single file."

"They're taking everyone away," Marion whispered in my ear.

"Sshh. Be happy it isn't us."

We sat on the floor of the closet and waited. A small streak of light filtered under the door. Then the light flicked off, and I heard a door clanking.

"Sounds like they've closed the Senior Center," Marion whispered.

"I guess it's safe to go out now." My hand felt along the door. No handle. I pushed on the door. Damn thing remained locked fast. I pounded on the door. No response.

"There should be a light switch here somewhere," I said as I began running my hand around the wall. Nothing.

"We're stuck," I said.

"Good thing we recently went to the restrooms. We'll have to make the best of it."

Marion stood up, and I heard rustling sounds.

"What are you doing?" I asked.

"I'm removing jackets and sweaters. I'll make a place for us to lie down. We might as well be comfortable since we'll have to wait until the janitor opens up in the morning."

"And for the first time all evening, I was just getting some good hands."

"Well, maybe you can put your good hands to another use." Marion snuggled up against me.

Suddenly our mouths met, and I felt a delightful pleasure course through me. An unused part of my body received the message and stood at attention.

My good hands became busy exploring interesting curves, and rather than protest, Marion leaned closer against me.

"I think this is all a plot to take advantage of me in my weakened mental state," I said.

"Good idea." Marion undid a button on my shirt.

We dispensed with clothes and in due course my saluting soldier found a warm cozy home.

I AWOKE WITH A START. It was dark, but a shaft of light peeked under the door. I remembered being in a closet at the Senior Center! And the warm body next to mine belonged to Marion Aumiller. What a strange situation. My usually defective brain could recall clearly the events of the preceding night.

Something jabbed my hip. I reached under my butt and found a cell phone imbedded in a jacket—part of our make-shift bed.

I shook Marion. "Time to rise. We have a way to escape this closet."

"Then we'd better dress." She reached over and gave me a kiss on the cheek.

We sorted through the pile of clothes until I retrieved my pants, shirt and shoes. My socks had disappeared so I dispensed with them.

I rummaged through my wallet and in the faint light found a scrap of paper. Placing it on the floor near the door, I could read Denny's phone number.

"Do you know how to use one of these damn things?" I asked Marion, handing her the cell phone.

"Let me turn it on, and then you just need to tap in the

phone number hit the large button on the top left and then place it against the side of your face."

She did her magic with the phone and handed it back to me.

I followed her directions and after a moment Jennifer answered.

"You need to come rescue your grandfather."

"Grandpa! We were all worried. Where have you been?"

"Just doing a little undercover work. You need to do me a favor."

"Sure, Grandpa."

"Before going to school, walk over to the Community Center and get someone to open the coat closet in the Senior Center."

Half an hour later, we heard a rustling outside the door, and it popped open.

I blinked as sun streamed in. Jennifer and a man stood there.

"Grandpa, what happened?"

"We conducted a test of the cushion properties of various types of jackets. The door doesn't have an inside handle."

The man in a custodian uniform standing next to Jennifer smiled. "But it has a release latch, right here." He pointed.

"I'll be damned. I never found that."

"Or you ignored it," Marion said, giving my arm a squeeze.

"And how come there's no light switch in your closet?" I asked.

"There's an overhead cord. There." The custodian pointed to what I had obviously missed in the dark.

We retrieved our own jackets, hung up the rest and then walked Jennifer to school.

"Do you remember how to get home, Grandpa?"

"I actually do. It's a few blocks away."

Marion and I strolled to the family digs, and I invited her in. Denny had gone to work, but Allison stood in the kitchen with her arms crossed like a mother waiting for an errant son. "It's about time you showed up."

"We just couldn't break away from the poker game," I said.

Marion called to leave a message for her daughter.

"As long as I'm here, show me your room," Marion said.

"My bachelor pad." I escorted her to my room.

She immediately looked at my dresser.

Uh-oh. Two framed photographs rested there.

"There's my picture," she said. "I hope the other one is your wife and not a new girlfriend."

NINE

I WAS FRANTICALLY searching my addled brain, trying to figure out how to explain why I had Helen's picture as well as Marion's on my dresser, when I was saved by the bell. The phone rang, and Allison called to Marion to say her daughter wanted to speak to her.

After Marion put the phone down, she said to me, "I need to go into Denver with my daughter in an hour."

Hoping to divert her attention, I asked, "Will you be back this evening?"

"Yes."

She wasn't smiling.

"Good. Let me take you out to dinner again."

She stared at me, and I felt like I was going to break out in a sweat.

"We'll see. You can call me later."

"I think I can manage that."

Allison and I gave Marion a ride to her hotel, and I walked her to the door.

"Thank you for an interesting night, Paul."

I went to give her a kiss, but she turned her cheek and then brusquely walked into the lobby.

I sighed and headed back to Allison's car.

When we returned home, I looked at the Boulder Daily Camera and saw a front-page article describing the raid on the Senior Center.

"Paul, how do you keep getting involved in these things?" Allison asked.

"I guess I'm just lucky. But at least this time I avoided being arrested."

"We were so worried about your disappearance and just about to phone the police when you called this morning."

"Nah. You can't get rid of me that easily."

Allison looked down at my feet. "Paul, you're not wearing any socks."

"I'm just trying to look preppy with my loafers and no socks. I have to keep up with the young chicks like Marion."

Allison shook her head. "Anyway, I'll cut out the article on this escapade of yours. Jennifer will want to save it in her scrapbook."

"I'm certainly contributing to her legal education."

THAT AFTERNOON I received a call from Meyer Ohana in Hawaii.

"I have some news for you, Paul."

"Before you tell me, I have some news for you. I woke up this morning and could remember everything from yesterday. That's the first time that's happened."

There was a pause on the line. "Uh-oh. Anything unusual happen last night?"

That stopped me cold. "Yes. Marion visited me."

He chuckled. "You old playboy. I bet you two had a romantic evening together."

"Why do you say that?"

"When you and I lived in the Kina Nani retirement home, we learned that only one thing jogged your memory."

"Unfortunately, I don't remember what that is."

"Think back to yesterday. What unusual activity did you engage in?"

"I just missed being arrested. I hid in a closet with Marion…and…and…"

"Now you're on track."

"Are you implying what I think you are?"

"Yes. You old stud."

"You mean sex clears up my foggy brain?"

"That's right. Your magic elixir."

"Damn. I'm too old for much hanky-panky."

"Just be aware that this newfound memory will wear off when you go to sleep again," Meyer said. "That seems to be the way that your brain works."

"Or doesn't work, as the case may be. Now, let's hear this news of yours."

Meyer cleared his throat. "I tracked down my contact in the Denver District Attorney's office. After I promised to send him a box of fresh pineapple, he shared some information on that airplane murder."

"So, did I do it?"

"They have your name on their list, but I can't see that you have the right skills to have committed the murder."

"What do you mean by that?"

"You described to me your military experience during World War II. You were a paper pusher, not in combat."

"Correct."

"You ever study martial arts?" Meyer asked

"A little marital arts, but no martial arts."

"That's what I thought. Here's the strange part. The coroner ruled that the victim was killed by a pressure point blow that had to be delivered by an expert in dim mak, a deadly killing technique."

"I may be dim in memory, but that's the closest I'd come to that."

"While people slept on the plane, someone delivered a deadly blow to your seat companion. Apparently no one saw the murder take place."

"And I'm guilty by proximity."

"Not guilty yet, but you are a person of interest given you were overheard arguing with the victim and later seen shoving him."

"But I'm not that interesting. I'm just an old fart."

Meyer chuckled. "It does seem that Marion finds you interesting."

"I happened to sweep her off her feet in a locked closet, that's all."

"Is this some new type of mating ritual?"

"No, it's a long story."

"What is it with you, Paul? Why don't you marry her?"

"I don't know. I can't take care of myself, much less a woman."

"Remember, you can always come join me here in this care home when you need additional assistance."

"I've forgotten. Tell me again what they have you locked up for?"

He chuckled. "Two things. Macular degeneration and incontinence. I'm on some medicine that seems to help the latter. How's your health?"

"Except for my crappy brain, I'm in good shape. I take walks, eat my daughter-in-law's good cooking and stay as much of a curmudgeon as possible."

We signed off. Meyer seemed to be a good friend and was certainly willing to help me. I just couldn't remember him. And the one thing that apparently unclogged my defective memory was a little romp in the hay, or closet as the case may be. What a life I led.

LATER THAT AFTERNOON, I called Marion, wondering what kind of mood she would be in.

Her daughter Andrea answered.

"This is Paul Jacobson. Tell your mother that her secret admirer would like to take her out to dinner tonight."

"I think she may be ready to speak to you again. Just a minute."

There was a pause, and I could hear some muffled background conversation. Finally, Marion came on the line.

"Yes, Paul."

"This old coot would be deeply honored if you would accompany me out to dinner."

"Since I haven't had any better offers, I suppose so."

"We'll have a more conventional date tonight. I'll make arrangements and pick you up in a taxi at seven."

"ANY IDEA WHERE I should take Marion to dinner tonight?" I asked Denny when he returned home from work.

"You might want to try Pasta Bella. It's an experience in eating."

The taxi showed up, and we picked up Marion and then arrived at the restaurant.

"This place is supposed to be an experience in eating," I said to Marion as I smacked my fingers, "and I'm ready for a robust meal."

We were escorted to a table in the corner, replete with white tablecloth, linen napkins in the shape of swans and a romantic candle.

An eager young waiter held the chair out for Marion and then unfurled her napkin with a snap. In the meantime I had disassembled my own swan. He took our drink orders, mine an iced tea and Marion's an Italian soda.

We revisited the events of the night before and both started laughing at the memory of our close encounter with the raiding police. Marion seemed to have forgiven me for the other picture on my dresser. Either that or her memory was getting as bad as mine.

Then our waiter bounded up to the table and gave my iced tea to Marion and vice versa.

"You have them backward," I said.

He wrinkled his brow, pursed his lips, and then as if he had made a major discovery, smiled and switched our drinks. He hovered over the table a moment then asked, "May I take your dinner order?"

"Sure" I replied. "But you may want to give us menus first."

His eyes opened wide. "Yes, sir." Then he galloped away.

Before you could say "rigatoni," he scampered back with the menus, proudly handing them to each of us.

We made our selections and when our young friend returned, Marion ordered a salad and shrimp scampi, and I ordered a salad and veal marsala.

"Aren't you going to write it down?" I asked the waiter.

He smiled like I had just jumped off the shrimp boat. "Of course not. We're trained to remember."

"Have it your own way," I said.

He charged off to the kitchen to inform the chef of our decisions.

"It is an interesting experience living with your kids," Marion said.

"You planning to stay there long?"

"I don't know yet. I may eventually go back to Hawaii. And you?"

"I'm enjoying seeing my granddaughter. I'll see how long they can put up with me."

The waiter returned and put minestrone soup in front of both of us.

"I hate to spoil your day," I said. "But we ordered salads."

He looked worried for a moment. Then the angelic smile returned to his face, and he grabbed both bowls and dashed off again. He returned shortly with the salads.

"He may not be very competent, but he's speedy," I said.

"He seems to enjoy his job, anyway," Marion said.

Our main courses arrived, and I took the first bite of mine. I chewed thinking veal, but somehow it tasted different.

I had another bite on my fork, when our waiter came rushing up, grabbed my plate away, and said, "Wrong order." He raced away.

Moments later he reappeared and set the right meal in front

of me. I would have been content to finish what he had first given me.

We had good appetites for two old coots and finished everything on our plates. We decided to top off our meal by ordering a tiramisu to share, and by then I nearly broke into a serenade in Italian.

Marion had achieved something rare for oldsters: no problems with memory, eyesight, hearing, walking, breathing, or eating—making for an attractive, intelligent and interesting companion.

After the speedy service so far, we waited and waited. No tiramisu. No waiter.

I finally flagged down another waiter and asked where our young server had gone.

"He went off duty ten minutes ago," the waiter said.

"Would you be kind enough to retrieve our dessert?"

"Yes, sir."

When it arrived, our forks sank into the soft blend of cake and liqueur, certainly making up for the delay. Our bill followed, and I noticed a charge for both chicken marsala and veal marsala. Now I knew what I had eaten a bite of. I explained the duplicate charge to our new waiter, and finally all was resolved.

We talked on and on, like we had known each other forever.

"We had discussed living together at one time, but it's probably best that we each have a chance to spend time with our families," Marion said.

I squeezed her hand. "I'm not the easiest person to be around."

We took a taxi back to Marion's hotel. We kissed goodbye at the door.

"Thank you for the experience in eating," Marion said.

"Yes, it certainly was."

Marion grabbed both my hands and took a step back to look at me. "How wonderful seeing you again, Paul."

"I certainly have enjoyed the last day being with you."

"Well, maybe we can get together in a week. My daughter and I are driving to Kansas to visit my younger brother who's hospitalized. We'll be passing back through the Denver area on our return trip."

"Let's get together then," I said. "I'll keep my social calendar open for when you'll be here again."

"I'll give you a call when we know our return plans."

I watched her go through the door. I would enjoy seeing her again. Not that I would remember her.

As I rode back home in the taxi, I felt in turmoil. It would be nice to spend more time with Marion, but I only remembered who she was because we'd had sex the night before. Not much of a basis for an on-going relationship if I couldn't remember her from day to day. No, I'd plug away and see if I could stay out of jail.

When I entered the house, I found Jennifer sitting at the kitchen table doing homework.

"Hi, Grandpa."

"What are you doing up so late?"

"I'm finishing my final science report that's due tomorrow. I'm studying buoyancy."

"That's not my best topic. When I go in the water, I sink."

"Oh, Grandpa. You need a little swimming practice."

"I'm too old for that. I'll stay out of the water and do fine, thank you."

She stared at me. "Are you and Marion going to get married?"

"What kind of question is that?"

"Well, she likes you."

"Yes. We're good friends, but I wouldn't want to foist myself off on her."

"Maybe she wouldn't mind."

"I'm not that easy to live with. It takes some work for me to just get used to myself."

WHEN SATURDAY ROLLED around, I still remained a free man. No police or lawyer or undertaker arrived to cart me away.

Jennifer came bouncing downstairs. "We have to go early to find a good place at the Kinetic Conveyance Race. I want to be as close to the reservoir as possible."

"I'm not much for oceans, lakes or reservoirs," I said.

"Grandpa, you need to think positive about water."

"It's okay for drinking, but that's it."

We piled into the family car and took off to wait in a line of vehicles entering the parking area. Then Denny handed over a ten-spot for the pleasure of leaving the car in a cow pasture.

Everyone seemed in a holiday mood. I looked out over a crowd dressed in a wide assortment of eclectic outfits on this warm May day.

Allison had provided a gallon of suntan lotion and outfitted each of us with a hat and sunglasses. We set up our folding chairs in the perfect picnic spot as selected by Jennifer, a knoll above a spit of sand with a worn wooden sign that read Chandler Beach. Various conveyances assembled along the lakeshore—a flotilla of boats, canoes and kayaks powered by bicycles, paddle wheels, propellers and oars to form forty or so people-powered sculptures. Costumes included chickens, purple-people-eaters, pink snakes, fruit, nuns, maharajas and dancing bears.

I felt like I had died and gone to a bizarre-o circus.

Remembering my mission, I strolled over to the staging area to see if I could spot the entry from Colorado Mountain Retirement Properties. I looked for a sign that would say "Scam Outfit" but didn't find it.

I wandered through all the contraptions, feeling like I was lost in a colony of seafaring space travelers escaped from an intergalactic zoo. I avoided a crowd of people dressed in red shark costumes and bumped into a silver creature with swim fins and a snorkel. I stumbled away and almost tripped over a vehicle with bicycle wheels and pontoons connected to a multi-colored snakehead poised ready to sink its fangs into me. Up ahead I noticed a large wooden head that resembled a barracuda, That had to be it.

And I was right.

I approached a man decked out in body paint with a shark tooth necklace around his neck, and asked for Gary Previn.

"Right over there." He pointed to a man with his back to me, engaged in a lively conversation with a group of men.

"Is he the leader of this motley crew?" I asked.

"He is. Gary knows this reservoir like the back of his hand. That's why we're going to kick ass today."

I had a different view. I was rooting for Previn to fall on his butt.

The group disbanded. Previn remained alone, standing a solid six feet tall with broad shoulders, one of which I tapped.

He spun around with his hands raised, then paused and smiled at me with steel gray eyes that locked onto my gaze. He had a firm jaw and closely-cropped dark brown hair. With the red and blue body paint he looked like the Caucasian answer to Geronimo.

"Mr. Previn, may I speak with you for a moment?"

He eyed me up and down. "It'll have to be quick. We push off in a few minutes."

"I sat next to one of your sales reps on a plane flight from Honolulu to Denver."

His eyes gleamed. "He had an accident. You didn't happen to be involved?"

"Someone else caused his death. And another thing. Someone murdered Randall Swathers at the Centennial Community Center. Your receptionist said you were supposed to be with him that day."

He shrugged. "My plans changed. I had some books to check out at the Boulder Library that afternoon."

"Awfully suspicious that two of your sales people died under strange circumstances."

"Fortunately, I've been able to replace them. Now, if you'll excuse me, I need to head out onto the reservoir."

"You'd never get me out there," I said.

"Why's that?"

"Being in water over my head scares me shitless."

"That so? By the way, I didn't catch your name."

"Cousteau. Jacques Cousteau." I turned and headed back to my family.

"WHERE DID YOU wander off to, Dad?" Denny asked.

"I checked out some of the conveyances. The one that looks like a barracuda, I hope it sinks."

I leaned over and whispered to Jennifer. "Now I've met the illustrious Gary Previn."

"What did you find out?"

"When Swathers met his maker at the Community Center, Previn claims to have been at the library."

"Either someone else did it, or he's lying," Jennifer said.

A gun fired. It wasn't someone trying to shoot Gary Previn. The race had begun.

I watched as people in the various contraptions thrashed, rowed, paddled and cycled through the lake. Only one word described this event: weird.

The people around me were consuming enough beer to fill the thirty-foot-high inflated brown Miller Lite bottle tethered to the sand on the other end of the beach.

Only two contraptions sunk, with the participants floundering back to shore. Unfortunately, this didn't happen to Gary Previn and his cronies.

Several conveyances moved quickly around a maze of three floats and disappeared toward the other side of the reservoir. Others moved in slow motion, probably more interested in enjoying the warm day than in winning the race.

I spent the next hour listening to too-loud music emanating from a soundstage while wandering through a collection of booths offering burnt cow meat, every imaginable brand of beer, Henna tattoos and jewelry. Having absorbed my fair share of the local culture, I returned to the family picnic spot. Shortly, Jennifer pointed. "Here comes the first one."

It was the damned barracuda paddling into shore. Then the crew carried their contraption through a mud hole, up a mound of gray dirt, over the other side and back into the reservoir for one last unsuccessful attempt at sinking. A group in pirate costumes followed close behind, and I watched both vessels disappear around a bend as they fought for first place.

After the race and all the hoopla was over, I considered visiting with Gary Previn again, but then realized I wouldn't find out anything new by doing that. As we trudged back to our car amid the crowd of happy alien creatures, I contemplated what little I had gleaned from Previn. My gut told me something about that shady outfit smelled bad, but I couldn't pin the murder on Previn. He was my own "person of interest." Either he or someone in his organization could be the killer.

When I encountered my buddy Detective Lavino, I'd have to point him in the right direction.

OVER THE NEXT several nights, if I could have remembered, I'm sure I had dreams concerning sharks and barracudas dancing with nuns and snakes on a lake. There were some benefits to having a crappy memory.

The following day Allison reminded me of my daily household task of walking the family critter, Max, and out we went. The frisky beast alternately tugged at the leash to charge off at full speed and then skidded to a stop to sniff every spot that had been visited by one of his relatives. He passed up the lawns of houses with no one home to disperse his presents on the immaculate lawns of homes with the owners watching. Fortunately, I was armed with plastic bags, a scoop and a thick skin to ward off disapproving looks.

As we strolled along the sidewalk, a gaggle of women approached. They stopped to pet Max. "Isn't he cute?" "How precious." "Hi, cutie."

They weren't referring to me.

Down the block I spotted the fattest cat I'd ever seen. It sauntered up and rubbed against my leg. I scratched him under the chin, and he purred loudly for a moment before hissing at me. Max was terrified and tugged on the leash in the opposite direction until we departed.

In honor of his escape from the monstrous cat, Max crapped on a neighbor's walkway between two of ten fir trees lining the path. A Bermuda shorts clad man with thinning white hair stood ten feet away with his arms crossed, glaring at me, so I diffidently cleaned up the mess. To make up for Max's impropriety, I struck up a conversation. "Nice trees you have there."

The man finally smiled. He appeared to be my height, probably ten years or so younger than me. "I planted them eight years ago. I wanted to have a row of trees all the same size."

"I know where to come when we need a Christmas tree," I said to kid him.

His smile changed to a glower. "I'm always concerned that someone will try to cut one down."

Seeing that he took his trees entirely too seriously, I couldn't resist a jibe. "Well, in that case I promise to cut only one down."

His mouth opened, and he made choking sounds.

Taking the cue, Max went over and lifted his leg on one of the trunks.

"You…you leave my trees alone," the man stammered.

"Come on, Max," I said. "We need to move along."

Max charged off again, and I followed in his wake. I thought that I should sic Max on Gary Previn's yard.

TUESDAY NIGHT after dinner, Jennifer said, "Grandpa, get ready. We have game night at my school."

"What shindig are you dragging me off to?"

Jennifer stomped her foot. "We spoke about this before. The end-of-the-year party at my school."

"In that case, let's go celebrate."

"I just wish Katherine was going to be there," Jennifer said.

"No word from her?"

"No, I guess she's still off somewhere with her dad."

Being such a nice evening and having only a short distance to walk, Denny, Allison, Jennifer and I strolled over to Marshall Middle School. The street in front of the school looked like a scene from rush hour in Manhattan, with people shouting from car windows and horns blaring. We had made a wise choice to avoid the parking lot crammed full of cars spewing out families with twitching pre-teens.

I felt the electricity in the air. Or maybe just the madness.

We entered the gym, resplendent with crepe paper streamers and balloons. All around the edge stood booths for different kinds of games. In the middle of the floor swirled a maelstrom of running, cavorting and laughing kids.

I thought back to my school days. We didn't have this much fun. Actually, we did. But we didn't show it in front of adults.

We bought tickets at a booth and proceeded to try our luck at various games. I threw darts at balloons and didn't win any prizes but did succeed at tossing a ring around a floating duck to win a small stuffed bear. I handed it to Jennifer.

She smiled. "Cool. I'll put it on my shelf with the Hawaiian beanies you gave me last year."

"I aim to please."

She skipped off toward another game, and I followed.

By investing five tickets, you could have the principal, dressed as a sheriff, drag someone off to a portable jail. I hoped no one did that to me. I had enough chance of that happening in real life.

We all entered a cake walk, but a small boy won and selected the largest chocolate cake from the twenty cakes sitting on a table.

I drank punch, munched on popcorn and trailed Jennifer as she charged around to try every game several times.

When the punch started sloshing around inside me, I excused myself and found the little boys' room. After taking care of my business, I was preparing to leave the restroom when two boys started splashing water at each other from the sinks.

I stepped in to separate them. "This is supposed to be a fun family event," I said. "Save the rough-housing for a school day."

They both glared at me and raced out of the bathroom.

I returned to the pandemonium and rejoined my family.

Five minutes later I noticed the two boys from the bathroom speaking to the sheriff and pointing toward me. He strode over and put his hand on my shoulder.

"Uh-oh," I said. "Did those kids decide to send me to your pretend jail?"

"We have something more serious. Come with me."

I followed him to the principal's office. I hadn't been in one of these since the time I put a tack on Ellen Sedgwick's chair in the third grade.

He motioned me to sit down on a hard wooden chair while he dropped into a padded armchair behind the desk. I regarded him. I had remembered principals being as big as grizzly bears. This guy resembled Don Knotts.

"There's been a complaint filed against you."

"Complaint?"

"Yes. I'll have to ask you to wait here until a police officer arrives."

I scratched my head. "What's the big deal? All I've done is play games and take a piss."

"That's the problem. Please wait." He stood up and walked out, shutting the door.

A few minutes later a tall, skinny man in a suit appeared. He looked at me and grinned. "Well, well, if it isn't Mr. Jacobson."

I stared at him. "Do I know you?"

"Yes, indeed. I'm Detective Lavino."

I looked at his fingers. "You're the detective who chews his fingernails."

He glanced at his fingernails and then blinked. "Mr. Jacobson, you and I have met on a number of occasions. Care to tell me what transpired when you went into the bathroom this evening?"

"I took a whiz and broke up some rowdy behavior between two young boys."

"Anything else?"

"Then I left the bathroom."

"Interesting. There's a report from two boys who claim you made indecent gestures in the bathroom."

"What? They're obviously making it up."

"That's possible.

"Well, you better grill them, Detective. I've done nothing wrong."

"I'll see what they have to say. At least in checking your background before I know you have no sex offenses."

"That's right. I've always defended sex."

"You stay put. I'll be back in a few minutes." He stood up, walked out and closed the door behind him.

This routine was getting monotonous. I had nothing to do but twiddle my thumbs and look at the principal's collection of books. I pulled one off the shelf titled *The Formative Years* and scanned an article regarding child development. It didn't say anything concerning little boys who lied. I was learning the length of average attention spans when Detective Lavino returned and closed the door.

"Mr. Jacobson, you've been accused of a very serious offense."

"And I've told you the children lied. Are you going to lock me up?"

"No, Mr. Jacobson."

I watched him carefully. "I bet when you interviewed those two boys, you found inconsistencies in their statements. Otherwise, you'd have shoved me in the slammer and thrown away the key."

He actually smiled. "You do have some keen insights for someone with memory problems."

"Not all of my brain is crapola. So what did the little squirts have to say?"

"I'm not going to relate the details, but you are right, Mr. Jacobson. Their stories don't ring true. But they haven't recanted their accusations against you, so I'll need to keep the investigation open."

"You do that, and you'll find I'm as innocent as the new driven snow. Now since you're interested in clearing the streets of criminals, I'd suggest you busy yourself with Gary Previn, the guy who runs sales for Colorado Mountain Retirement Properties. He was on the plane when one of his sales people was killed by a deadly pressure blow."

Lavino gave me a cunning grin. "And how would you know the nature of his death? That information hasn't been released."

TEN

OH, SHIT, I THOUGHT to myself. Here I've gone and stepped in it. Meyer tracked down the information for me concerning the murder on the plane. Since Lavino didn't know of my insider knowledge of death by martial arts blow, he could only conclude that I had done it. I decided to take the offensive. "And another thing. Previn claims to have been at the library when the murder took place at the Community Center. I'm not convinced of that. You should check him out to see if he's lying."

"I've spoken with Mr. Previn," Lavino said with his intense eyes on me.

"Go grill him again. You seem to have no qualms against constantly harassing me."

"That's because you happened to be the only person in proximity to both murders. Crimes seem to congregate around you like flies on horses."

"Now if you're through with your earthy agricultural analogy, may I rejoin my family?"

He regarded me carefully, then threw up his hands. "Go on."

I stood up and headed for the door. "And you really shouldn't bite your nails so much."

Outside in the school hallway I braced myself against a not-too-clean wall. Here I was getting deeper in cow pies. Every time I turned around, something happened to link me to some crime I didn't commit. I felt like that L'il Abner character with the cloud always over his head. I had to suck it up and get on with things. I knew I was innocent and had to find a way to convince Detective Lavino of the fact. I'd keep plugging away and see what I could learn. With that in mind, I ambled back to the gym.

"Where have you been?" Denny asked.

"I had a conference with the principal." I spotted the two boys running toward a ring toss booth. I leaned toward Jennifer. "Do you know those two?"

"Yes. Teddy Bishop and Randy Buchanan."

"What do you think of them?"

She pursed her lips. "The principal and teachers think they're wonderful, but I know they're sneaky."

"They also made up some lies about me." I felt like tanning those two little troublemakers, but that would only put me in deeper dog poop.

Her eyebrows lowered, and she scrunched her lips together. "I'll get to the bottom of that, Grandpa. Don't worry."

AFTER WE RETURNED HOME, I received a call from Helen Gleason.

"Paul, my family's having a party tomorrow night. Would you like to join me?"

"Sure."

"I'll be by to pick you up at seven."

I decided that would be a good diversion from my crime spree.

THE NEXT EVENING, Denny, Allison and Jennifer went on a shopping expedition, so Max and I waited for Helen.

The doorbell rang, and Max went into his run-and-skid-toward-the-door routine.

I let Helen in.

"Welcome to my humble abode."

Max greeted her by putting his paws on her knees.

"What a cute puppy," she said, giving him a scratch behind the ears.

Max knew how to play a crowd.

"Would you like a tour?"

"A quick look-see, and then we need to leave for the party."

I showed her my room.

She stopped in front of the two photos on my dresser. "Who's in the other picture?" she asked.

Uh-oh. I had Marion's picture as well as Helen's on display.

"I hope that was your wife and not a girlfriend," she said.

I looked at my watch. "Time to get going."

On the drive we discussed the distant past, since the last five years or so remained frustrating territory for me. Helen grew up in New York and moved to Chicago, raised her family there before retiring with her husband to Arizona. He died approximately when my memory went south, so we both had a loss at the same time.

I told her of my experience in World War II and my life running an auto parts supply business in Los Angeles.

We arrived at Helen's place, and I met her daughter Madge, son-in-law Hector, granddaughter Lauren and grandson Bruce. The family sat in the backyard, while Hector tended a man-sized, natural gas-powered barbecue grill. "How do you like your steak?" he asked.

"Nice and dripping red," I replied.

"A man after my own heart. Say, what do you think of this upcoming city council race?"

"To be honest, I'm new to Boulder and don't know anything regarding the local politics yet."

"There's a big battle brewing over prairie dogs. The city council's mulling over the disposition of a parcel of land north of town. Full of prairie dogs. Some want to pave 'em over, some want to leave it as open space and some want to relocate the critters."

"What do the prairie dogs want?" Lauren asked.

Hector scratched his protruding belly. "Right. There's a fresh viewpoint."

Madge, a mousy woman with large eyes, came over and started asking me questions about my family.

We determined that Jennifer and Lauren had some of the same interests—tennis and swimming.

"Lauren doesn't plan to be a lawyer by any chance?" I asked.

Madge furrowed her brow. "Why no. She's too young to be considering a profession yet."

"Just wondering," I said.

We demolished the singed cow accompanied by corn on the cob and Caesar salad. I felt well-fed and well taken care of.

As we sat around enjoying sunset and having chocolate cake, Hector asked me, "How long do you plan to be in Boulder?"

"Good question. I came to stay with my son and his family after living in a retirement home in Hawaii. I'll have to see how long they can put up with me."

Hector and Madge exchanged knowing glances.

"We're enjoying having Mom here," Madge said. "She's independent and takes care of herself."

I smiled. "This image some people have of us old folks needing to be waited on hand and foot is way off base. As long as we stay healthy, we can fend pretty well for ourselves."

"Besides, having grandkids keeps us sprightly and alive," Helen added.

"Although I can't talk Grandma into learning the computer," fourteen-year-old Bruce chimed in.

"My granddaughter has the same complaint," I said. "But we enjoy watching what you kids can do with the blasted things. There has to be something to make you feel superior, given our wisdom and experience."

As dusk fell, I put on my light jacket to protect against the high altitude coolness. My blood had thinned from living in Los Angeles and Hawaii for all those years.

As we prepared to leave, I marveled at the pleasant evening with no lawyers or Detective Lavino to harass me. I noticed a book of Sudoku puzzles on a bookshelf in the family room. I figured the Japanese had definitely found a new way to take over American minds.

Afterwards, Helen dropped me off at home. I could tell that the chemistry between us had changed. Chalk it up to having two pictures on my dresser. Oh well. At my age, I could only handle one girlfriend anyway.

THE NEXT SATURDAY Jennifer had her first summer swim meet. At the crack of dawn, I helped load the family van with towels, snacks, suntan lotion and various accoutrements.

"Who's the opposing team?" I asked Allison after we unfolded our chairs along the side of the pool.

"This is a practice meet for just our club."

I settled in for a morning of watching kids struggling to stay afloat. Actually, that would have been me if I fell in the pool because I floated like a brick, but these kids, including Jennifer, zipped through the water like motorized porpoises.

The sun shone brightly, and by 9 A.M. I discarded my light jacket to expose my arms to skin cancer.

"Put on lots of sunscreen," Allison said to me. "You can get a bad burn at this altitude."

"Yes, ma'am," I replied. She took as good care of me as she did of Jennifer.

Jennifer placed second in the fifty-meter freestyle race for her age group and, after scrambling out of the pool, came over to visit with her fan club. "I took half a second off my best time from last summer!" she said, beaming.

"And you nearly touched out that other girl," Denny said.

"Almost. I'm going to practice really hard so I can beat her in the finals at the end of the season."

"But she could also improve," I added, helpfully.

"Oh, Grandpa. That might be the case, but I'm more motivated than she is. Besides, we can work to place first and second in the league championship against the other teams."

I sighed. "Jennifer, you'll be president of the country some day."

"No, but I do plan to be a successful attorney."

I shook my head. "Can't you think of a more respectable profession?"

"Oh, Grandpa. You're too negative about lawyers."

With that she spun on her heels and skipped off for her next event.

JENNIFER WON the one-hundred-yard freestyle and touched out the girl who had beaten her in the earlier event. Within a few minutes she strolled up to where I sat.

"You did it!" I gave her a congratulatory pat on the back.

She smiled. "What did I tell you?"

"How do you do that? My own flesh and blood swimming so well, when I hate going in the water."

"You have to be more positive, Grandpa."

Allison had gone to help at a poolside bake sale, so I wandered over to select a muffin to munch on.

"Paul, could you mind the table for a few minutes?" Allison asked.

"Sure. What do I need to do?"

"Just collect money and put it in the cash box. All the prices are marked."

"I can handle that."

Allison stood up, and I took her place sitting on the folding chair. I felt like I was back behind the counter of my auto parts store many years before in Los Angeles.

I sold a few chocolate chip cookies, some donuts and a bagel.

Then all of a sudden, a mob of kids descended on the table,

like a piranha feeding frenzy. Kids grabbed things and I tried my utmost to collect money and maintain order. I had a handful of quarters and after the crowd departed I prepared to deposit the money in the cash box. I scanned the table. No cash box. Uh-oh.

When Allison returned, I explained what had happened.

"I better report this," she said. "You stay here."

"Yes, ma'am."

I continued to collect money for food and dropped it in a Styrofoam coffee cup. An hour later a policeman arrived and took down my name and a statement. He checked around and found the empty cash box in the men's locker room.

On our way home, Jennifer bounced up and down in the back seat. "Two firsts and one second! And my two relay teams won!"

"Pretty good start for your season," I said. "Only disappointment being that someone stole the bake sale money."

Jennifer pursed her lips. "Why would someone want to ruin a perfectly good swim meet by doing that?"

"Maybe the person didn't win as many ribbons as you."

THAT AFTERNOON Denny answered the telephone and said a man wanted to speak to me.

I picked up the phone.

"Mr. Jacobson, this is Detective Lavino."

"What can I do for you?"

"I received a report that your name came up in connection with a petty theft earlier today. You back on your crime spree, Mr. Jacobson?"

"No way. I have Social Security for pocket money."

He chuckled. "You're a witness once again. You do seem to have a way of being in the vicinity when crimes are committed."

"I'm just lucky I guess. On a more important subject, did

you ever find out if Gary Previn was really at the library the day of the murder at the Centennial Community Center?"

"Look, Mr. Jacobson, I don't have to answer your questions."

"I know. I'm just an old fart. Humor me."

I heard a sigh on the phone. "Yes, a witness confirmed Previn's presence at the library at the time of the murder."

"How can you be so sure?"

"A librarian remembers him checking out two books, and I collected the library record of his account."

"Crap. It must be someone else in that slimy organization who's the murderer."

"We're still investigating."

After I hung up, I sat there with the weight of the world on my chest. One more crime happening around me and staring down my throat. This was getting old, quickly. Then I started thinking. Maybe I needed to do a little more investigation of my own.

I wandered into Jennifer's room. "I need your help."

"Sure, Grandpa."

"Can you find a picture of Gary Previn?"

"Grandpa, we printed one out for you already. Let's look in your room."

We returned to my room and searched through my stuff.

"Here it is." She held up a business-schmaltzy picture of Previn she found in my dresser.

"So that's what the scumbag looks like," I said.

"You met him at the Reservoir, Grandpa. And we don't know if he's the killer. Innocent until proven guilty."

"You sound like a lawyer."

She gave me her most winning smile. "Of course. And I'm going to check around the club tomorrow to see if I can find any clues regarding the missing bake sale money."

"I'd appreciate that. Every time something happens in this town, Detective Lavino wants to talk to me."

"You have to admit that you're around an awful lot of crime."

"Rather than persecuting me, the police should use me as a criminal magnet. Arrest everyone around me."

"But not me, Grandpa. I have to keep my record clean if I'm going to become a lawyer."

THE NEXT AFTERNOON, armed with the picture of Gary Previn, I took the number six bus. Allison had been kind enough to look up the right bus route and with one transfer, I negotiated the trip.

An interesting thing I observed while riding the bus in Boulder. Mainly young kids and old farts like me. Not too many riders in between. The middlesters all drove around in BMWs and Mercedes.

At the library I admired a modern glass structure jutting up with the foothills in the background. I thought of all the books I had read over the years, having been an avid reader. Then I thought of all the books I'd read in the last five years. Who knows—it could have been a hundred or zero since my sieve-like brain cells had retained no recollection of any books.

The library spanned Boulder Creek with a glass-encased second-story walkway connecting parts of the building on each side of the stream. I wouldn't want to be there when a hundred-year flood surged out of Boulder Canyon, given my swimming ability.

I moseyed up to an information desk, manned or, I guess, womaned by the perfect image of a librarian. She was probably in her late fifties or early sixties, had gray hair neatly pulled back in a bun, wore glasses which hung on a black cord around her neck and possessed lips that just begged to be pursed.

"Good afternoon," I said with my most sincere smile. "I'm trying to get some information concerning a patron who visited the library three weeks ago. Does the same staff always work on Sundays?"

She looked at me with intense brown eyes and, as predicted, pursed her lips. Then she spoke. "Why yes. Unless someone takes a vacation."

I gazed past her to a man and woman at counters scanning books and library cards. "So those two over there are your regular checkout people?"

She turned her head. "That's correct. Plus Maggie at the circulation desk."

I thanked her and ambled over to the first line. When my turn arrived, I flashed the picture of Previn. "I'm trying to determine if this man checked out books three weeks ago."

The woman pushed a strand of black hair back from her forehead and peered at the picture. "We see a lot of people here."

"Does he look familiar?"

She stared again and then shook her head. "No, not at all."

I tried the other line with equal lack of success. Crap. One option remained—Maggie. Crossing my fingers and toes (possible, since I wore sandals), I approached the circulation desk. A young woman in her forties sat there writing numbers on a sheet of paper.

"Excuse me," I said. "I wonder if you might help me?"

She looked up and gave me a charming smile as if she had been waiting all day for someone to ask her assistance. "Yes, what can I do for you?"

I handed her the picture of Previn. "This man may have checked out books three Sundays ago. Do you recognize him?"

She scrunched up her nose, squinted at the picture and tapped it with a fingernail replete with sparkling pink polish. "Why, yes. I do remember. It's the man the police inquired about recently. Is this the same matter?"

"Yes. Tell me what you remember."

"As I told the officer, I recognized the person in this picture as the one who checked out library material. Yes, indeed. The very same."

"With all the people passing through here, how do you remember him in particular?"

She gave a smug smile. "I always pay attention to the patrons coming through the line. But this man had one distinguishing characteristic. He had a tattoo of a surfboard on his left wrist."

"Did you tell the police about the tattoo?"

"No. The officer only asked me to identify the man from a photograph."

"Do you remember what materials he checked out?"

She shook her head. "That would be asking too much of my memory."

"Yeah, I know how memories are," I said. "Thank you for your assistance."

So Previn had a surfboard tattoo. Went with him pedaling that contraption out in the Boulder Reservoir.

That evening I took Max for his usual walk, and we journeyed through the whole neighborhood so Max could fill his nostrils with doggy aromas and I could think what to do next to clear my name. Max accomplished more than I did and probably remembered his experience the next day.

THE FOLLOWING MORNING before Denny and Jennifer left for work and school respectively, we heard a loud rapping on the door. Max growled and stood back from the door. When Denny opened it, a man with thinning white hair and a red face stood there. When I approached the door, he wagged his index finger at me. "You…you…you cut down my tree."

I blinked. "What do you mean?"

He sputtered and spittle flew out of his mouth. "You came by walking that white dog last night." He now aimed a finger at Max.

Allison stepped forward. "Yes. Paul took Max for a walk last night."

"Then this morning I find one of my trees has been cut down."

"What does that have to do with me?" I asked.

He pointed at me again. "You recently made a snide comment concerning cutting one of my trees down. I see you skulking around, and the next morning, one of my trees has been sawed off."

"I didn't have anything to do with it. How could an old geezer like me take your tree away?"

"I sleep very soundly. I bet you and your family came and chopped it down last night and hauled it away. I'm reporting my suspicion to the police."

"My dad didn't harm your tree, Mr. Fisher," Denny said, trying to calm the man down.

Fisher continued to splutter. "Yes…yes he did. He's the culprit." He turned and stomped down the walkway.

So much for neighborly relations.

"Mr. Fisher is very protective of his yard," Denny said as he closed the door.

"I don't blame him. I'd be pissed if someone sawed off one of my trees."

"And he does what he says, so I expect he will contact the police and file a complaint."

"Great. That's all I need. Yet another reason for me to be on the bad side of the local cops."

"That's why you need a lawyer."

I held my hand up. "No. Anything but a lawyer."

"I'll help you," Jennifer said.

"You're hired. When you get home from school, we'll review all the crimes I've been around and what we can do."

"I'll see that you stay a free man, Grandpa."

"I'm sure you will, and then I won't have to deal with any blood-letting lawyers."

"I'll take your case on contingency," Jennifer said. "You can pay me a Hawaiian stuffed animal for each crime that's resolved."

"Uh-oh. You're already starting to think like a lawyer."

"Of course." She skipped off to get ready for school.

I turned toward Denny. "This is one hell of a situation. Every time I turn around someone's pointing a finger at me concerning some transgression. Crap. I might as well be accused of leaving dog poop on someone's lawn as well since I take Max for a walk every day."

ELEVEN

RATHER THAN DROWN in self-pity, I decided to take a walk. I needed some time to myself without having to stop at every tree and mailbox, so I left Max at the door, whining.

As I wandered through the neighborhood, I tried to put all the pieces together. Somehow I stood at the top of Lavino's person of interest list, linked to a myriad of crimes. First, and foremost, were the two murders. Two salesmen for Colorado Mountain Retirement Properties had been knocked off. Gary Previn had been my number-one suspect, but he had an alibi for the second murder. Maybe he conspired with the CEO, this guy Peter Kingston. These two were involved in something crooked because that outfit wasn't all it was cracked up to be.

Then I had the little matter of the misguided Mrs. Milo thinking I was at fault for allowing her ex-husband to abduct her daughter. Hopefully, her initial irrational reaction had now been replaced by sanity. And I had witnessed a bank robbery, been accused of accosting two boys in the bathroom at Jennifer's school, been at the scene of stolen money at a swim meet and now had a crazy neighbor implying I had sawed down a tree.

Every time I turned around, someone suggested I hire a lawyer. No thank you. I'd stick with Jennifer's help. I took a deep breath. I had to think positive. I lived with my family in a beautiful place and remained in good health for an old poop, memory excepted. I looked up at the Flatirons: pointy peaks surrounded by pine trees, wispy clouds above and sunshine warming my old body. Feeling better, I actually started whistling.

All of a sudden a small white dog appeared. It looked a little like Max. "Hello, boy," I said, reaching down to pat it on the head. "You thought I whistled for you."

It scampered off the sidewalk onto a lawn and proceeded to fertilize the yard. Man, that little dog had a lot inside him.

I heard the screeching of tires and a white van came to a stop beside me. At the sound of the vehicle, the white dog dashed off into the bushes. I looked at the van and saw the words: City of Boulder Animal Care and Control.

A squat little man in a dark blue uniform hopped out and approached me. He held a clipboard and wrote furiously. "May I see some identification, please?"

I reached in my wallet and showed him my ID card.

He wrote my name down, then ripped off a piece of paper and handed it to me.

"What's this?" I asked.

"It's a citation for violation of City Ordinance 6-1-16."

"What the hell is that?"

He pursed his lips, then spoke. "Dog running at large prohibited. Must be on a leash. You also violated 6-1-18."

I started at him. "You mean I'm a two-time loser? What's 6-1-18?"

"Removal of animal excrement required. Each violation should net you a fine of five hundred dollars because of your dog."

I laughed. "You mean that white dog? I'm not his owner."

The man grimaced. "Sir, in Boulder we have no dog owners, only dog guardians."

"Well, la-de-da. I'm not its guardian either. It just appeared when I walked by."

He laughed. "I hear that one a lot." He wagged his finger at me. "You're not getting off by pretending not to be the violating guardian."

A man with thinning white hair approached us from the yard. Uh-oh. It was my accuser, Mr. Fisher. I scanned the yard. Sure enough, a well-manicured lawn, colorful flower garden and a neat row of fir trees with one sawed off a foot above the ground.

"I overheard what's going on here." He pointed a thick finger at me. "This guy walks that white dog by here almost every day. He's a bona fide criminal."

I peered at Mr. Fisher. His face was red again. If he kept this up he'd be like a balloon ready to burst.

"Yes, I walk my son's dog Max, but this dog isn't Max. I always walk Max on a leash. This is a stray dog."

The radio in the van squawked, and the animal control officer stepped over to answer.

When he returned, I said, "If you come with me to my son's house, I'll show you that Max is there."

"I don't have time for that. I received a call that a vicious pit bull is lose in Frasier Meadows."

"But I want to prove my innocence—"

"He's guilty," Mr. Fisher said helpfully.

"Sir, you can contest the tickets if you disagree," the animal control officer said as he climbed in his van and drove away.

Mr. Fisher stood there with his arms crossed. "Now—regarding this dog crap on my lawn."

THAT EVENING I shook my head in disgust. Too many crimes had been heaped upon my innocent head. As I sat there feeling sorry for myself, Jennifer skipped into my room.

"We need to work on your cases, Grandpa."

"I appreciate your enthusiasm, but don't you have homework to do?"

"Nope." She smiled. "School's over in two days, and I'm practically free." Then her face turned serious. "Now we have to make sure that you stay free."

"I'm all for that."

"Let's proceed into my office."

I followed her to her room, and she motioned me to sit in one of the two chairs by her desk.

"Okay," Jennifer said. "First step. Let's start with my friend Katherine Milo's disappearance."

I thought for a moment. "Here's what I read. I walked you and your friend to her house after school. We left her there and the next thing I knew her crazy mother accused me of being at fault in her daughter's disappearance."

Jennifer pursed her lips. "That was the last time I saw Katherine. She didn't return to school."

"The logical explanation is that her father spirited her away somewhere."

"Yes. The police are looking for Mr. Milo. Mrs. Milo had the illogical notion that you aided and abetted that kidnapping."

"You sound so lawyerly."

Jennifer smiled. "You're getting the best representation money can buy."

"Uh-oh. What are you charging me?"

"See? You've forgotten. We settled on one Hawaiian stuffed animal for each case I take. With all the trouble you're in, Grandpa, I'll soon have a huge collection."

"It'll be worth it. Besides, I don't have anything else to spend money on. You and your folks will inherit any savings left when I kick the bucket."

"Don't talk that way, Grandpa. I know you'll live to be a hundred."

"Only if you save me from the electric chair."

She nodded her head. "Okey dokey. Back to the case. Mrs. Milo has even offered a reward for information leading to Katherine's return. Five thousand dollars. We need to track down where Mr. Milo is hiding Katherine. Then when he's captured, Mrs. Milo will forget about trying to blame you."

"Did Katherine ever mention to you any place her father had taken her before?"

Jennifer scrunched her nose and looked upward. Then her eyes lit up. "Yes! She once told me he had a cabin up in the mountains. I'm going to call Mrs. Milo."

"Be careful of the dragon lady."

"There's no problem. She likes me." Jennifer reached for the phone extension in her room and punched in some numbers.

"Mrs. Milo, this is Jennifer. I'm trying to help find Katherine… No, I haven't heard from her… Yes, but I do have an idea. She once referred to visiting a mountain cabin with her dad. Do you know anything about that?… Okay, just wondering… Yes, I'll let you know if she contacts me. Thanks."

Jennifer put the phone down and wrinkled her brow. "Mrs. Milo doesn't know anything about a cabin her ex-husband owns. They never had a cabin when they were married."

"You have a good lead then," I said. "A cabin only he knows of would be a logical place for him to go."

"I can't remember Katherine telling me where it was." Then her eyes gleamed. "But there's someone else who might know. When she went to spend weekends with her dad in Lakewood, she made a friend in the neighborhood named Annette. She told me that she, Annette, Annette's dad and her dad went fishing one time. Maybe they went up to the cabin."

"Did you tell this to Detective Lavino when he questioned you?"

She shook her head. "No. I didn't think of it until this moment."

"You better watch yourself, young lady. You don't want to end up with a memory like mine."

She grinned. "No problem. I can always keep a journal like you do, Grandpa."

"Speaking of which, somewhere in my room I should have Detective Lavino's phone number. I'm going to call to tell him to track down this Annette and her dad to see if they can locate Milo's cabin."

I returned to my room, rummaged through some papers in the dresser, noticed the business cards of the murdered salesmen and eventually found a slip of paper with the name Lavino and a phone number. Success!

I called the number, and a female voice answered.

"I have some information on one of Detective Lavino's cases," I said.

"Please wait a minute. I'll try to locate him."

I twiddled the piece of paper while listening to static on the line. Reminded me of how my brain cells worked when I woke up in the morning.

"Detective Lavino here," a clear voice said.

"Detective, this is Paul Jacobson."

"Well, well. How is my favorite witness and person of interest?"

"I guess I should be proud that you're so interested in me, but I have some information for you. My granddaughter, Jennifer, came up with something that should help you in regard to the Katherine Milo disappearance."

"I'm all ears."

"Katherine mentioned to Jennifer that her dad had a cabin in the mountains."

"That would have been useful information to tell me when I interviewed her."

"She just remembered it," I said.

"Memories have a way of coming and going in your family."

"With me it's mostly going. One other helpful thing, Detective. Katherine had a friend in her dad's neighborhood in Lakewood named Annette. Jennifer remembers Katherine saying that Annette and her dad had gone fishing with Mr. Milo and Katherine. There's a chance that they went to the cabin and know where it is. If I were you, Detective, I'd track down Annette and her father. I bet that Milo has Katherine in that cabin."

"Do you have any additional basis for this suspicion?"

"No. It's my geezer intuition. And by the way, I didn't cut down any trees."

"Is there something else you should be telling me, Mr. Jacobson?"

"If you hear any more wild claims concerning yours truly, I'm innocent."

After hanging up, I returned to Jennifer's room.

"You've given him a lead now, Grandpa. We'll see how good a detective he is."

"I hope he's as persistent in following up on what I told him as he is in bugging me."

"Maybe he likes you, Grandpa. I know I do." She gave me a hug.

How could you argue with logic like that?

Jennifer stepped back and looked at me. "Do you remember your dreams, Grandpa?"

"What kind of question is that?"

"With your memory problems do you remember dreams?"

I thought back. "I can't remember any recent ones. As a boy I had dreams of flying. We had a big oak tree in the pasture behind our house. I dreamt once of soaring from a branch in that tree. A red bird flew with me. That's when I knew I dreamed in color."

"That's a nice dream. I sometimes dream that I'm floating around the house. I like that kind of dream."

Allison looked into the room. "Speaking of dreams, it's time for you to get ready for bed."

"Aw, Mom. Grandpa and I are making progress on one of his cases."

"You two can continue tomorrow night, and then once summer vacation begins, you'll have time during the day."

Jennifer's eyes widened, and she turned toward me. "That's

right, Grandpa. We'll be able to do some of our own investigating and follow clues. We'll have lots of time between
morning swim practice and afternoon tennis team."

"Ah, the wonders of youthful energy," I said.

THE NEXT NIGHT Jennifer and I continued our planning.
After reviewing the litany of charges, Jennifer bit her lip
and then said, "With tomorrow the last day of school, I'd
better get cracking on talking again to Teddy Bishop and
Randy Buchanan. I already spoke to them once regarding
the false claims they made in the bathroom at the game
night."

"What did they say?"

"When I confronted them one at a time, each stuck to his
story. I caught them together later and told them they could
get kicked out of school for lying."

"Did that have any effect?"

Jennifer smiled. "I'll say. They both looked at each other
guiltily. Then they ran off. I think they're worried. I'll have
to put some more pressure on them tomorrow to see if I can
get them to crack."

"Even if you get them to confess to you, it doesn't mean
they'll admit it in front of the police."

The corners of Jennifer's mouth turned up and her eyes
sparkled. "I'll do what you did in Hawaii that one time. I'll
record my interview with them. Mom has a small tape
recorder. I'll borrow it."

"I don't know if that will work."

"I'm going to try. I can use the same pressure techniques
Detective Lavino always uses on you."

"Are you turning into a cop as well as a lawyer?"

She smiled. "Maybe I can combine private investigation
with my law practice."

"Don't get too carried way. You're only twelve."

"I know. But I'll train now and be ready by the time I

graduate from law school." She rubbed her stomach. "You want a snack?" So saying, she skipped off toward the kitchen.

THE NEXT MORNING Jennifer headed off to school armed with a recording device.

"She only has a half day of school today," Allison said.

"That daughter of yours will clear my good name. She's quite a pistol."

"When Jennifer sets her mind to something, she's very persistent."

"I bet when she's old enough to have a boyfriend, he'll have to toe the line."

"She already has a boyfriend," Allison said.

"What? She's too young."

"Paul, at this age it means that they ignore each other less than usual. He's a boy on her swim team named Neal Wooten."

I shook my head. "I can't even imagine what kind of boy Jennifer would choose as a boyfriend."

"You can find out for yourself. There's a swim meet on Saturday."

"I don't know if I should show up at the swim and tennis club again, being the scene of the lost money box."

"I won't make you take over the bake sale this time," Allison said and patted my arm.

THAT AFTERNOON when Jennifer returned from school, I met her at the door. "Any luck?" I asked.

She gave me a sunny smile. "Wait until you hear the tape."

"Did it turn out?"

"I haven't listened to it, but I forced them to admit that they made up the story."

"Tell me exactly what happened."

"I caught up with Teddy and Randy before school. They were sitting on the wall in front of the building. I looked each of them in the eyes and said, 'It's a shame you two will be in the school detention program all summer.'" She giggled. "You should have seen how big their eyes grew. Then I told them that if they confessed to making up the accusation, the principal would go light on them."

"And what did they say?"

"They both blurted out that it was a joke and they didn't mean any harm. That's what's on the tape. I told them to go speak with the principal immediately to clear things up."

"Did they do that?"

Jennifer frowned. "I don't know for sure. The bell rang. We aren't in any classes together, and I didn't see them when school let out."

"Let's hear the tape," I said.

Jennifer rewound and played it. You could hear Jennifer clearly, followed by the voices of the two boys. She had definitely put the fear of God in them.

"Good work," I said. "We'll give this to Detective Lavino the next time he comes sniffing around."

That night Jennifer and I discussed the Colorado Mountain Retirement Properties outfit.

"Let me see if I can find anything new on the Internet," Jennifer said and began tapping on her keyboard. "Here's an article from the *Chaffee County Times*." She pointed to the screen.

I read the article which described zoning hearings taking place concerning the proposed site for a new retirement facility.

"They don't even have approval yet on that property," I said. "They're selling lots which may or may not ever be available. We need to print this out for Detective Lavino."

"I can do one better. I'll email it to him."

"How do you know where to send it?"

"I'll search for his email address." She clicked away on the keys again. "There. I found it."

I scratched my head. "How do you do these things?"

"Easy, Grandpa. I scanned the Boulder Police Department web site and found a list of detectives and contact information. I'll write him a note and attach the article."

Minutes later she had completed the task, none too soon because the warden showed up.

"Okay," Allison said, with her hands on her hips. "There's a swim meet tomorrow. Lights out in ten minutes."

"I need to log off, Mom. We're making progress on helping Grandpa."

"Well, you help yourself into bed, young lady."

THE NEXT MORNING Allison made sure we rose early. After eating a hearty breakfast, we clambered into the family van along with a pile of towels, folding chairs, sweatshirts, blankets, ice chests and extra swim goggles. I didn't know if we were going to a local swim meet or the Olympics.

When we arrived at the club, we set up alongside the pool.

Jennifer dashed off to swim her warm-up laps, and Allison signaled for Denny and me to follow her. "I need you two big, strong men to help me blow up balloons."

"We having a party?" I asked. "I used to blow up balloons for Denny's birthday parties all the time. You remember that, Son?"

"I sure do. You and Mom always decorated the house for my birthdays."

"While you two reminisce, grab some balloons and start blowing so we can decorate the club with our team's colors," Allison said as she handed each of us a bunch of green and white balloons.

I huffed and puffed and discovered that I still had good lung power. I tied off my first balloon with a flourish.

"How'd you do that so quickly?" Allison asked.

"The secret is in the placement of a finger on the stem and

a quick flick of the wrist," I said, demonstrating it. "Not bad for an old fart, eh?"

I finished off a dozen balloons, knowing I had done my part for the home team.

Then I prepared for a morning of watching kids thrash in the water. Only they didn't thrash. They zipped along like baby seals. If I had been in the pool, I'd have been the one thrashing.

Allison leaned over and said to me, "There's Jennifer's boyfriend, Neal Wooten."

"Where?"

"In the third lane."

I squinted. I could only see a head covered with goggles and a swim cap, bobbing up and down, arms churning like a windmill. When he finished his heat, he jumped out of the pool and disappeared into a crowd of kids so I couldn't get a good look at him.

An hour into the event Jennifer came over, leading a boy three inches shorter than she was. "Grandpa, meet my friend Neal Wooten."

I examined him up and down. Skinny, with a little belly that didn't fit for a swimmer, pimples, braces, orange-ish complexion and a squashed face.

He gave me a shiny grin. "You're the guy who took money at the last swim meet."

I felt like drowning the little whelp. "Where'd you hear that?"

"Some of the fifteen-to-eighteens mentioned it in the locker room. They said Jacobson, and Jennifer's the only Jacobson in the club."

"I didn't take any money, and I'd appreciate it if you would set the record straight with whoever is spreading false information."

"Okay. I need to get ready for my next heat." He turned and jogged off toward the staging area.

"Isn't he cool, Grandpa?"

I didn't want to dispel her enthusiasm. "I guess he's all right." I didn't share my view that he reminded me of something you'd find in an aquarium.

TWELVE

ON SUNDAY AFTERNOON, Jennifer raced into my room. "Grandpa, we have a lead on the stolen money. One of my friends, Annie, saw some funny looking bills in the toy store at the Pearl Street Mall."

"Let's go check it out."

Jennifer hung her head. "I'd like to, but my friend, Rebecca, is coming over to play in an hour."

"I'll go have a look."

"Great, Grandpa. Here, Mom gave me her cell phone for you to use. You can call home with any report."

I eyed the electronic contraption she handed me. "I don't know how to use those damn things."

"It's easy. Just push the green button and talk."

"If you say so." I took the cell phone and stuffed it in my pocket. "Now where am I going?"

While Jennifer looked up the address for me, I found a notepad to put in my pocket. Then with some further guidance, I took the number 203 bus which picked me up right in front of the middle school and deposited me at the end of the line on 14th and Walnut. From there I navigated the short distance to the Pearl Street Mall.

At the designated address I found a window displaying some stuffed animals. I decided I could kill two birds with one bus ticket. I'd buy Jennifer a present as a first installment on her attorney fees and see if any funny money showed up. As I entered the shop, a bell jangled and a brown-haired man in crumpled jeans and sweatshirt appeared from a back room.

"May I help you?" he asked.

I appraised him carefully, noting a triangular face with a few freckles and a serious, intense expression on his puss.

"I'm looking for a stuffed animal."

"All along the shelf over there," he waved his hand to the right.

I ambled over past some toy cars and airplanes and inspected the collection of furry creatures.

"There's a line of Hawaiian stuffed animals, each with a passport. Do you have any?"

He grinned. "As a matter of fact I have one in stock." He drifted over, bent down and rummaged through the shelf. He thrust his hand up like he'd found a treasure and exhibited an orange crab.

I inspected it closely. The label indicated the name "Hihe'e," meaning sideways running Hawaiian crab. It looked just like the description I remembered of Jennifer's boyfriend Neal Wooten.

"I'll take it," I said. "You stocking any more of these?"

"I have to order them on-line."

"I'd suggest bringing in a boatload. I may be needing to buy additional ones."

Reaching into my wallet, I found only one bill, so I handed the fifty-spot over to pay.

"You the proprietor of this place?" I asked.

"Yeah. Owner and sole employee."

"Do much business?"

He shrugged. "Not too busy lately, but it should pick up in a few weeks when more tourists visit Boulder." He handed me two twenties, a dollar bill, some coins and the crab in a brown paper bag.

I almost dropped the money when I saw red blobs on the two twenty-dollar bills.

After leaving the shop, I found a bench to sit down on. Once the adrenaline rush had worn off from finding the marked money, I looked up at the blue sky and sat comfortably in the warmth of a late spring afternoon. I yawned. Then I took out the notepad and jotted down what had happened.

I AWOKE WITH A START. A pigeon sat a foot from my face staring at me. I blinked. Where the hell was I? I stretched my arms, and the pigeon hopped off and began pecking at something on the ground. I surveyed my surroundings and discovered I was attached to a bench on some sort of downtown mall. Didn't recognize it. Standing up I decided to explore.

Groups of teenagers sat on the lawn by a three-story building, some talking, some kicking a hackie-sack, some smoking. Boy, was I glad I never took up smoking. I'd probably be dead from lung cancer if I had.

I entered a shop and wandered through aisles of crafts, shirts, refrigerator magnets and maps of Colorado. I decided I must be in Colorado. Then in a rack of bumper stickers, one caught my eye. I chuckled. I had to buy that one. It read, "Old age is not for sissies."

At the counter I extracted a twenty-dollar bill from my wallet and shoved it over the counter to the clerk.

He stared at me and said, "May I see some ID? I can't sell this to you unless you're over seventy-five."

I did a double-take, but since I already had my wallet out, I showed him my identification.

He looked at it, then smiled. "Just kidding, Mr. Jacobson. You're a good sport."

I laughed. "You got me on that one."

The clerk stared at the twenty-dollar bill I had given him. "Look at this. It has red marks on it."

I examined the money. Since this guy had a good sense of humor, I replied, "Left over from a bank robbery."

He gave me a wan smile. "Just as long as it's not counterfeit."

He forked over my change, and I told him to drop my purchase in the brown bag I already had.

"Thanks, Mr. Jacobson. You can buy more bumper stickers any time…without your ID."

Just then music started playing in my pocket. "What's that?" I shouted.

"Sounds like your cell phone."

I reached in my pocket and extracted a silver object that I had never seen before. "How does this damn thing work?"

The clerk leaned over. "Push the green button and speak into it."

I whacked the button and put it in front of my mouth. "Hello?"

"Hold it to the side of your face."

I did as instructed. "Hello?"

"No you have it upside down."

I flipped it over. "Hello?"

"Grandpa, are you all right?"

I didn't recognize the voice. "Who's this?"

"This is your granddaughter Jennifer."

"You sound older than I remember."

"Did you fall asleep?"

"Yeah, I just woke up from a nap. Where am I?"

I heard a sigh on the phone. "Let me give you directions on how to get home."

WHEN I ARRIVED AT the address given me, my daughter-in-law met me at the door. "I understand you fell asleep downtown."

"Something like that. Where's Jennifer?"

"She went off to Rebecca's house to spend the night. She asked me to remind you to write in your journal and to tell you she'd catch up with you tomorrow."

I opened the paper bag I was carrying and found a stuffed

animal crab. "I guess I bought this for Jennifer." I handed it to Allison. "You can give it to her from me if you see her before I do."

THE NEXT MORNING I slept late. Upon awakening, I spotted a note and a journal on the nightstand. "Read this before you get in any more trouble, you old goat." I examined it closely: my handwriting. I read a few pages recounting how I had flown to Denver to live with my family. I thumbed through some more pages and then read a random section about Jennifer being my lawyer. I decided I'd finish the missive after I shaved and dressed. I put on Bermuda shorts, sandals and a T-shirt with a picture of a whale on it. I had finished shaving when Allison called to me.

"Paul, you have a visitor."

"Is it a long lost girlfriend or have I won the Publishers' Clearing House sweepstakes?"

"No, it's a detective to see you."

Why would a detective want to see me? I ambled out into the living room to find a tall, skinny man in a suit.

I stared at him. "You an undertaker? I didn't think I'd died yet."

"Very funny, Mr. Jacobson."

"Do I know you?"

He held out police identification.

"I see you chew your nails." I read the name Detective Lavino. "I don't recognize the name or face."

He pulled back his identification and stood with his hands behind his back.

"Mr. Jacobson, I'm here to take you to police headquarters for questioning. You have the right to remain silent—"

"What's this all about?"

"Anything you say—"

"I need my lawyer." I turned and hollered, "Jennifer!"

"She's at swim practice," Allison said, wringing her hands.

"You have the right—"

"Hold it. You don't have to go through all that Miranda crap."

"If you cannot afford—"

"I know the words but not why you're going through this."

"You can decide at any time—"

Denny heard the commotion and rushed into the room. "What's happening?"

"Your father has been implicated in a serious crime, and new evidence directly links him to it. I've read him his rights and will take him to the station for questioning."

"What? Are you arresting him?"

"Not at this time."

Denny dropped onto the couch. He was taking this harder than me. "Is he a suspect?"

"Let's just say that I need to ask him some tough questions."

"Dad, I'm calling an attorney."

"I don't want any lawyer. I can clear this up myself."

"It's gone way beyond that." Denny looked toward Lavino. "May I accompany him now?"

"No. But you and your lawyer can speak with him at the police station."

"You going to cuff me, Detective?"

"Not unless you put up resistance."

"I don't have any resistance left in me."

I waved goodbye to my family as Lavino escorted me to his beautiful Crown Victoria parked at the curb. My next stop might have been death row.

"I'll think of something," Denny shouted to me.

"Either that or hire the cavalry to rescue me."

After an all-expense-paid ride while sealed in a back seat that felt like a medieval torture chamber, we arrived at an in-stitutional off-white building swarming with police, grumpy-looking people and various hangers-on from both sides of the law.

I twiddled my thumbs while Lavino filled out some paperwork. Then he led me to a small room.

"Please wait here for a few minutes," he said and left the room. At least I hadn't been thrown in a jail cell yet.

While I sat there, I looked around my new comfy surroundings. One other chair, a beat up desk and bare walls except for a picture of a large brown institutional building with no windows.

Before you could have said, "Olly olly oxen free," Detective Lavino reappeared and sat down in the other chair facing me.

"What's the picture on the wall?" I asked.

He smiled. "That's the county jail. A reminder of where people go when they are arrested."

I flinched. "Oh. I think I'll just stay here."

"We'll see after you answer some questions," Lavino said. "Before you were just a witness, but now there is evidence that directly links you to a bank robbery."

"Give me a hint what you're referring to."

"Yesterday afternoon you spent a twenty-dollar bill at a shop on the Pearl Street Mall. The clerk remembered your name."

I looked at him blankly.

"That bill had red identification marks on it indicating it came from the Boulder Central Bank that was robbed earlier this month."

"So?"

"The same bank that was robbed when you were found by a police officer holding a bag of stolen money outside. I considered you only a witness at that time, but one of the bank employees, a Mr. Kraus, was certain that you caused a distraction during the robbery. He felt you might be working with the perpetrator. I had nothing specific enough to consider you a suspect at the time, but I do now."

"I have no clue what you're referring to." I opened my wallet. "I don't remember anything about a twenty-dollar bill yesterday." I looked to see what might be in the folding money section. "I seem to have one in my wallet now." I handed the bill to Lavino.

He stared at me. "This one has the red marks as well. We now have further evidence linking you to the bank robbery."

"None of this makes any sense to me."

"Where did you get this twenty-dollar bill, Mr. Jacobson?"

I scratched my head. "Good question. I don't remember."

He extracted another twenty-dollar bill in a plastic bag. "How about this one?"

I shrugged. "Same thing. No idea if that was even mine."

"Why did you tell the clerk in the store on the mall that this twenty-dollar bills was, quote, 'left over from a bank robbery'?"

"You got me. I must have been joking."

"Pretty serious joke when the twenty-dollar bill came from the very bank robbery that you witnessed. I'm wondering if Mr. Kraus is right and you aided that robbery."

"Not an old coot like me. I don't go in for that type of thing."

"Are you still claiming you don't know the bank robber?"

"Since I don't remember the event, I can't say anything about the robber."

"Is there any further statement you'd like to make, Mr. Jacobson?"

"Yeah. I'm ready to go back to my family now."

He watched me carefully. "I'd like to ask you to have a photograph taken for our files."

"I have no problem posing for you although I'm sure you could find some more attractive models. Don't you want fingerprints as well?"

"No, Mr. Jacobson. We already have your fingerprints on file."

I looked down at my sandals. "You can also have my toe prints, if it will help."

I think I had convinced Lavino that I was more trouble than it was worth keeping in this tiny room. "Come with me." He stood up and I followed.

Lavino led me down a hallway. I expected the lights to blink and dim as someone met their doom in an electric chair in a hidden chamber. But we marched onward, and I encountered no guard dogs frothing at the mouth, no hooded executioners, nor any rooms with racks and water torture devices. We simply arrived at another hallway where several men sat in chairs outside an office. An officer in uniform stood with his arms crossed overseeing the operation.

"Take a seat here, Mr. Jacobson, and it will be your turn shortly."

I plunked my butt down on a chair next to the carcass of a big burly man with tanned arms covered in tattoos. He reminded me of a refugee from a weightlifting camp. "What 'dey bring you here for?" he asked in a whisper, leaning toward me.

"Bank robbery."

"No kidding." He raised his eyebrows.

"And you?"

"I beat up my ex-girlfriend's current boyfriend."

I looked at him carefully. "Not a pleasant sight, I bet."

He chuckled. "Mashed da guy up pretty good."

I wouldn't want to get on this guy's bad side.

The policeman indicated the bruiser's turn had come, so the brute lumbered into the adjoining room.

I looked to the other side of me, and a hairy face appeared inches from mine.

"Boo!" it said.

I nearly peed in my pants.

The face chuckled. "Gotcha good, old man."

"Who the hell are you?"

"I'm Al."

"You shouldn't scare old guys, Al. Might lead to homicide being added to whatever you're in here for."

He laughed. "Nothing bad. Just drugs. I'm here to be processed."

"You make it sound like you'll end up in a tuna can."

"Not dissimilar. You got a cigarette?"

"No. I don't smoke."

"Too bad. I could use one real bad." He scratched the back of his neck that was covered by long dirty brown hair. "What brings you here?"

"I'm suspected of aiding a bank robbery."

"If they lock you up, you'll be able to get out until your trial. You can post bail."

I squinted at him. "How do you know so much?"

"Easy. I'm a lawyer."

"Couldn't be much of one if you're sitting here."

"I don't practice anymore. Drugs paid better. Until I got busted."

At that moment Allison, accompanied by a police officer, came charging up the hallway and handed me a cup of water and three pills. "You're supposed to take your medicine."

I looked at the three gigantic capsules she'd given me. "Can't I offer these to my friend here? He does drugs."

Allison glared at me. "Don't make a fuss. I had enough trouble getting in here. Just do what you're told."

I knew better than to argue, so I struggled to gulp down the three rocks. Once I knew they had arrived safely in my stomach and not my lungs, I handed the paper cup back to Allison.

"Who's the chick?" my hirsute neighbor asked.

"She's from Special Forces. Come to spring me."

"Damn," he said. "Maybe she can get me out too."

"Don't count on it," I said.

"We'll be waiting for you out in the lobby." Allison gave me a furtive glance and disappeared from view accompanied by the police officer who had brought her in.

"Looks like she didn't break you out," Al said.

"Not yet. She's reconnoitering before bringing in the heavy artillery."

The watchdog police officer indicated it was my turn, so I waved goodbye to Al and proceeded into the room to find a bored-looking woman sitting there. She was attractive in a no-makeup way but didn't make eye contact.

"Please stand on that line." She pointed to a strip of tape on the floor.

"So you want me to toe the line just like Detective Lavino does."

She finally gazed up at me. "Yes."

"Don't you want to make sure I'm not armed?"

She finally exhibited a hint of a smile. "I don't think we need to worry about that."

"You never can tell. We old guys are pretty dangerous. Do you want a smile or a scowl?"

"Look natural."

I considered striking a pose like a bodybuilder, then thought better of it. Police personnel weren't noted for their sense of humor.

After a flash blinded me, I asked, "What's the next stop on my guided tour?"

"Detective Lavino will take you up front."

"That's good," I said. "I've always tried to be up-front with him."

She groaned just as Detective Lavino reappeared.

"Are you harassing our personnel?" he asked.

"No. Just entertaining them."

Lavino shook his head. "Mr. Jacobson, you have a very unique way of expressing yourself."

"You stick with me, Detective, and you'll have so much fun that you won't ever consider chewing your nails again."

I didn't think I was winning Detective Lavino over, but he did lead me out to the lobby where I immediately spotted Denny, Allison and Jennifer.

"Thanks for rescuing me," I said as Allison and Jennifer gave me hugs.

Jennifer immediately approached Detective Lavino and stood inches from him looking up into his face with her hands on her hips. "Why did you bring my grandfather here?"

He smiled down at her. "I had some questions to ask him concerning the bank robbery."

She now raised her right hand and shook a finger at him. "He's completely innocent. He had no motive for robbing a bank."

"But he has some very suspicious links to the robbery."

Jennifer shook her head. "Not good enough, Detective. My grandfather was only in Colorado two days before the robbery took place. He has no connections with the bank robber."

"And besides," I said. "I don't need the money. I'm mooching off my son, and my daughter-in-law is keeping me well-fed."

Lavino let out a sigh. "You're free to go for now, Mr. Jacobson. I'm sure we'll be speaking again soon."

As we left the building, I said to Jennifer, "I'm retaining you as my lead attorney."

"Cool. I'll see that you're cleared of all charges. We'll start planning your defense tonight." She gave me another big hug, and I knew I would be well represented.

THIRTEEN

BACK AT THE OLD HOMESTEAD, I discovered the notepad from my foray to the toy store and read the last few entries in my journal, but I couldn't relax. I paced the room, trying to figure out how I could stay out of Lavino's clutches. I would end up with an ulcer or dead if this continued.

I quickly realized why Lavino had brought me in for questioning. I would have done the same. I had passed a marked twenty-dollar bill at a store where the clerk remembered my name because he had played the little joke of asking for my ID. Then I had compounded the problem by showing Lavino another marked twenty-dollar bill at the police station. Not only mentally defective, I had been stupid. And since I had already been seen at the scene of the bank robbery, there could be only one conclusion. I was in cahoots with the robber.

I needed to clear this up. I searched through my room until I found Lavino's phone number. Calling, I waited as some brisk-voiced broad tried to track him down. No luck. I slammed the phone down. I'd have to try another time.

Then I decided to stretch my legs. I needed some time to contemplate my future. As I approached the door, Max, always ready for a walk, jumped up and down to catch my attention. "Sure, boy. You can accompany me on my expedition."

The sun had dipped behind the Flatiron rock formation, and a golden lenticular cloud hung in the sky above, resembling a large oval spaceship.

I mulled over what I should do: how to figure out the two murders, how to clear my name of the litany of miscellaneous charges I had attracted like a magnet sucking up iron filings.

I hiked until only a faint glow of light remained in the western sky, then retraced my steps. Up ahead a van nestled against the curb, its engine idling. I looked inside from the passenger's side. No one in the driver's seat. All of a sudden a man came running up, opened the back and thrust a fir tree inside.

Something clicked. The tree thief!

"Hey!" I shouted.

But the man jumped in the van, stepped on the gas and shot away from the curb.

In the dim light cast from a nearby street lamp, I caught a view of the license plate.

"There we go, Max. We've found the culprit who sawed down Mr. Fisher's tree."

Back at Denny's house, I retrieved Detective Lavino's phone number that I had left out and called again. To my surprise, he answered on the second ring.

"Detective Lavino, this is Paul Jacobson, your favorite suspect."

"You have something new to tell me?"

"Yes, indeed."

"Your confession?"

I chuckled. "You are a persistent cuss. No, nothing to confess, but I have two leads for you. First, I saw a man load a sawed-off tree in a van a few minutes ago. And here's the license plate number." I gave it to him.

"Let me tell you something I find very interesting, Mr. Jacobson. When we spoke recently you made an obtuse comment concerning not having cut down a tree. Afterwards I checked and, sure enough, a complaint had been filed about you. And now you call to say you saw someone else loading a tree into a van."

"Check out the license plate, Detective. Now here's the second item. I read my journal when I returned home from the nice visit to the police station you sponsored. Guess what I discovered?"

"With you, Mr. Jacobson, I wouldn't even venture a guess."

"I found where the marked twenty-dollar bills came from."

"I'm all ears."

"I received them in change from a toy store on the Pearl Street Mall."

"Name of the store?"

"Hell, I don't know. I didn't write it down."

"You'll have to be a little more specific, Mr. Jacobson."

"Go check out all the toy stores down there."

"We'll see what we can do."

I sighed. "And while we're talking, I want to follow up on another item."

"I can hardly wait."

"This is important. Colorado Mountain Retirement Properties. Detective, this outfit is peddling property that hasn't even been zoned yet. My granddaughter emailed you an article. Have you busted those crooks yet?"

"We're looking into it. You've been witness to or implicated in every category of crime except drugs, Mr. Jacobson."

"I don't do drugs. I hate pills, and my brain is already screwed up enough without artificial assistance."

"Is there anything else you have for me at this time, Mr. Jacobson?"

"No. I think I've shot my wad for now."

After hanging up, feeling satisfied I had done my civic duty, I grabbed my journal and various notes and joined Jennifer in her room to work on my defense.

When I arrived, Jennifer held up the orange crab. "Oh, Grandpa, it's so cute. Its face reminds me of something, but I can't place it."

I bit my tongue and didn't mention her boyfriend Neil Wooten.

"Consider this a first installment for the legal services you're performing for me."

"Cool."

I let Jennifer read selected sections of my diary while I finished reading the entry from the day before.

"How come you didn't give me the parts about Marion to read?"

"That's private, young lady."

"I read the details when you kept a journal in Hawaii…" She gave me a smug grin and wagged her finger at me. "I know all about you and Marion."

"There are some things best not divulged to a twelve-year-old."

Jennifer clicked her tongue. "Come on, Grandpa. I can handle it. And besides, as your attorney, we have no secrets. I'm sworn to keep them to myself."

"Fine. Anything relevant to the cases at hand."

She gave me one of her winning smiles. "Well, it's my professional opinion that you and Marion should live together."

"That's a subject we can revisit once you clear me of all charges."

"It's a deal. But I'll bring it up again then."

"Let's start with you getting me off the hook for the bank robbery."

"Okay." Jennifer swung her head to the side, and her blond ponytail bounced. "It's obvious that the shop owner who gave you the marked twenty-dollar bills in change committed the bank robbery. We need to find a way to make him confess. Your notes say the owner told you he has no employees."

"That's correct."

"I'm going to try something." She looked up the phone number of the one toy store on the Pearl Street Mall and called from the phone in her room. "Yes, I'm trying to find out if you carry lines of stuffed animals… Yes, that's right… And who am I speaking with?… Mr. Slade, thank you very much." She put the receiver down. "There, Grandpa. Mr. Benjamin Slade becomes our prime suspect!"

"So all we have to do is convince Slade to confess."

"Yes. We have to trap him, like you did with that thief at the retirement home in Hawaii."

"I don't remember."

"You and Meyer Ohana set him up, and he went for the bait. We'll have to try something similar."

"I understand. If the guy lusts after money, we dangle something in front of him that appeals to his greed."

"Exactly, Grandpa."

"You think it over tonight, and we'll talk more in the morning."

When I returned downstairs, Denny sat hunkered down by himself reading a magazine.

I plopped down next to him. "Catching up on world affairs?"

He lowered the magazine. "I'm reading an article regarding memory loss."

"That's my field. I'm an expert."

Denny frowned. "I know you've been through a lot with your memory problems, and I'm concerned I'm facing the same thing. My test results should be back next week."

I patted him on the shoulder. "It's crappy to be dealt mush in the brain, but I'm grateful to be healthy and still alive. Let's see how your tests turn out, and we can discuss what it will mean to you."

I returned to my room and mulled over Denny's concerns. With me as the model of mental acuity, I could understand his worry. If I had watched my father lose his marbles, I would have been anxious too. My father died young, but Denny had this old goat of a dad who couldn't remember up from down after falling asleep. What a pisser. If he followed my example, at least he'd be around for a good many years.

I could have wallowed in feeling sorry for my son and myself, but the telephone rang and Denny shouted for me to pick up the phone.

Who would be calling me? I wondered. Someone from my fan club?

A pleasant female voice greeted me, "Paul, this is Helen Gleason."

"Helen, it's good to hear from you."

"I wanted to let you know that tomorrow night we're having an old movie night at the Senior Center and thought you might enjoy attending."

"Well, I can handle the old part."

"I can't pick you up since I've committed to drive a car full of ladies from Meadows Manor, but you can meet me at the center. It starts at seven."

"Sounds good. I'll see you there."

THE NEXT MORNING after breakfast, Jennifer accompanied me back to my room.

"We'll do some more plotting when I get back from swim practice."

"I'll have what's left of my brain cells ready for action."

Jennifer stared at my dresser. "Grandpa, you still have two pictures."

"That's right."

"I warned you that it wasn't a good idea to have pictures of two girlfriends. You should choose one."

"Why do you say that?"

"If Neal had another girlfriend as well as me, I'd pop him in the nose."

I laughed. "I see your point." I regarded the pictures again, trying to remember either Marion or Helen. Marion and I had a long history together, although I could only recall it from my journal. Both attractive young ladies. "I'm not the kind of guy that plays the field. I really should have only one girl-friend."

"Good, Grandpa. And which one will it be?"

"If you're going to force me to make a decision, I guess Marion."

"You have chosen wisely." With that she skipped off to get ready for swim practice.

AFTER DENNY LEFT for work, Allison picked up a Sudoku puzzle to work, so I hunkered down to read a short story. Within half an hour Jennifer barged through the door.

"What happened to swim practice?" I asked.

"We had a problem with the pool. The chemicals aren't right so they closed the pool for the day."

"No practice then?"

"It's delayed. We're going to use the pool at the Centennial Community Center in an hour."

"Why don't I walk over with you? I need to stretch my creaky old legs."

"Your legs aren't that creaky, Grandpa. You move very well for a gentleman of your age."

"Why thank you. I'll take that as a compliment, I guess."

I donned my tennis shoes, and a little later Jennifer and I ambled off to the Community Center.

"I've been thinking up ways to trap Benjamin Slade, the suspected bank robber," Jennifer said.

"What're your thoughts?"

"He has the bank money stashed somewhere. He brought some of it out, and that's how you ended up with two marked twenty-dollar bills."

"We need to find a way for him to surface more of the cash and then sic my buddy, Detective Lavino, on him."

"Exactly, Grandpa. What would convince him to get a lot of the cash out?"

"We have to tempt him with something. He needs money, so if we can dangle a deal he can't refuse under his nose…"

"I've got it! If he could pick up a bunch of rare Beanie Babies for a low price, he could sell them for a high price. I could go into the shop and say I have a valuable collection that I need to unload quickly because my mom is sick and needs the money."

"How would you do that?"

"I have a catalog. I can tabulate a list of expensive Beanie Babies and see what price he offers to buy them for. I'll tell him I'll be back the next day with the stuffed animals and need cash. He'll bring in money from the bank robbery."

"That's crazy enough to work," I said. "We could leave a message with Detective Lavino to check the cash at the toy store that morning. Then Lavino will see who really stole the money."

"And since the detective thinks you're in cahoots, he'll find out that Benjamin Slade doesn't even know you. I'll think some more while I'm swimming laps, Grandpa."

"That's a good idea for you to noodle on it, but don't you have to concentrate while you're swimming?"

"Nah. I like having something to ponder when I'm doing laps. Races are a different matter. Then I have to concentrate."

We arrived at the building, and Jennifer bounded off toward the pool. I sank down onto a bench to watch the kids do their thing in the water. I spotted Jennifer as she adjusted her swim cap and goggles. She waved to me, then dove in and began swimming freestyle behind a line of a dozen kids going back and forth in one lane. Amazing. I swam like an oyster, and my granddaughter zipped along like a salmon.

When the excitement reached a crescendo, I sauntered outside for some sunshine and to enjoy the view. Rounding the building, I spied a children's play area replete with a huge sandbox and climbing equipment. Several women sat on a bench, laughing and watching children digging in the sand. At a picnic table under an awning sat a man with thinning white hair overseeing a young boy, probably his grandson, pushing a truck along the sidewalk. As I approached, the man's head jerked up and his eyes grew wide. "You...you... you're the one who sawed down my trees." He shook his fist at me. "Not one tree but two. And your dog crapped all over my lawn."

Uh-oh. This must be Mr. Fisher.

"Look, Mr. Fisher. I know you're upset about your trees, but I didn't saw them down. I can assure you that the police have a lead on who the real culprit is."

"How...how do you know that?"

"I saw a man load a tree into a van parked in front of your house."

He continued to splutter. "I...I think you're the one."

"I guess I can't change your mind now. Please be patient and have an open mind."

I walked away before he had a conniption fit or died of apoplexy. Much like with Detective Lavino, it wouldn't be easy to convince him of my innocence. Oh well. The challenges faced by a brain-impaired geezer.

Strolling over to an area with three handball courts, I sat on a bench to watch two young men pound a ball back and forth. They wore jeans and no shirts so their shoulders glistened with sweat in the warm sunlight.

I thought back to my college days. I had played a little handball then. One of my fraternity brothers had a nickname of Brick, derived from the fact that he stood only a smidgen over five feet tall and almost as wide. He planted himself in the middle of the handball court, and although he didn't move that well, he allowed no balls by and placed his shots so his opponent had to scramble like a scared jackrabbit. Good old Brick. Built like the proverbial brick shithouse.

I leaned back and watched a puff of cloud sail eastward. A

hawk circled searching for a mouse in the adjoining field. Kind of like Lavino waiting to pounce on me. I had to think positive. With Jennifer's assistance, we continued to make inroads on the long list of crimes I had to deal with. If I could only shorten the list before Lavino added any more offenses.

Standing up, I stretched my arms. I had to count my blessings. I remained free of arthritis and was healthy for an old poop my age. Had to walk and keep those legs in shape.

I wandered back toward the play area, giving a wide berth so as not to inflame Mr. Fisher again. I noticed that he had nodded off. Seeing me had obviously exhausted him. I strolled down to the pond and halted at the edge to watch some bluegills drifting through the mucky water. Algae had accumulated on the edge of the pond, which dropped off steeply.

I heard a giggle. Twenty feet away a little boy tottered toward the water. It was Mr. Fisher's grandson. A duck swam past. The boy reached out toward it, stumbled and splashed into the pond.

FOURTEEN

THE BOY FLAILED in the water.

Fear gripped me.

He would drown.

I saw no one else close by.

Across the pond in the dog park, a woman screamed.

My head jerked from side to side. I couldn't swim any better than the toddler, but I had to do something. I raced over and catapulted into the pond. I sank into water over my head. Bubbles emerged next to me and I grappled in the water, until my hand struck something solid. I felt a T-shirt, grabbed it and lifted the boy out of the water. He spluttered. I gulped a mouthful of muck. With my other hand I paddled toward shore. My head went under. I struggled to hold the boy up while attempting to regain the surface.

I flailed again, trying to reach the edge of the pond. How could something so close be so far away? My head went under again, but I held the boy above the water. My right foot grazed something. I flinched and kicking, freed my foot from a web of algae.

I thrust my head up and gulped air again.

I heard the boy crying. A good sign. I felt like crying too.

I kicked and one-arm-stroked.

The edge of the pond appeared almost within reach.

I went down for the third time and my feet struck bottom. I stood up, never so glad to feel something solid under me. Pushing the boy onto the grass lining the pond, I pulled my old body up next to him, scraping my hand in the process. Exhausted, I closed my eyes. So sleepy.

Then I remembered.

Don't fall asleep you old coot, or you won't have a clue what happened.

I opened my eyes.

A group of people had gathered.

I heard, "I've called 9-1-1."

Another voice said, "Someone went to find the lifeguard from the swimming pool."

I lay there gasping.

Shortly, a muscle-bound young man in skimpy swim trunks dashed up to me. He stared at me with a look on his face as if he'd been the one dragged from the pond. "You have blood all over your hand," he said. Then he bent over and puked. So much for guarding my life.

I raised myself up on one elbow as the lifeguard continued to nourish the lawn with the contents of his breakfast. I noticed my minor scrape and rubbed the blood off my hand onto the grass.

The toddler sat on the ground, sniffling, but alive. Mr. Fisher had his arm around the boy.

A woman said, "Did you see that? The old man's a hero. He saved the little boy's life."

Another woman said, "If he hadn't been nearby, the boy would surely have drowned."

The distant wail of a siren increased in volume, and, in moments, two men in white uniforms came running up to me.

"Check out the boy first to make sure he's okay," I said.

One medic attended to the child while the other bent down to wrap a blanket around me. That helped absorb some of the water from my T-shirt and Bermuda shorts, and I used it to wipe off the pond scum. I would have to put up with squishy tennis shoes for a while.

"Are you having trouble breathing, sir?" he asked.

"Not now. I caught my breath."

"We can take you to the hospital."

"That's not necessary."

I looked up to see Jennifer running toward me. "Grandpa, what happened?"

"I decided to go for a little swim."

"But you hate the water."

"I know. I still do."

The emergency team tended to the lifeguard, the only one requiring treatment. They gave him oxygen from a portable unit and then, with a paramedic supporting him on either side, dragged him to their emergency vehicle.

I stood up and shook my arms and legs. "A little damp, but it's a warm day. I wouldn't want to have done that on a winter morning."

"You should head home to change," Jennifer said.

"I can walk back."

"Okey dokey. I'm glad you're fine. I need to go back to swim practice." She raced off.

Mr. Fisher came up to me. "I can give you a lift to your house. I need to take Ralphie back to dry off."

"Thank you," I said. "I'll take you up on that."

He met my gaze directly. "And thank you for saving my grandson. I guess I misjudged you."

I shrugged. "No problem, Mr. Fisher."

"And please, use my first name. Nate."

"And I'm Paul."

We shook hands. Then he reached down to clasp Ralphie's hand, and we headed toward the parking lot.

Ralphie seemed no worse for wear, and as a gaggle of geese flew overhead, he pointed and giggled. Ah, the resilience of youth.

"Let's stop at my house first so I can get Ralphie changed into dry clothes." His brow wrinkled. "My daughter-in-law will be by in half an hour to pick up Ralphie. Please don't mention anything regarding the incident. If she finds out I fell asleep when I was supposed to be watching Ralphie, she'll never entrust him to me again."

"My lips are sealed."

We pulled into his driveway. Nate extricated Ralphie from his car seat, then turned to me. "Come on in for awhile. I'll fix you and Ralphie a snack after I change his clothes."

I scanned the front lawn. Well-trimmed grass, no weeds, rosebushes in full bloom…partial row of fir trees with two stumps in the middle. No wonder he had been so pissed.

Inside, I waited while Nate and Ralphie disappeared down a hallway. Not wanting to dampen his furniture, I strolled around the living room inspecting an old, comfortable, blue flower-patterned couch and matching chairs. Pictures on the wall displayed a consistent theme: each a still life of a different flower. I felt like I had entered a plant nursery.

Everything appeared clean and neat. The only thing out of place in the otherwise immaculate room was a pile of cardboard boxes tucked away along the wall behind an end table supporting a lamp and yellow-flowered shade.

Nate reappeared with a dry and combed Ralphie. Nate puttered around the kitchen, opening and closing the refrigerator, banging dishes and making rapping sounds. I sauntered over to join him and studied him carefully. He must have been in his seventies, approximately my height, a small paunch, thinning white hair, but otherwise a healthy-looking young whipper-snapper.

"Anyone else live here with you, Nate?"

He visibly slumped. "No. My wife died a year ago. I'm on my own."

"I'm sorry to hear that. I'm in the same boat. My wife Rhonda died some time ago. Any girlfriends?"

He shook his head. "I've kept to myself since Harriet died. Maybe one of these days…"

An idea occurred to me. "Say. I'm going over to the Centennial Community Center to see a movie tonight. You care to join me?"

His eyes lit up. "Sure. I haven't been to a show in ages."

I thought back to my conversation with Jennifer that morning. I had one too many girlfriends and Nate had none. What if…?

"Here are some crackers and cheese for you." Nate handed me a plate.

I sat down on a plastic-covered stool and munched away while I plotted. What if I fixed Nate up with Helen?

After we finished eating, Ralphie toddled off to play with a toy car on the living room rug.

The doorbell rang, and Nate shuffled over to open the door. A frazzled-looking woman with short brown hair stood there. Ralphie jumped up. "Mommy!" he shouted. The first word I'd heard him speak.

"I'm running late," she said as she lifted up Ralphie. "Thanks for watching him." Then she turned and disappeared.

Nate shook his head. "This generation. They're always in such a hurry."

"Good thing she didn't ask why Ralphie had a different outfit on."

"Yeah and I'm lucky that Ralpie's only word is 'Mommy' so he won't be able to tell her what happened."

I surveyed the living room. "I was wondering. What do you have in all the boxes?"

"They're a collection of Beanie Babies. Harriet collected them and after she died…well…I boxed them up. It's a valuable collection, but I haven't had the heart to do anything with it yet… Say, maybe your granddaughter would like some. I could let her pick out ones she likes."

"Beanie Babies," I said to myself, remembering what Jennifer and I had discussed on the way to the swimming pool that morning. "Tell you what, Nate. Rather than giving my granddaughter some Beanie Babies, could we borrow a box of them?"

"Borrow?" He looked at me quizzically.

"Yeah. We're working on a project, and if we could use them for a day, it would really help. I promise to return them in pristine condition."

He shrugged. "Well, I guess I owe you one."

"One favor. Let me have a box that contains high-priced stuffed animals."

He pointed toward the boxes. "The box on the top has the early ones. Harriet started collecting right when they first came out. Those should be worth the most."

I ambled over and picked up the bulky box. "Now if you'll give me a ride down the street with this big box, I'll get out of your hair."

He coughed.

Damn. I guessed I shouldn't have said that to a guy going bald.

NATE DROPPED ME and the box of Beanie Babies off at the old homestead and said he'd pick me up at a quarter to seven for the movie at the Senior Center.

I waved goodbye as he drove away, glad that I had young friends who could still drive. What a change in his attitude toward me as a result of a little thing like saving the life of his grandson.

Jennifer had returned from swim practice and sat in the kitchen with her mom.

"I understand you've become the man of the hour," Allison said.

"Just doing my civic duty."

"Sounds like a lot more than that."

"Some good news. Nate Fisher and I have become best buddies."

"He told you his first name? Wow. That's really something."

"He's basically a nice guy, but lonely."

"He always seems so crotchety."

"Losing a wife will do that to you."

"What's that?" Jennifer asked, eyeing the cardboard box.

"It's a surprise," I said. "Let's go to your room, and I'll show you."

"What are you two up to?" Allison asked.

"We're plotting and scheming," I replied. "Now let's get started."

In Jennifer's room, I opened the box.

"Cool." She pulled out several stuffed animals. "These are expensive Beanie Babies."

"You said this morning that you had a book that lists their value. Why don't you calculate what we have here? This can be our hook to catch Benjamin Slade. We'll dangle these in front of him and see if he retrieves cash from his stolen loot."

"I get it. We don't have to go to his shop pretending to sell Beanie Babies. We'll take the box in and say we're selling the whole caboodle."

"Exactly. We'll ask him to appraise them and give us an offer. We'll say we want cash and will return the next day to complete the deal."

Jennifer rubbed her hands together. "This will be so cool. We'll nail him, Grandpa." Then a serious expression returned to her face. "But you've been in his shop before. If he remembers you, he might start wondering what's going on. If I take the box in on my own, he's less apt to be suspicious."

"I can wait for you outside. I'll keep an eye on him from there so he doesn't try anything fishy."

Jennifer clenched her right hand into a fist. "Nobody's going to mess with me."

I stepped back in mock terror. "I wouldn't want to be in Slade's shoes if you go after him."

Jennifer flicked her ponytail. "Now I want to find out the value of the Beanies." She removed a book from her shelf, lined up all the Beanie Babies on her bed and retrieved a pad of paper and pencil. She licked the tip of the pencil, thumbed through a few pages and began jotting down numbers.

"You look like a serious entrepreneur," I said.

"Absolutely. When I'm tired of being a lawyer, I'll probably start my own business."

"I wouldn't put it past you. Or running the country."

She grinned. "That might be later."

When she had completed her research, she showed me the list and grabbed a calculator to tabulate the numbers.

"Okay, here's the total." She showed me the number.

"Wow! Almost ten thousand dollars."

"These are all valuable first generation Beanies. The tags don't open like a book, but are a single-layer heart shape. The more recent tags unfold." She picked up her list and an alligator. "Here's Ally, it's worth three hundred dollars… And Spot the dog, over a thousand dollars…and here's a neat one, Slither the snake. Twelve hundred and fifty dollars."

I whistled. "People pay that much for these little critters?"

Jennifer shrugged. "That's what the books shows. We have twenty-four first generation Beanies. That's quite a collection."

"It will be interesting to see what Slade offers for these—I'm sure a lot less since a dealer has to make margin, but I wonder how much he'll try to cheat you."

Jennifer smiled. "I'll have to negotiate with him a little."

I looked at my watch. "Let me change out of my damp clothes, and we can catch the bus downtown."

"Okey dokey. I'm ready to catch this guy."

AS WE BOARDED THE BUS, the mustached driver wrinkled his brow. Maybe he thought we had a bomb in the cardboard box.

"Let's sit in the back, Grandpa." Jennifer skipped down the aisle.

I followed her, noting the nearly empty bus—two young boys playing handheld video games and a shopping bag-toting woman who looked even older than me, if such a thing were possible.

After several stops where a teenager with earphones danced aboard and the old woman departed, we arrived at the end of the line. We strolled the short distance to Toys 'n Stuff.

"Okay, Grandpa. You wait here on this bench. You can see inside the shop through the glass door. Time for me to make a deal." She pranced into the shop.

I heard a bell jangle and could see a man appear at the back counter. Jennifer placed the box down and began waving her hands. On one occasion she punched her right fist into her left hand. Then she began to extract the stuffed animals from the box and deposited them on the counter.

The man picked up each one, examined it and wrote something down. Then he turned his back for a few minutes. When he turned back he pointed to something on the counter.

Jennifer shook her head.

The man picked up a pen and scribbled for a few moments. He pointed again.

Jennifer threw her hands up in the air.

The man looked startled and jotted down something.

Jennifer put her hands on her hips and shook her head again.

The routine continued until, finally, Jennifer nodded her head. Then she returned all the Beanie Babies into the box, picked it up, turned and strolled out of the shop:

"Follow me, but don't look like you're with me," she whispered as she loped past me.

I waited a moment and then traipsed after her until we were out of sight of the store.

"How'd it go?" I asked.

"Like you suspected, he tried to cheat me at first."

"What did he offer?"

Jennifer laughed. "He said he'd give me ten dollars per Beanie."

"That's nothing. He must have thought you just got off the banana boat."

"Exactly. And I told him so."

"I can imagine you did."

"I indicated I knew what they were worth and wanted a serious offer."

"Did that work?"

She frowned. "Not the first time. He raised his offer to a thousand dollars."

"But you kept after him."

"Yes. He finally reached two thousand dollars and I figured that would be enough for him to have to resort to some of his stolen stash."

"Didn't he want to buy them right then?"

"Since I told him I'd only take cash, he said he'd have to bring in the money tomorrow. We know where that's coming from."

"What's the next step?"

"I'm supposed to return at noon to finalize the deal."

I smiled. "I'll have to let my friend Detective Lavino know. Maybe he can waltz into the shop and check for marked money."

"Then we'll be able to clear your name, and you'll owe me another Hawaiian stuffed animal."

I sighed. "You lawyers always want your payment."

"You bet, Grandpa."

I looked at my watch. "It's two o'clock, and I only had a snack at Nate's house, but no lunch. You hungry?"

"I'm always ready to dine with my grandfather."

We stopped at a hamburger shop and ordered. The clerk

filled up a large brown bag with cheeseburgers, fries and milk shakes and we headed out to find a bench to sit on.

"I like this town," I said to Jennifer as we munched away. "Warm weather, but not too hot. And all kinds of strange characters to watch." I pointed to a guy riding a unicycle who held a flag of Brazil in one hand while licking a chocolate ice cream cone.

After lunch I gathered all the wrappers, stuffed them in the brown paper sack, strolled over to a garbage can and dropped the bag inside.

Suddenly, a man in tattered jeans elbowed me aside and reached inside the trash container. He extracted a brown bag, looked from side to side with frantic eyes and started running. Before I could regain my composure, another man vaulted a bench and tackled him. They crashed to the ground, and a third man in a blue windbreaker jogged over and pulled out handcuffs.

Within seconds the guy who had pushed me wore cuffs.

The man in the blue windbreaker strode over to me and held out a police badge. "I need to speak with you."

"Here I am."

"No, I mean down at police headquarters."

"Jennifer, come over here."

Jennifer bopped over. "What's happening, Grandpa?"

"This undercover cop wants to give us a ride down to police headquarters."

"Cool."

WHEN WE GOT THERE, Jennifer said, "I've seen the lobby before and now the inside of the police station, Grandpa."

"You stick with me, and you'll see all the exciting parts of the city."

We were escorted to a small room, Jennifer carrying the box of Beanie Babies.

"I always wanted to see how they take videos during interrogations," Jennifer said, as she jumped up and skipped over to inspect the camera in the corner of the room by the ceiling. She tilted her face up and stuck out her tongue.

Moments later a tall, skinny man in a suit strolled into the room.

"We meet again, Mr. Jacobson."

"And who are you?"

"Detective Lavino."

"Say. I want to talk to you. Here's something important regarding the money from the bank robbery. When we last talked I told you I received the twenty-dollar bills as change from a toy store on the Pearl Street Mall."

"So?"

"My granddaughter and I checked it out, and it turns out I paid for a stuffed animal in a shop called Toys 'n Stuff on the Pearl Street Mall." I paused.

"Go on, Mr. Jacobson."

"The shop proprietor and only employee is a man named Benjamin Slade. I gave him a fifty-dollar bill and received two twenties in change. I suggest you visit Mr. Slade and investigate him. He should have a large amount of cash tomorrow when he opens the shop."

"And why would that be?"

"Because he thinks he's buying a number of valuable stuffed animals. He'll have cash that, if my guess is correct, will be some of the money you're looking for. When you put pressure on him like you're always doing with me, maybe he'll confess. And you'll find that I had nothing to do with the bank robbery."

"Quite a story, Mr. Jacobson."

"It's absolutely true," Jennifer said. "I spoke to Benjamin Slade. He tried to cheat me, but he's greedy enough that he'll bring some of his stolen loot to his shop tomorrow. You can catch him red-handed."

"What are you two up to?"

"Just check it out, Detective."

"Now, the matter at hand. I recently mentioned to you that you'd been near every crime except drugs. Looks like you're making up for that now."

"I didn't do anything."

"I understand, but I want to hear from you what you witnessed on the mall."

"We had something to eat, I threw away the bag and your undercover guys arrested a man."

Lavino laughed. "The undercover officer reported that you threw something away just before a drug bust."

"Show the detective the receipt for our food, Grandpa."

I reached in my shirt pocket and extracted a receipt that I handed to Lavino.

"Two cheeseburgers, an order of fries and two milk shakes," Jennifer said. "If you go back and check the trash can, you'll find two wrappers, a fries container and two cups in the brown paper bag that my grandpa put in the trash container. And his fingerprints will be all over our trash, but not the drug bag."

"My granddaughter knows what she's saying. Now, Detective, we need to mosey along."

THAT EVENING I changed into slacks and a clean long sleeve dress shirt. I sauntered into the hallway and called up the stairs to Jennifer.

Moments later she came bounding down. "Yes, Grandpa?"

"I need your assistance."

We went into my room, and I pointed toward the two pictures on my dresser. "I can't tell the difference between Marion and Helen."

Jennifer rolled her eyes. "Grandpa, we've been over this before. The one on the left is Marion."

"Good. I wanted to make absolutely sure."

At precisely 6:45 a car beeped in front of the house.

"I'm off for an evening with my younger friends," I said.

"What does that mean?" Denny asked as he looked up from a Smithsonian magazine.

"Young people. You know, in their seventies."

I jumped in Nate Fisher's brown Buick, and as he looked to his left to pull away from the curb, I surreptitiously placed an object on the floor.

"I didn't know they had a Senior Center in the community building," Nate said. "I've only visited the playground but never been inside."

"It's quite a facility. They have all kinds of activities, so you may want to look into other things as well."

When we arrived, I set my plan in motion. I introduced Helen and Nate to each other and suggested we find chairs. I made sure that Helen sat between Nate and me. Helen was decked out in a pretty blue flower-patterned frock. Perfect.

"Helen, Nate is quite a gardener."

"Is that right?" She turned toward him, and suddenly they became engaged in begonias, petunias, mums and crab grass prevention. Then the movie started and we settled in to watch Betty Grable, Marilyn Monroe and Lauren Bacall scheme to marry millionaires. I purposely sat away from Helen and noticed that her body had shifted toward Nate. Success!

Halfway through, the video stopped and a woman in a bright green dress stood up, clapped her hands to get everyone's attention and announced an intermission, with refreshments being served in the back of the room. Chairs scraped as a mad shuffle toward the restrooms ensued. I stood up and noticed that Nate and Helen had re-engaged in perennials, annuals and leaf worm. I slipped away and picked up two cups of punch and several cookies that I took back and offered to my companions. They accepted the refreshments without even looking up at me. Things were progressing even better than I expected.

Then I made my final move. "Nate and Helen," I said, "I'm

feeling a little under the weather, so I think I'm going to head home."

Nate looked up, concern on his face. "Do you need a ride?"

I waved my hand. "No. It's a short walk. I could use the fresh air."

Nate looked relieved.

I said my goodbyes, and they continued their animated conversation, now into soil acidity, root care and grafting.

AT HOME I immediately went into my room and admired the picture of Marion on my dresser. Helen's picture now rested in Nate's car.

FIFTEEN

I FELT BETTER NOW. Things had returned to a natural state. I had one woman in my life, and Marion would be back soon to visit me again. Now my main goal remained to clear my good name. That and stay alive a day at a time.

I decided I needed to have a confab with my lawyer, so I went to Jennifer's room.

"We're making good progress on the crime-scene front, but there's one other issue we need to address," I said. "We need to figure out what happened to the money stolen from the bake sale at the swim meet."

Jennifer scrunched up her nose. "Yes. We need to do something. I'll check it out at the club tomorrow."

"You do that if you expect to earn another Hawaiian stuffed animal."

"Oh, Grandpa. I'll earn it fair and square."

THE NEXT MORNING Jennifer took off for the club, eager to start tracking down the culprit from the great bake sale heist. I settled in for a morning of watching Allison defeat the Sudoku puzzle gods and listening to Max whine as he tried to convince me to take him for a walk. Then the ringing doorbell interrupted my busy schedule. Max's ears perked up.

"Don't lose your concentration," I said to Allison as I ambled over to open the door while Max growled. A guy my height, a little younger than me, but with thinning white hair, stood there. "Paul, may I speak with you?"

He knew me, but who the hell was he? Nate Fisher?

"Sure, let's take a walk." I turned and shouted to Allison. "I'll be back in a little while."

She didn't even look up. "All right, Paul."

I stepped outside and closed the door. "Those damn puzzles are more addictive than heroin… Now, what can I do for you?"

He cleared his throat as we sauntered down the walkway toward the sidewalk. "Well, it's regarding last night. I know Helen is your friend, but she and I hit it off so well."

It was Nate! I held up my hand. "Say no more. Helen and I are only acquaintances. We don't have that much in common, whereas you two gardening fanatics fit like two eyes in a face."

Nate looked relieved. "Thanks, Paul. I really like her and think she likes me. I didn't want to interfere if you…you know…had something going."

"Not to worry." I clapped him on the back. "She's all yours. As long as you don't try to have me arrested for sawing down trees."

He gave me a wan smile. "No, I know now I shouldn't have blamed you for that. But I'd still like to find the bastard who destroyed my trees."

"The police will be on it hot and heavy. The guy should be strung up by his thumbs any day now."

"That would be too good for him."

Wow. This guy Nate really loved his trees. Must have been like if someone tried to take Allison's Sudoku puzzles away.

We strolled on, and Nate said, "You know, Paul, a strange thing happened last night."

"Other than the magic in the air?"

"Yeah. When I returned home last night, I noticed something on the floor of my car—on the passenger's side."

"Do tell."

"I found a picture of Helen."

"Imagine that."

We circled the block, and when we arrived back in front of Denny's house, I remembered something from my journal. "Wait right here." I scooted inside and retrieved the cardboard box of Beanie Babies.

Back outside, I handed the box to Nate. "Thanks for the loan."

"I still can't figure out what you needed a box of Beanie Babies for."

"Undercover work."

WHEN JENNIFER SKIPPED INTO the house after swim practice, she had a smug look on her puss.

"You look like the cat that swallowed a flock of canaries."

"Yes, indeed." Her chin wagged up and down. "I made progress on tracking down a suspect for the bake sale heist."

"Give me the details."

"Well, I started snooping around during practice, asking if anyone had extra money. No clues there. But afterwards I went up to Barb, who runs the snack concession at the club. And guess what I found out?"

"That Barb fences candy for the Mafia?"

"No." She stomped her foot. "Barb told me that one Jeremy Wilkins had been buying lots of candy and cookies."

"And this raises suspicion because he's diabetic or something?"

Jennifer glared at me. "Grandpa, pay attention."

"Yes ma'am."

"Jeremy's mom never gives him money to buy snacks. She only wants him to eat fruit and yogurt, which she provides for him in a cooler every day."

"So suddenly Jeremy becomes the high roller of the candy set."

"You got it, Grandpa."

"Have you busted him yet?"

The corners of her mouth raised in a delighted grin. "I have a plan. I enlisted Neal to check out his locker. I'll have a full report tomorrow."

"I'd hate to be Jeremy with you on the case."

She punched her right fist into her left hand. "Nobody escapes the Jennerator. Nobody."

I wondered what I had unleashed. Maybe I should have turned her over to the American Bar Association ethics committee before she went too far.

AND THE NEXT DAY, true to her word, Jennifer sat down with me when she returned from swim practice. "It's all worked out now," she said.

"Meaning?"

"Like I told you yesterday, Jeremy Wilkins has become my chief suspect. Neal had a chance to look in his locker before swim practice today and what do you think he found?"

"Parts for weapons of mass destruction?"

"No." She glared at me. Then her smile returned. "A wad of cash. And not neatly organized. Loose bills tossed inside. Like someone had grabbed them from the bake sale."

"There might be some other explanation."

"Possible, but that's not the case. I confronted Jeremy in the clubhouse after practice today, and he confessed."

"What kept him from pleading innocent?"

"A little friendly persuasion." Jennifer held her fist up. "Nobody gets away from this. Nobody."

I laughed. "I've created a monster."

"No. Only a very focused and motivated enforcer."

"I know. I owe you one more Hawaiian stuffed animal."

"That's right." She gave me her sweetest smile.

THAT AFTERNOON I sat in the living room and calculated how much of my social security check would be going to paying off Jennifer. Oh well. Pay me now or pay me later. Whatever money remained when I kicked the bucket would be going to Denny, Allison and Jennifer anyway.

The ever-ringing doorbell jangled, and I lifted my old body up to answer the door as Max skidded to a stop in front of me. Two men in suits stood there, one tall skinny one and the other with a mole on his cheek.

"I'm sorry," I said. "I'm not interested in a subscription to Watchtower."

The taller of the two said, "Very funny, Mr. Jacobson. We need to speak to you."

"And you are?"

They both held out police identification. "Detectives Lavino and Hamilton. You're each investigating a murder."

"Very good," Lavino said. He turned to his companion. "Mr. Jacobson always comes up with the most interesting things he remembers."

"Hey, I aim to please. Anything I can do to help the Fraternal Order of Police."

Hamilton nodded. "May we come inside to talk?"

"Be my guest," I said. "You gentlemen can sit on the couch."

They settled in, and I sat down in a chair facing them. "To what do I owe the pleasure of your visit?"

"As you so eloquently stated, we're both investigating interlocking murder cases," Lavino said.

"I thought different police jurisdictions didn't cooperate much with each other," I said.

"That's a myth." Lavino gave Hamilton a wink. "We work together when there's a link between crimes in each of our cities. Both victims worked as salesmen for Colorado Mountain Retirement Properties. Ring a bell?"

"Although I don't remember specifically, I have read notes I made in my diary concerning the two murders."

"And, Mr. Jacobson," Lavino continued. "You've mentioned to me numerous times that you had suspicions regarding the legitimacy of the victims' company."

"That's right. I'm convinced that outfit has been perpetrating fraud."

"And we agree with your conclusion," Hamilton said. "Through the cooperative efforts of our two departments, we are investigating the president of the company, Peter Kingston."

I clapped my hands together. "Good work, Detectives. How soon will you have him locked up?"

"These things take time," Hamilton said.

"Have you linked him to the two murders as well?"

Hamilton shook his head. "No, he's innocent of the murders. He didn't fly back from Hawaii when Daniel Reynolds was murdered, and he had business in New York when Randall Swathers died."

"Too bad," I said. "I remember reading that Kingston was a lawyer. He would have been a good candidate to be arrested for whacking two of his sales people."

Lavino wrinkled his forehead and leaned forward. "That's still the interesting part. We've been able to find only one person who was both on the plane and at the Centennial Community Center: you, Mr. Jacobson."

I gulped. "There has to be someone else. Or maybe two killers." I thought over what I had read. "The really suspicious guy is Gary Previn."

"I've spoken to you in regard to this before," Lavino said. "Previn was on the plane so he remains a person of interest for the first murder, but he was at the Boulder Public Library at the time of the second murder. That leaves only you, Mr. Jacobson, at the scenes of both crimes."

"There needs to be a motive. I had no motive to kill anyone."

Hamilton smacked his lips like he had spied a big piece of pie a la mode. "In comparing notes with Detective Lavino, we found a pattern. On the plane you argued with the victim about the treatment of old people."

Lavino smiled. "And at the Community Center, you threatened Randall Swathers minutes before his death."

I sat there trying to get my bearings.

Hamilton pointed his right index finger at me. "Is there any chance, Mr. Jacobson, that you have anger management problems?"

"Only when detectives ask me dumb questions."

"Are you threatening us, Mr. Jacobson?" Hamilton said.

In spite of the situation, I couldn't contain myself. I laughed. "You've got to be kidding. I limit my anger to a few cuss words and shouting at people once in awhile. That's it."

Lavino frowned. "This is very serious, Mr. Jacobson. We need your full disclosure."

"Detective Lavino, I know you mean well, but you've been pestering me about a whole list of things I didn't do."

"I'm not convinced of your innocence," Hamilton said. "Both victims were killed after you had arguments with them. And the murder on the plane—you were the one who was seen striking the victim right before he was found dead."

My decrepit mind started churning, and suddenly I realized something. "Wait a minute. I didn't strike him, only shoved him. Reynolds must have already been dead when I pushed him off my shoulder. He looked all gray."

The detectives look at each other.

"You never mentioned that before, Mr. Jacobson," Hamilton said.

"I just made the connection. So keep searching for the murderer. Someone else dispatched Reynolds and Swathers. It wasn't me."

At that moment a cell phone chimed, and Hamilton reached into his pocket and snapped open a tiny instrument.

"Hamilton here…yeah…right." He flipped it closed and stood up. "I need to handle another case ASAP."

"I'll spend some more time with Mr. Jacobson," Lavino said.

"Gee, you give me such personalized attention," I replied.

Hamilton strode to the door and exited the scene.

"Very intense fellow," I said to Lavino.

"A lot more crime in Denver than Boulder, Mr. Jacobson."

"I'm glad to hear our sleepy little burg isn't the crime capital of Colorado."

"We still have our fair share."

"I'm curious. I gave you the license plate number of the guy who had been sawing down trees in a neighbor's yard. Have you collared the rascal yet?"

Lavino leveled his gaze at me. "You understand I don't have to share any information with you."

"I realize that, Detective. But as a citizen concerned over local crime in our neighborhood, I was just wondering."

"Becoming more civic-minded?"

"Absolutely. Please tell me what you can."

Lavino looked like he had tasted a lemon. Then his face relaxed. "Why not? We traced the license number to a local artist named Mallory Pitman. His landlady reports he's gone out of town. Since this isn't a big enough crime to waste any more time on right now, we're not pursuing him."

"But I'm anxious to see the culprit caught. And Benjamin Slade? Did you nab him as the bank robber?"

"Awfully inquisitive today, aren't you, Mr. Jacobson?"

"I gave you a good lead and want to make sure you followed up on it."

"Thanks for your concern. We're working the case."

"You keep after him, Detective. And how about Katherine Milo's father? I provided a lead there as well. Any luck?"

"We're still trying to track him down."

"So, Detective, I've provided you with all this useful information. Don't you think it's time to stop harassing me?"

He smiled. "No. I enjoy our conversations far too much. I can't wait for our next encounter. Besides, there is still the matter of two murders. Any parting words for me?"

"Keep investigating people in that slimy retirement property outfit. And if I have any new information, you'll be the first to know."

"We'll be speaking soon, Mr. Jacobson." He stood up and headed toward the door.

Just then Jennifer burst through the door. "Hi, Detective Lavino. Say, we have something to give to you." She dashed upstairs and returned moments later to drop an object in Lavino's hand. "Here's a recording of the two boys admitting they lied about my grandfather at the game night."

"And one last thing, Detective. If you'll check on it, you'll find that someone has confessed to stealing the money at the swim meet bake sale."

He turned back toward me. "As I said, these are all minor issues compared to the murders."

"I know. I only want to set the record straight."

THAT EVENING I told Jennifer we needed to have a conference.

"Cool. I'll grab a snack, and we'll adjourn to my office."

I regarded the back of her head as she bounced into the kitchen. Damn wannabe lawyers.

In Jennifer's room I sat down. "We're making good progress on a number of my so-called crimes, but the two killings remain unsolved. Both Lavino and Detective Hamilton from Denver are most anxious to pin those two murders on me and throw me in the clink."

Jennifer placed her index finger on her chin. "Let's both read through your journal again."

"Good idea."

I retrieved my stack of paper and with a few off-limits sections covered up, reviewed the material with Jennifer.

Once I'd read it through, I dropped the sheets of paper onto Jennifer's desk. "I don't have any fresh insights here."

"I can see why the detectives want you, Grandpa. No one else appears as suspicious as you."

"Thanks for the vote of confidence."

Jennifer shrugged. "Only being realistic. If I were Detective Lavino, I would wonder about you since you were the only one near both crimes and you argued with the victims ahead of time. We both know you're innocent since you don't know any super karate, so we have to figure out who else it could have been."

"Previn presents another alternative. He was on the plane with me. He's trained in martial arts. He could have sneaked up and whacked Reynolds while everyone else slept."

"That's possible. And Swathers died from a lethal blow. Previn has the right skills for both murders. But he has the alibi of being at the library at the time Swathers was killed in the Community Center parking lot."

"Unless there were two assailants." Then a thought occurred to me. "Or if Previn wasn't really at the library."

"Your journal indicates that Detective Lavino and you both verified that Previn had been at the library."

I slumped back in the chair. "That's right. Still, Previn remains the best lead we have. Maybe I can find something to break his alibi. I need to confront him again."

"You tried at the Kinetic Conveyance Race."

"I need to find another neutral site where I can accost him. From what I read he never answers his phone. Strange that the head of sales is so hard to reach."

"Let's see what we can find on the Colorado Mountain Retirement Properties web site." Jennifer pounded on her keyboard, and shortly a picture of a modern building surrounded by white-capped mountains appeared.

"That's a fake picture, if I ever saw one," I said.

"Be patient, Grandpa. Let me search through their site."

She clicked away and finally tapped the screen. "Here's something. Previn is hosting a promotional event next Saturday night at the Millennium Harvest House Hotel here in Boulder."

"You'd think that AARP would have shut those guys down by now."

"It's open to the public, so you can attend, Grandpa."

"Yes. I'll have an opportunity to see Previn in action. Then I'll have a friendly little chat with him."

"Be careful. If he's a murderer, he could be dangerous."

"I should be safe in a crowded room. I'll avoid ending up in a dark alley with him."

"Okay, let me read you the details. It starts at seven P.M. with a drink and dessert bar, followed by a presentation and entertainment. Wow. There's also a raffle. They're giving away a prize of two tickets for an Alaskan cruise."

"If I win, I can take my lawyer."

Jennifer pursed her lips. "No, if you win, I think you should take Marion. You two deserve some time with each other."

"I suppose you're right. I'm no spring chicken."

Jennifer gave me her lawyerly stare. "You and Marion should get together."

"You branching off into the matchmaking business as well?"

"Yes. Now that you've intelligently reduced your girl-friends to one, Marion would be the perfect cruise companion for you."

"You trying to get me to make Marion an honest woman?"

"I think she'd welcome the opportunity."

"But I don't know if she can put up with me."

"Grandpa, if Mom, Dad and I can do it, so can Marion."

"I'll consider it."

"When Marion comes back through Boulder, you two should discuss your future."

"At my age, my future could be twenty minutes."

"Oh, Grandpa. You're going to be around for many more years. You might as well have a companion."

"You sound like you're trying to get rid of me."

"No. I like having you here. But it would be better for both you and Marion if you lived together."

"You're sounding like one of Previn's salespeople."

"Only this is legitimate and good for you."

"I'll see. This all remains academic until I can clear myself of the murders."

She crossed her arms and leveled her gaze at me. "We'll make that happen. You talk to Marion when she visits."

I could see why Jeremy Wilkins had caved in and confessed to stealing the bake sale money.

THE FOLLOWING WEDNESDAY I received two phone calls. Nate Fisher invited me out to dinner on Thursday night. I readily accepted. Then within the hour Marion telephoned.

"Paul, I'll be passing through Boulder on Friday."

My heart jumped. I didn't know if it was love or fear of pressure from Jennifer. "That's great news. How'd you like to join me for a romantic dinner for two?"

"That would be wonderful. I'll be at the Days Inn again."

"I'll be by at six."

"I've missed you, Paul."

"I've missed you too, Marion. I'll see you on Friday."

After I hung up the phone, I stood there contemplating my strange existence. First, nothing planned, now I had engagements for Thursday, Friday and Saturday. Would I live through all three events?

SIXTEEN

ON THURSDAY EVENING a horn beeped, and I raised myself up from Denny's couch to open the front door. A brown Buick idled at the curb. "My chariot has arrived," I announced to my family. "I'll be back by 4 A.M."

"Earlier than that, I trust, Paul," Allison called back without looking up from her Sudoku puzzle.

When I reached the car, I saw a woman in the passenger's seat, so I climbed in the back seat.

"Helen and I both wanted to take you out to dinner," Nate said.

"And here I thought we were going to have a bachelor outing."

"How have you been, Paul?" Helen asked.

"Still alive."

We pulled into the parking lot at the Broker Inn.

"I like that this place serves a huge bowl of shrimp for appetizers," Nate said. "They're the kind you have to peel."

"Sounds good to me," I said. "I find shrimp most appealing."

Helen groaned.

"Hey," I said. "That's why Nate offers better companionship for you. He doesn't tell dumb jokes."

We sat in a corner booth and soon loaded up with shrimp.

Nate cleared his throat. "Paul, we invited you here because we have an announcement to make."

"I know. You're going to kick me out of the Senior Center for telling bad puns."

"No, something very important." Helen held out her left hand. "Notice anything special?"

"Your fingers appear very clean." Then I spotted the rock. "There's a diamond!"

"Yes. Nate and I are engaged."

"Well, I'll be damned." I reached across the table and gave Nate's hand a thorough shake. "Congratulations. This calls for a celebration." I waved to a passing waiter. "We need a truck-load of bubbly here."

When the champagne arrived, we had a round of toasts.

"And, Paul, thank you for bringing us together," Nate said.

"I'm delighted. What a whirlwind romance."

"It was love at first sight," Helen said.

"And both being avid gardeners didn't hurt either," I said.

We ate a fine meal. I patted my stomach, as a result of one fewer trout in the wild, and settled back to watch the glow in the eyes of Nate and Helen.

"You really should find a good woman," Helen said over dessert.

"I already have. She's coming to visit tomorrow."

WHEN I RETURNED HOME, I found Denny sitting alone in the living room.

"Seems so quiet here. Allison given up on her puzzles?"

"Yes. She finished her puzzle book and has sworn not to start another."

"We'll see how strong her willpower is."

"Dad, I want to talk to you."

I settled down into a chair. "Fire away."

"My tests come back tomorrow."

"Tests?"

"Yes. I went through a whole battery of scans to see if I'm developing any memory problems."

"You've been worried that you'd end up with a mushy brain like mine."

"I have been concerned that my memory is failing."

"It's a matter of seeing what the tests indicate."

"What if there's a problem?"

"Son, the one thing I've learned in all my years is that there's no sense worrying when there's no confirmed evidence yet. Get a good night's sleep and see what the medics report back tomorrow."

He sighed. "I guess you're right, but it has been on my mind."

"See, if you can remember that you're worried, you're still in fine shape. It's when you forget you're concerned that you have a problem."

"Thanks, Dad. I guess I'll head upstairs now."

I watched him stroll away. My perverse logic seemed to have helped. I just hoped that Denny wouldn't have to suffer memory loss.

LATE FRIDAY AFTERNOON, Denny burst through the door.

"My tests came back. They're all negative!"

Allison came up and gave him a hug. "That's great news."

I let out a sigh of relief.

"Yes. I have no unusual problems. I've been experiencing normal memory loss according to Dr. Johnson. He suggested I exercise regularly and watch my diet."

I came over and patted Denny on the back. "See. You can inherit my good traits, not the bad. You need to plan to come on walks with Max and me to stay in shape."

"Let's celebrate," Denny said. "Mama Mia is playing at the Denver Performing Arts Center. I'm going to call to make reservations for all of us."

"Count me out," I said. "I have a hot dinner date tonight."

Denny scrambled over to the phonebook, thumbed through it and then punched in some numbers on the telephone. "I'd like to reserve three tickets for tonight's performance."

His shoulders suddenly slumped. "Sold out? Could you check to see if anyone has cancelled at the last minute?"

He drummed on the phone stand.

Then he shot erect. "There are? Great. I'll take three seats. Here's the Visa number."

When he hung up the phone, he had a huge smile. "We're in luck. I reserved three tickets."

DENNY, ALLISON and Jennifer all charged off to prepare for the event, and I ambled toward my room to take a shower and spruce up for my date with Marion. I admired the picture on my dresser. So Jennifer thought Marion and I should be together. Marion was a very attractive woman. Damn. If only I could remember her day-to-day. Would she really tolerate an old poop like me?

After a good scrubbing, I donned a clean pair of brown trousers, a fresh striped long-sleeve shirt and my sports jacket. I admired myself in the mirror. Not bad for an old fart. Marion and I would make quite a pair.

My family scrambled out the door, and I called for a cab. On Denny's advice, I had booked a reservation. He had warned me of the expense of his recommended choice, but hey, what else did I have to spend money on other than the one woman now in my life?

When I arrived at the Days Inn, I spotted Marion standing next to a younger woman. I noticed the resemblance.

"Paul, I want you to meet my daughter, Andrea."

I took her hand and she pulled in close and gave me a hug.

"I've heard so much about you, Paul."

"Don't believe any of it," I said.

I stepped back and looked at her intelligent brown eyes, light brown hair in a flip, even white teeth and friendly smile. She and Marion made a striking pair.

"What do you two have planned tonight?" Andrea asked.

"We're dining at the Flagstaff House, the restaurant that overlooks Boulder. It comes highly recommended."

"I've heard of it. It's supposed to be one of the best restaurants in town."

"Nothing but the best for your mother."

We waved goodbye and stepped into the cab.

"Take us to the Pearl Street Mall," I instructed the cabbie. I turned toward Marion. "My family went into Denver for a theater performance tonight so I have the run of the city—unchaperoned."

"We'll have to make the most of it," Marion said with a coy smile.

"Since we have a little time before our reservation, I thought it would be nice to take a stroll on the mall. We should be able to see some interesting street performers and displays there."

"There's an art exhibit going on," the taxi driver said. "An excellent display of Boulder modern."

"You very familiar with art?"

"Oh, yes. I have a PhD in art history."

I shook my head. Only in Boulder.

When we arrived, I paid the cab driver and said, "If you want another fare, we'll meet you here in thirty minutes and give you a full report on the exhibit."

The man gave me a smile behind a full gray beard. I noticed that he had a shiny bald head and wore a pair of oval-shaped silver-rimmed glasses. "Look for the Pitmans. He does superb work. I'll be back for you."

Something clicked. "Did you say Pitman?"

"Yes, Mallory Pitman. He's an up-and-coming local artist. Does environmental sculpture."

I'll be damned. Just the guy I wanted to track down.

We strolled along the mall as an early summer stream of tourists, locals and gawkers surged by.

"Look at all the colorful flowers," Marion said as she

squeezed my hand. Brick-lined squares contained a vibrant mix of colors. I thought of the gardening-maniac couple I had brought together. All was well in the universe. Sort of.

Up ahead, the pulsating mob coalesced into a stationary assemblage. We had arrived at the art exhibit. Marion snuggled up against me as we sauntered through the various displays of watercolors, oils and pastels when suddenly, in front of us, materialized the most God-awful modern sculpture I'd ever seen. Mounted on a puke-green wavy platform that looked like seasick waves, stood a row of silver-coated fir trees. Mallory Pitman had taken Nate Fisher's trees, plus some others selected from around town, and turned them into the tin man's frozen forest. I shook my head in disbelief. Pushing through the mass of onlookers, I accosted a man with wild red hair, silver-speckled black pants and a torn T-shirt.

"Are you the artist who created this monstrosity?" I asked.

He glared at me and thumped his chest. "I'm Mallory Pitman."

"I wanted to make sure." I turned and walked back to Marion.

"I need to check out a couple of things," I told her.

"Fine. I'll explore the rest of the exhibit and meet you back here in fifteen minutes."

I needed to get word to Lavino that the elusive Pitman had returned. I spotted a blue uniform and strode over to the officer. "I'd like to report a suspect in a theft."

The officer gaped at me and pointed to a decal on his shoulder. "I'm an animal control officer. I'm searching for a stray dog."

"Damn. I need to reach Detective Lavino of the Boulder Police Department."

"I can help you with that." He unhooked a cell phone from his belt and punched in some numbers. "Please connect me with Detective Lavino."

Then he handed the phone to me. I examined it as if he had

given me a live coal. How did anyone talk into these tiny devices?

It rang a few times, and then Lavino answered.

"Detective, this is Paul Jacobson."

"Mr. Jacobson, I can hardly hear you. Where are you?"

"I'm at the Pearl Street Mall. I've located Mallory Pitman, the artist who's been stealing trees. He has the evidence in plain sight. Come nail the bastard."

"Thanks for the tip. I'm tied up right now but will check it out later."

"You do that. You can get one more criminal off the street."

So I needed to do whatever I could to keep Pitman here until Lavino arrived. I remembered reading that I had seen Pitman stuff one of Nate's trees into a white van. He obviously used that to transport his ridiculous sculpture here.

I noticed an alley off to the side of the mall. Moseying over, I spotted a white van. Success.

I searched near a trash bin and found a nail. Then I unscrewed the cap on one of the back tires out of view of the crowds, pressed the nail against the valve and listened to the satisfying hiss of air escaping.

Suddenly someone tapped me on the shoulder.

I shot upright as if I had been burned.

A street person in scruffy clothes, a scraggly beard and unkempt hair stood there scratching himself. "Whatcha doing, man? Why're you letting air out of the dog catcher's van?"

I peered at the letters I hadn't noticed on the vehicle. Shit. I had the wrong van.

"Just testing tire pressure," I said as I tossed the nail into the trash bin and then sauntered back to find Marion.

Oh, well. One stray dog would have a little more free time before being locked up in the pound.

I rejoined Marion who smiled at me as she stood in front of Pitman's fiasco. She turned toward the so-called sculpture and stared at it thoughtfully.

"What do you think of the exhibit?" I asked.

"Some very good paintings. I particularly liked a set of mountain scenes, but this is something else." She pointed at Pitman's folly.

"I know what you mean. That artist should be locked up."

WE MET OUR TAXI DRIVER back at Pearl and Fifteenth.

"Enjoy the exhibit, folks?"

"Very enlightening," I said. "Now we're ready to chow down. On to the Flagstaff House."

The cab driver chuckled. "You're in for quite a treat. A marvelous wine selection."

"You a wine connoisseur as well as an art expert?"

"Yes. During my art studies on the continent, I picked up a passable knowledge of wine. You have to try their Domaine Harmand-Geoffroy Gevrey Chambertin 2001. It's a fine red burgundy with a spicy bouquet and a tang of ripe cherry." He took a hand off the steering wheel and kissed his fingers.

I stared at the back of his bald head. "You have any other sidelines, like advice for the lovelorn?"

"Why yes. I also have a Masters in psychology."

"If we start fighting, I'll seek your services."

Marion snuggled up against me, and I decided that we wouldn't need his assistance.

The driver cut over to Baseline, and we headed up the winding road on the side of Flagstaff Mountain. Out on the plains, the shadows from the Flatirons slowly lengthened as sunset approached.

"You will have a lovely view at this time of evening," the cabbie said.

"You give sightseeing tours?"

"I do. On weekends I guide a Tours 'R Us bus up into Rocky Mountain National Park."

"Is there anything you don't do?"

"I don't do dishes. Working in a restaurant is beneath my calling."

I gave him a five-dollar tip, and a doorman ushered us into a glass-enclosed dining area.

Marion gasped. "What a view!"

"As promised."

We sat at a table next to the window, and neither of us said anything as we surveyed the rooftops, sandstone buildings of the University of Colorado, green trees and ponds dotting the outskirts of town.

We ordered some zinfandel, which, when served, we raised in a toast to our reunion. After scouring the elaborate menu and placing our orders, the feasting began. A waiter materialized and proceeded to deliver in perfectly timed sequence a plate of the chef's hors d'oeuvres, a salad a bunny would die for, lightly browned crab cakes and mandarin orange sherbet to cleanse our palates. I didn't even know my palate was dirty. Then as Marion and I gazed into each other's eyes, the main course magically appeared. Marion had a petite filet mignon, big enough to choke a vegetarian horse, and I had a salmon that practically jumped off the plate and into my mouth.

"At our age it's fantastic to be able to eat a delicious meal like this," I said.

"Speak for yourself. I'm nowhere near your age."

"I know. You're still a young chick. But old farts like me have to take time to appreciate these things."

Marion squeezed my hand. "You're not that old. I find you very handsome."

I squeezed her hand back. "Thank you. I'm privileged to be in the company of such a wonderful woman."

We gazed again into each other's eyes. I felt that special warmth. Even though I couldn't remember her from the last time I'd seen her, I experienced a heart-felt connection. As Jennifer said, Marion and I should be together.

The arrival of the baked Alaska interrupted my reverie.

Since this meal would eat significantly into Denny's inheritance, I decided to make the most of it and did my fair share of demolition on the dessert. After licking the last bit of ice cream off my lips, I reached over and took Marion's hands in mine.

"As you know, I have a very intelligent granddaughter."

"Yes, Paul. She's quite a young lady."

"Well…er…she told me that she thought you and I should…well…get together."

A twinkle appeared in Marion's eyes. "Is this some sort of proposal?"

"I guess you could call it that." I took a deep breath. "I care a great deal for you, Marion. I would like to be with you, but I have trouble reconciling that with foisting my memory problem off on you." *That and I needed to find a way to keep out of jail.*

Marion smiled. "I appreciate your concern, Paul, but I know what I'm up against. Don't you think that it's my decision whether I'm willing to accept your limitations?"

"Absolutely. I know I'd be hard to live with. Most mornings I wake up and can't remember anything from the day before. That would mean that I wouldn't recognize you either."

"You and I spoke of this when we lived at the Kina Nani retirement home in Hawaii. Back then, I didn't think I was ready for that type of relationship, and I decided to go live with my daughter in California. But I've been reconsidering it. During the road trip, my daughter and I have talked a great deal, and she helped me to recognize something. People always have issues: differences of opinion, baggage brought into the relationship, health concerns, worries and so on. Your memory presents a significant problem, and it's a condition that isn't easy to deal with. But you're a vital, vigorous man, and I love you."

I sat there dumbfounded. "If you're willing to put up with my little deficiency, I think we should get hitched."

Marion laughed. "Before we rush into anything, why don't we live together for awhile? I've discussed this with my daughter, and you could come live with me in Southern California. I have a separate apartment, and we could see how we get along."

"I'd like to be with you, Marion, and I see no reason not to make it a formal commitment."

As I held her hands, I noticed that her ring finger was the same size as my little finger.

She squeezed my hands. "Let's discuss it again in the morning."

"We run the risk of me not remembering. We'd have to discuss this all over again. Maybe I'd forget that I offered to marry you."

Her lips curled into a smug smile. "Paul, I have something to tell you. I know you haven't wanted to discuss this, but I figured it out. When we have sex, you remember things the next day. I think we should make sure that your memory works perfectly tomorrow morning."

"I can't argue with that suggestion. I hope I'm up to it."

"You will be. I'll see to it."

After forking over a good portion of my life's savings, I requested to have a cab called.

"Your place or mine?" I asked.

"Andrea is in our hotel room and since your family has gone to the theater, we better go to yours."

When the taxi arrived, I checked to see if we had the Renaissance man from before. No. This time the cabbie pushed sixty with remnants of gray hair sprouting out on the sides of his head.

"Are you a PhD in art history by any chance?" I asked him.

"No. My PhD is in literature."

"Are you driving a cab because it gives you new insights into the human predicament?"

He sighed. "I wish. I had tenure as a full-time professor at

CU and retired with a solid portfolio, but I imprudently invested it in some up-and-coming Internet companies. Then poof!" He snapped his fingers. "Into Dante's hell. I tried to reclaim my job, but it was too late, so here I am. A Sisyphus rolling my cab up Mapleton Hill."

"Seems like the taxi cab union in Boulder requires a prerequisite of a doctorate degree."

"There are a number of us. We like living here, and the cab pays the bills."

I thought over what he said. If I had a choice of being in jail or driving a cab, I'd take the cab. But it wasn't likely that I'd ever receive a driver's license again.

We climbed out of the taxi in front of Denny's house, and I wished the driver well with a thirty percent tip. Hey, I had to do my part to support the liberal arts.

Inside, we hung up our coats.

"Care for a nightcap?" I asked.

"Sure. What do you have?"

"Good question." I rummaged through kitchen cabinets and found a half-full bottle of Jack Daniels and some Smirnoff vodka. "Name your poison."

"I'll have a small bourbon and water."

With drinks in hand, we clinked glasses and sat down on the couch.

"So tell me where you're staying in California."

"My daughter Andrea and her family live in Venice, not far from the canals."

"Are there really canals in Venice?"

"Yes. A grand canal connects with four feeder canals that each runs approximately two blocks. Paul, it's so beautiful: the morning reflection off the water spanned by a white, arched bridge in the distance and colorful cottages with neatly trimmed hedges lining a walkway…"

"All those years I lived in Los Angeles, I never visited

Venice. We often traveled to Santa Monica Beach or Redondo, but somehow I missed Venice."

"It's very unique. The town I've described represents calm and beauty. There's another side to Venice. Along the beach from the Venice Pier to Santa Monica on a weekend you find every variety of normal person and weirdo that Southern California can produce. Street vendors hawk their wares. You can buy anything from sandals to hookah pipes. You find street performers, artists, protesters, rollerbladers, bicyclists, belly dancers, kids with every imaginable form of musical device, families heading to the beach and plain tourists."

"Sounds like quite a mob scene."

"Take the Pearl Street Mall here, add the ocean, an onshore breeze, multiply the craziness a hundredfold and you have Venice. I can sit on a bench for hours watching all the strange characters parade past."

"Sounds like I would fit right in."

"You would. You'd never be bored. Venice is a tale of two cities. It has the two faces—the calm and the frenetic. Much like my daughter Andrea in her teenage years. During the day she charged around at two hundred miles an hour. At night I'd look in on her when she slept—a peaceful angel."

"And you think your family would be ready for me to invade their domain?"

"Of course, Paul. They'd love you as much as I do. You'd be very comfortable in Andrea's home. They bought it twenty years ago, fixed it up and added an apartment over the garage, where I live. I have a private residence with bedroom, living room, kitchen and bathroom. I can spend time with my family or, when I want, be on my own. It's big enough for two." She gave my arm a squeeze.

"And you'd really put up with an old coot joining you?"

"Of course. If it's the right old coot."

Suddenly we were caressing each other and our mouths met like attracting magnets. I felt a little-used part of my anatomy come alive. All the delicious tastes of the evening couldn't compare with the sweetness of Marion's lips.

I came up for air. "Would you care to see my etchings?"

"And anything else you have to show me."

This was getting interesting.

We adjourned to my bedroom.

Marion gave my room the once-over. "I'm glad to see only my picture on your dresser this time."

"You're the only woman for me."

Our bodies pressed against each other, and not-too-nimble fingers began fumbling with buttons and zippers. As the joints loosened up, clothes began to fly faster than at a day-after-Thanksgiving sale.

We were in luck. Allison had changed my bed that day, so we snuggled in fresh sheets.

I began exploring intriguing curves and indentations. My equipment kicked into gear.

"Oh, Paul."

"Marion!"

Then we engaged and revved up our engines like two finely-tuned, but seasoned, machines. I hadn't forgotten what to do!

My old body and selected parts hung in there to do their job, and at the moment of release, I flung my arm out.

My hand hit the nightstand lamp that teetered and plummeted to the floor to the sound of shattering glass.

SEVENTEEN

I LAY THERE SPENT, basking in the aftermath of lovemaking with Marion. My room in Denny's house seemed to be swirling around me.

"My goodness, Paul. People describe hearing bells ringing or fireworks going off, but that crashing sound—how unique."

"We old guys have special music."

We snuggled together for a while before I lumbered out of bed. "We better put some clothes on. My family will be home soon."

Marion sighed. "I guess you're right. We don't want to shock the kids."

I considered cleaning up the broken lamp, but decided I'd do that after escorting Marion back to her hotel.

"It's a quarter-of-a-mile walk," I said. "You up to a moonlight stroll?"

"Sure. Is that how you stay so fit, Paul? Taking walks?"

"Every chance I can. Whether walking Max or wandering around on my own, I try to put in several miles a day."

"That's another thing you'll love about Venice. Along the ocean, a winding bicycle path traverses the distance from Marina Del Mar to Will Rogers State Park. You'll have lots of places to roam."

That would sure beat time in jail. I needed to find a way to distance myself from all these crimes I'd been associated with in Colorado. Then I could consider this possibility of a new life with Marion.

We arrived at the hotel.

"Thank you for a wonderful dinner." Marion reached up and pulled my head toward hers and planted a delectable kiss on my puss.

I hugged her, and we separated at arm's length to gaze into each other's eyes.

"There's a restaurant in the hotel," Marion said. "Come join me for breakfast."

"What time do you want this old fool to show up?"

"Eight o'clock."

"I'll be there with bells on."

We parted with another kiss. I waved as she entered the lobby and then floated back toward Denny's house. Damn. What a woman. And she wanted to be with an old poop like me. Who wudda thunk?

As I strolled along, my reverie was interrupted by the sight of a white van parked with its right front wheel over the curb. Then I heard the sound of sawing. Could it be Pitman up to his old tricks?

I peered into the yard and, sure enough, I spotted a shadowy figure hacking away at a fir tree. This guy had to be stopped.

I picked up a stick and sneaked up on the culprit.

With his focus upon the destruction of the tree, he didn't notice me.

I jammed the stick into his back. "Reach for the sky or I'm going to blast you into smithereens."

He let out a yelp, dropped the saw and thrust his arms toward the Milky Way.

"Now lie face down, unless you want your organs splattered all over this lawn."

He flopped down faster than Max dropping into his doggy bed.

"Don't move a muscle if you want to see tomorrow."

He shook and whimpered.

I strode toward the house and knocked on the door.

A man opened the door.

"Why hello, Paul. What brings you here?"

Although I didn't recognize him, this had to be Nate Fisher.

"I caught the wacko who's been cutting your trees. He's lying face down in your yard."

An attractive gray-haired woman joined him.

"What did you do to him, Paul?"

"Just put the fear of death in him. Call the police, and I'll make sure he doesn't escape."

I returned to the yard to find Pitman still face down. I stuck the stick into his back again. "Make my day, slimebag."

He continued to quiver. I hadn't had so much fun since hitting the bull's eye at a carnival in San Pedro and winning a stuffed bear when I was courting my now departed wife Rhonda.

Nate came out to join me.

"The police should be here soon. Helen's on the phone with them." Nate stifled a laugh when he saw me with the stick in Pitman's back. He quickly joined in the spirit of the situation. "Lordy, please don't shoot that man. I don't want blood all over my yard."

"As long as he stays still. If he so much as lifts his head, though, you'll have blood-spattered grass."

Pitman moaned again.

When the police arrived, I removed the stick from Pitman's back.

Nate explained what had happened to an officer who wrote everything down in his notebook.

Pitman stood up, his wild red hair poking out like he'd put his finger in an electric socket. "I sawed the trees down. I'll never do it again, but save me from this maniac with the gun."

"What gun?" I asked as I leaned on the stick.

Pitman's eyes widened.

"This guy's been sawing off trees," I said. "He's guilty of that and of producing awful sculpture."

After the police led Pitman away, Nate invited me inside.

"Thanks, but I need to head home. Besides, I don't want to interrupt anything between you and Helen."

His cheeks reddened. "We were…uh…only enjoying a little time together."

"Hey. It doesn't matter. You're practically married."

I waved goodbye and continued on my journey, knowing I had done my part to make the world a safer place from criminals and lousy artists.

When I arrived back at my domicile, I found that my family had returned.

"How'd you enjoy the show?" I asked.

"Great, Grandpa. Terrific singing."

Allison came up to me. "What happened to the lamp in your room, Paul? I went in to check on you, thinking you might be home, and I found broken pieces all over the floor."

"I meant to clean that up. I had an exciting evening and got a little carried away."

I WOKE UP REFRESHED and stretched my arms. Damn, what a beautiful day! I hadn't even read my journal, and I could remember the day before and my date with Marion. Our little romp the night before had certainly cleared my pipes. I even remembered having a dream. The image lingered of me prancing around in a meadow full of sawed-off trees with a group of red-headed midgets in orange crab outfits. Maybe it was just as well that I normally couldn't remember my dreams.

After dressing, I came into the kitchen, whistling. Jennifer, Allison and Denny were all gathered at the table.

"You certainly seem chipper today, Paul," Allison said.

"Yes. I feel like a young man again. Not a day over eighty."

"Are you ready for breakfast?"

"No. I'm meeting Marion over at her hotel. But I'd like to take everyone out to lunch today. I thought we could get together with Marion and her daughter."

"That works for me," Jennifer said. "No swim meet today."

I asked Denny for a suggestion of a good restaurant.

"Why not go to the Boulderado? It's a nice spot, right downtown on Spruce and Thirteenth."

With that settled, I hiked over to Marion's hotel and called her from the lobby. She said she would meet me in the restaurant on the second floor in five minutes.

I took the elevator up and selected a corner table for us next to tall windows covered by filmy curtains. I looked up at a balcony on the floor above that was covered with paintings of geese, salmon and a fishing bear. The far wall was made of knotty pine. I felt like I was in a modern log cabin in the wilderness of Boulder.

Marion arrived wearing a black pantsuit with silver trim. Damn, she looked good.

"Have you reconsidered?" I asked.

She placed a finger to her chin. "I seem to be having memory problems this morning. You'll have to remind me."

I took a deep breath. "We discussed living together in your place in Venice."

"Oh, that." She smiled. "Of course I'd still like to do it."

I let out a sigh of relief. "Before you leave today, I want to take you and Andrea to lunch so she can meet my family."

"That can be arranged. We'll check out, eat with you and then hit the road."

"Great. I have an errand to run this morning, and we'll meet you two at the Boulderado at eleven-thirty."

We feasted on unfertilized chicken babies and pig parts and washed it down with gallons of caffeine.

With my stomach full, I sat back and admired my companion. "I feel so comfortable with you, Marion."

"That's good to hear. We'll see how you feel after we're around each other every day."

"I'm looking forward to the opportunity."

I now had to figure out a way to direct Detective Lavino to the right criminals so I could leave the state.

"But, Marion, you have to be aware that I might not be around that much longer."

"All the more reason for us to live together now. We have no time to waste." She smiled at me. "I think you're going to last a good many years. I know from last night that you have a lot of energy left."

We parted. I caught a bus into town to run my errand and returned to Denny's digs to collect my family for lunch.

After sprucing up, I shouted upstairs. "Let's get a move on."

Allison strolled downstairs. "You seem awfully nervous, Paul."

"I don't want to keep Marion and Andrea waiting."

I herded everyone into the family jalopy, and we cruised to the Boulderado.

After all of my hassling, we arrived first. Within five minutes, Marion and Andrea joined us. Allison and Andrea hit it right off, talking of schools, raising kids and the differences between Boulder and Southern California. Marion and I held hands under the table like teenagers.

After we had ordered, I picked up a knife and clinked it against a water glass. "I have an announcement to make."

"Paul, you have moisture on your forehead," Allison said.

"I am a little nervous." I extracted a handkerchief and wiped off the perspiration. I returned it to my pocket and pulled out a small box. "I wanted all of you to be here for this." I pulled an object out of the box and held it out toward Marion. "Marion, will you marry me?"

There was a hushed silence.

Marion put her right hand to her mouth.

I took the opportunity to grab her left hand and slip the ring on her finger.

"I don't know," Marion said, tears in her eyes. "We only discussed living together."

"If you don't marry him, Mother, maybe I will," Andrea said.

"You can't, dear. You're already married. Besides, he's mine."

I wondered momentarily if I had been played like a trout on a line. Then I shrugged. So what? I wanted this. And at eighty-five I should have my own way. Provided I could get Lavino off my back.

"If we live together, we can consider it part of an extended engagement," I said.

Marion admired the ring. "It fits perfectly. How did you arrange that?"

"Just lucky, I guess."

"This calls for champagne," Denny said. He snapped his fingers toward a waiter.

"Can I have a taste, Dad?" Jennifer asked.

"No."

"Aw, Dad."

When the champagne arrived, the waiter filled glasses. We raised them, Jennifer holding up her water glass, and we clinked them together.

"Marion and I have decided to spend all our money so we won't burden you with the hassle of an inheritance," I said.

Marion punched me in the shoulder. "We did not!"

"Just testing the sense of humor of the younger generation. So am I marrying you for your money or are you marrying me for my money?"

"I think that it's probably a pretty even playing field," Marion said.

"Good. We won't have to hire any slimy lawyers for a pre-nuptial agreement."

After lunch, Marion and I stood in the parking lot saying our farewells.

Marion handed me a piece of paper. "Here's Andrea's cell phone number. Give me a call tomorrow while we're on the road."

"I'll be happy to."

"When do you think you can join me in Southern California?" Marion asked.

"I have a few things to wrap up." If only it were that simple. "I'm hoping within a few weeks." Dreamer.

"I'm missing you already."

"Why don't you wait for that until you're on the road?" I hugged her tightly, and then she and Andrea drove off.

"Grandpa, this is so exciting. I knew you and Marion belonged together."

"This puts more pressure on you, young lady. You need to help me get cleared of all charges so I can join Marion."

"Not to worry. Your cases are in capable hands."

I punched my right fist into my left hand. "I want to see some results, damn it."

"Oh, Grandpa. You say the funniest things."

THAT AFTERNOON Jennifer and I took a walk together so we could connive over my evening plans.

"At the Colorado Mountain Retirement Properties' promotional program tonight, I'll have to find a way to determine if Previn is the murderer."

"See if he slips up, Grandpa."

"I need to confront him again. He's arrogant enough that I might be able to force that."

"Be careful. If he's the murderer, he knows how to kill people with his bare hands."

"Maybe I should wear body armor."

"You'll have to outsmart him, Grandpa."

"That's my plan. My mental acuity against his. As long as I don't fall asleep."

"Keep on your toes."

"You're my backup. If I'm not back by eleven, call Detective Lavino. I have his phone number in my room."

"I'll do it, Grandpa."

With that settled, we completed our walk and headed back to our humble abode.

I now had a good woman counting on my ability to escape from Lavino's clutches. I couldn't let Marion down.

THAT EVENING AFTER DINNER, I dressed for my evening escapade and returned to the living room.

"Do you want a ride?" Denny asked.

"That's okay. The bus goes right by the Millennium Harvest House. I can catch it there and back."

"If you're stuck, call."

If I were to be stuck, it would probably require more than a phone call. I'd have to see what I could do on my own.

I caught the bus, paid my fare and sat down. Then I spotted a familiar face across the aisle. I savored this experience of remembering something from the day before, thanks to Marion.

"Aren't you the taxi cab driver with a PhD in literature?" I asked.

His eyes shot up to see me. "Yeah. Do I know you?"

"You gave me a ride from the Flagstaff House last night."

"Oh, yeah. Now I remember."

"Why are you riding the bus?"

"My cab broke down."

"I can identify with that. My memory is kind of like your taxi cab."

EXITING THE BUS, I waved goodbye to my ex-taxi buddy and strolled along Twenty-eighth Street toward the Millennium Hotel. The warm June air rustled through my hair as I looked toward the Flatirons, now hiding the setting sun.

So into the lion's den.

In the lobby a bright banner identified Colorado Mountain Retirement Properties Gala Event with a large red arrow pointing down a hallway with yellow duct tape strips marking the way. I followed the yellow brick road to a conference facility reception area littered with people. Bright red, blue, green and yellow balloons covered the walls. I felt like I had found the circus. A sign over the doorway read, "Win an Alaskan cruise for two."

"What's going on?" I asked a matron sitting at a table.

She gave me a tired smile, like her lips were ready to wear out. "We're holding a raffle for a cruise. Just fill out a form."

"Where do I get one?"

"From any of the sales people. They're wearing red jackets."

What the hell? I would add my name. If I won, Marion and I could go on a honeymoon cruise. I wouldn't mind visiting Alaska. As long as I had a sound ship under me.

I spotted a few red jackets in the crowd. Shit. Except for them, all the other people milling around were old farts. More women than men.

I selected one red jacket-clad man, an innocuous fellow who didn't fit the Special Forces mold, and approached him.

"I understand you're my ticket to Alaska."

Like a light switch, a smile appeared on his face and his hand shot out. "Miles. Miles Haviland. And you are?"

I shook his hand. "Oh, I'm having a good time."

His smile disappeared momentarily. "I meant your name."

"Well, why didn't you ask? I'm Paul Jacobson. I'm seeking you out to enter your cruise raffle."

"Let's sit down at that table over there." He pointed toward a table covered with a white linen tablecloth.

Once seated on folding chairs facing each other, he said, "Now, I need to discuss with you our wonderful Colorado Mountain Retirement Properties."

"You can spare your breath. I've been to a pitch before."

He wagged his finger at me. "You can't get off that easy. You have to listen to my presentation to enter the raffle."

I stared him in the eyes. "I've seen drawings of the facility, and I've visited the place where your so-called retirement home is supposed to be built. Do you know that the land isn't even zoned yet?"

"There must be some mistake."

"No, your bigwigs are leading you astray. Unless you're in on the scam as well."

He turned his head from side to side like he was searching for an escape hatch.

"Are you going to offer me a founder's spot for a mere two hundred thousand dollars?"

"Sshh." He put his finger to his lips. "We aren't discussing that tonight."

I did a double take. What the hell was going on? "And by the way, did you know Daniel Reynolds and Randall Swathers?"

His smile had now disappeared entirely. "Yes. They were associates of mine."

"Any idea what happened to them?"

"A couple of unfortunate events."

"Right. Someone murdered them. Any chance Peter Kingston or Gary Previn wanted them out of the way?"

Beads of sweat appeared on Haviland's forehead. "I see a customer I need to meet with." He jumped up.

"Don't you want to give me your sales snow job?"

"I don't have time now."

"Don't I receive a raffle ticket?"

"No. Complete this form and turn it in for the drawing."

He dropped a sheet of paper on the table and shot away like a deer being chased by a hunter.

I filled out the form with my name, address, phone number and age. Then I answered several questions including one asking where I'd like to live: mountains, ocean, desert. Funny, it didn't include jail as an alternative. Then I wandered back to the woman sitting at the other table.

"I have my raffle entry. How do I win?"

She gave me her tired smile again. "Drop it in the box over there." She pointed. "The drawing will take place at the end of the show. You have to be here to win. We'll announce the winning name."

"Do you know anything about being able to purchase founder's lots for two hundred thousand dollars?"

She looked at me quizzically. "I don't understand."

"I heard that old coots like me could plop down two hundred thousand dollars and be assured of a garden spot in your retirement community."

"I'm not aware of anything like that. You'll have to speak with one of the sales people."

"No thanks. I've already had that questionable pleasure."

I folded the sheet of paper and dropped it in the shiny silver box. Now set to win a cruise, I scanned the room. My attention again focused on all the colorful balloons lining the wall. I guessed the holiday atmosphere would take peoples' minds off of being fleeced. The balloons gave me an idea. I could surprise Jennifer by decorating her room with balloons. I wandered over to a corner where I found a box of balloons not yet inflated.

I approached a woman sitting at a table nearby.

"Okay if I take some of the balloons?" I asked.

She shrugged. "Help yourself."

And I did. I filled up a pocket with a handful. Next time I spotted Jennifer leaving her room, I'd sneak in, blow up the balloons and tape them to her wall.

I mingled with the flow of the crowd toward a bar serving beer, wine and soft drinks. I picked up a glass of Sauvignon Blanc and ambled into the main room. Crap. This place also was crammed full of old people. You'd think they had attracted every oldster in Boulder to this event. Previn and his

gang seemed poised to extract hard-earned money from all
these gullible seniors. Give up your two hundred thou and see
it disappear into a scamming outfit that had squat to show for
it. Made me want to puke like that lifeguard tossing his
cookies at the Centennial Community Center.

The lights flashed and people began to scramble for the
folding chairs that rested in neat rows. Once everyone sat
down, the audience must have been two hundred people. I did
the math at two hundred thousand dollars a pop; this room represented forty million dollars to the eager sales staff.

An old broad in a flowered hat squirmed in the chair next
to me.

"Are you planning to invest in this?" I asked her.

Her eyes lit up. "Oh, yes. I've brought my checkbook. But
don't tell anyone. I've been made a special offer. They aren't
discussing it at all tonight. My salesman told me he'd secretly
process my paperwork during intermission."

"Why the rush?"

"He says tonight might be the last chance to hold property
in my name at the low rate. I'm ready to make my reservation."

"I wouldn't advise that. Did you know they might never
even build on the property they're describing?"

Her hand came up to her mouth. "Dear me. How can that
be? I've seen beautiful pictures of the facility."

"Artist's renditions. Keep your checkbook in your purse
and save your money for something legitimate."

Before I could scare her further, music began playing and
a spotlight focused on the stage in front of us.

"Ladies and gentlemen. Welcome to Colorado Mountain
Retirement Properties' June Extravaganza."

Hands clapped and whoops emerged from the back of the
room. I turned my head to see the noise coming from a row
of red jacket-clad automatons lined up along the rear wall,
trying to set the appropriate mood.

The show started with a John Denver look-alike singing Rocky Mountain High. The woman next to me sighed. I wondered if sanity or emotion would control her checkbook. Slides flashed above the singer's head with pictures of snow-capped peaks and fake drawings of the facility. I had to admit, it appeared appealing. As the singer reached a crescendo, a strobe light flashed and an emcee in red jacket vaulted onto the stage.

He held a microphone in his mitt. "We have a special treat for you tonight, ladies and gentlemen. I'm Gary Previn, and I want to thank you personally for joining us." Another round of applause and cheers from the peanut gallery.

I stared at the illustrious Gary Previn, noticing his square jaw, short-cropped hair, fierce eyes and muscular build.

He leered out at the audience. How could anyone trust this guy?

"Colorado Mountain Retirement Properties represents a new concept in luxury living. We're pleased to provide an evening of entertainment to you as a preview of all the evenings of enjoyment you have in store when you have your own private cottage. Our staff will be available during inter-mission and after the show to answer any questions."

Something didn't smell right. After the hard pitch I'd received at the Centennial Community Center, what caused Previn to be so low key tonight?

"And now back to the show."

A beautiful soprano appeared and whirled around the stage, singing the theme song from *The Sound of Music*. The words almost fit for this event. The hills were alive with the sound of money.

I could understand why Previn willingly sprang for a door prize of a cruise for two. That was a spit in the wind compared to the money they would collect from this unsuspecting crowd of eager crones and geezers ready to open their wallets.

Then another honcho in a red jacket with white hair and a pearly smile appeared on the stage.

"Is everyone having a good time?" he shouted into the microphone.

The woman next to me shouted, "Yes," along with a chorus of two hundred others.

"I'm Peter Kingston, the president of Colorado Mountain Retirement Properties. I want to add my thanks as well for spending your evening with us. We hope to see many of you spending many evenings with us in the future."

Was he encouraging us to join him in prison? This guy was going to be locked up in the very near term. He seemed awfully confident for someone that Detectives Hamilton and Lavino were ready to haul in.

I scrutinized Kingston. Athletic build like Previn, short haircut, strong jaw, glint in the eyes. The Special Forces mold.

"Now back to the show."

A dance troupe tromped on stage and to Beethoven's *Pastorale* cavorted around like sheep and shepherds in a mountain meadow. Man. These guys laid it on thick. I looked over at my companion. She was eating it up like a banana split.

After the sheep pranced off-stage, hopefully to be shorn, Previn returned to the microphone on the left side of the stage.

"We will soon break for a short intermission, but now…"

The lights blinked out and on again. Previn stood at a microphone completely over on the right side of the stage. "You are in for something special…"

The lights flashed off and on again. Previn now stood back on the left side of the stage. "Straight from Austria for your listening enjoyment…"

Off and on went the lights and Previn appeared on the right side of the stage. "With no further ado…"

Another switch and Previn stood on the left. "The Chorale Masters."

While a group of old snots in lederhosen marched on stage and began yodeling, I sat there dumbfounded. Either Previn was a magician or…

I had to find out.

At intermission Previn came down the stairs on the left side of the stage and headed toward the lobby. While everyone in the audience tromped out into the lobby as well, I looked around to make sure no one saw me and then scrambled up the stairs on the right side of the stage and headed into the wing.

I found no one there. A small hallway led further to the right, so I began exploring. I tried a door. It opened to a dark room. I tried the next door. It swung open. There sat Previn smoking a cigar. His red jacket lay across another chair, and he had his sleeves rolled up.

"What the...?" I said, then realized that I had surmised correctly. "You're a stunt double for Gary Previn."

The guy put his fingers to his lips. "Sshh. It's supposed to be a secret."

I entered the room and closed the door. "I'll keep it to myself. You do this routine often?"

He shrugged. "I can't help it if I look like the big cheese. He hires me from time to time for sales meetings and other events. It's easy work and it helps pay the bills." He stubbed out the cigar.

I looked at his wrist. He had a tattoo of a surfboard.

EIGHTEEN

I LOOKED AROUND this backstage room and then my gaze returned to the Gary Previn look-alike. "That's quite a performance you put on. Are you available for freelance gigs?"

"Sure, any time."

"How would I reach you?"

He reached in his shirt pocket and held out his hand. "Here's my card."

I inspected it. Matt Larson. Actor. And a phone number.

"Matt, did you ever go to the library for Gary Previn?"

"Hey, I can't discuss my gigs with you," he said. "Now you better leave. Previn will be pissed if he finds you talking to me."

I stared into his eyes. "I know that you went to the library and impersonated Previn. You may not want to discuss it, but you better listen to me."

He swallowed. "Why's that?"

"Because while you pretended to be Previn, he murdered one of his salesmen at the Centennial Community Center."

His eyes expanded to the size of light bulbs. "You're kidding."

"I wish I wasn't. And I think you're in a heap of trouble. When Previn finds out that I know of his little ruse, he's liable to treat you the same way he did two of his employees. You'll end up dead."

"Previn asked to meet me later tonight."

"I wouldn't advise keeping that appointment. I think Previn

will eliminate the one witness who can prove he wasn't at the library that afternoon."

He gulped, and his gazed darted around the room. "I have to get out of here."

"I have a suggestion. Call Detective Lavino of the Boulder Police Department. He'll be very interested to learn that you went to the library in Previn's place. You've done nothing wrong so you have nothing to fear from the police. But if you don't seek protection from the police, Previn will kill you. Clear enough?"

His head bobbed up and down. Then he grabbed a duffel bag and charged out of the room.

I needed to get word to Detective Lavino. Damn. I didn't have his phone number. I dashed out into the convention center lobby and scanned the area for a telephone. Nothing.

I scurried up to the woman sitting at the table in the entryway.

"Where can I find a public telephone?"

"Back in the main lobby."

I scampered in the direction she pointed. Finally, a phone. I found a slip of paper in my wallet with Denny's phone number and dropped a quarter in the phone slot.

Allison answered.

"I need to speak to Jennifer."

"You're breathing hard, Paul. Is everything all right?"

"I'm just in a hurry. Please ask Jennifer to pick up the phone."

In a few moments I heard, "Hi, Grandpa."

"Jennifer, Previn's the murderer."

She lowered her voice. "How did you find out?"

"He has a stunt double who went to the library the day of Swathers's murder. I need to reach Detective Lavino. I have his number somewhere in my room. Find it and call him. Tell him what I told you. Also, the name of the guy who impersonated Previn is Matt Larson." I gave her Matt's phone number.

"I'll call the detective and pass on the information, Grandpa."

I returned to the event and found Previn in the lobby.

"I need to have a word with you, Mr. Previn," I said.

His eyes lit up, and then a frown appeared. "I recognize you."

"Yeah. I'm Paul Jacobson. I spoke with you at the Kinetic Conveyance Race."

He narrowed his gaze at me. "You're the guy who sat next to Daniel Reynolds on the plane."

"I also found Randall Swathers after he was bumped off in the parking lot of the Community Center. Any chance you happened by that afternoon?"

He leered at me. "No. As a matter of fact, I was at the library that afternoon."

"Not exactly accurate. Your stunt double was at the library that afternoon."

The lights flashed.

"I have a show to put on, Mr. Jacobson. We can talk later."

"I'll wait with bated breath."

I returned to the auditorium and plopped down next to the woman in the flowered hat.

She turned to me. "I'm now owner of the last early sales unit."

"I'm sorry to hear that. You'll never see your money again. You should stop payment on your check immediately."

"You're wrong. My salesman assured me that everything is legitimate."

"Right. And SUVs don't guzzle gas, and I have a special deal for you on a bridge in San Francisco."

She glared at me, then turned her head away as she held her chin high and harrumphed at me.

Oh well. I tried. Old farts can be so stubborn some times.

The show resumed with Previn leaning toward the audience and acting like nothing had happened. He was a good actor.

The second act started with a chorus line of eighteen young women in Tyrolean skirts. At one point they all sat on the stage and lifted their feet toward the audience. The bottoms of their shoes spelled out, "Colorado Mountain Retirement Properties."

I felt like repeating the performance of the queasy lifeguard.

After several more equally appalling acts and a grand finale with the sheep and shepherds prancing once again, Previn reappeared.

"And now ladies and gentlemen. What you've been waiting for. The announcement of the winner of the Alaskan cruise for two. The envelope please."

A skimpily-clad wench appeared and handed Previn an envelope.

"Drum roll please."

Canned music blared through the loudspeaker.

With a flourish, he tore open the envelope and lifted out a sheet of paper. "I'm proud to announce that the winner is…Paul Jacobson. Mr. Jacobson. Please identify yourself and come up on stage."

People applauded and whoops emerged from the back of the room.

I lifted myself up and waved.

The woman next to me flashed a fetching smile in my direction. Uh-oh. The unattached ladies would be coming after me.

I had two emotions. First, I felt excitement. Then the reality of suspicion settled in. Something didn't seem right.

I climbed up the stairs and approached Previn.

He put his paw on my shoulder, and I winced as a vice-like grip bore down on me. With his other hand he presented me with two tickets.

"Mr. Jacobson has won an all-expense-paid trip for two on an Alaskan cruise this August. Congratulations."

More applause and hollering.

"This completes our program, and thank you all for coming," Previn announced.

The lights went down. With his shoulder-numbing grip, Previn steered me backstage. I tried to shout but Previn clamped a hand over my mouth, and with the applause still going on no one would have heard me anyway. He shoved me inside a small room and jerked the door shut.

"You're in way over your head, Mr. Jacobson."

"So, why'd you bump off Reynolds and Swathers?"

"Let's say they didn't realize when they had a good thing."

"Maybe they had second thoughts regarding this scam of yours."

Previn laughed. "I set it up for you to win the raffle so you and I could have a little chat." He reached over and grabbed the two cruise tickets out of my pocket. "You won't be needing these, so I might as well take them back."

I slapped at his hand, but he pulled away out of my reach.

"Hey, I had plans for those," I said.

"Your plans won't last much beyond an hour."

"You going to whack me with one of those martial art blows like you did to Reynolds and Swathers?"

"We'll see."

"Is your buddy Kingston in on this as well?"

Previn chuckled. "Peter will take the fall for the company being a sham."

Then it all clicked into place. "Now I get it. You set up Kingston. You've had this scam of collecting two hundred thousand dollars a pop. That's why there's no mention of this up-front money tonight. You don't pitch that when Kingston is around."

"Very clever, Mr. Jacobson. Too bad you'll never have a

chance to tell anyone. The money and I will be bound for Rio in the morning."

"You'll never make it, Previn. The police will nab you."

"Nice bluff, but they haven't figured it out yet."

Think. I had to keep this guy talking.

"If you're running off with all the money, I still don't understand why you had to resort to murder."

"I had to keep the operation going long enough to earn my retirement funds. Reynolds started acting nervous in Hawaii. Swathers caught the same bug. I couldn't have two wussy salesmen blow my plan."

"So you chopped Reynolds on the plane. Then you had your stunt double cover for you at the library while you killed Swathers in the Community Center parking lot."

"Too bad you won't have an opportunity to share your knowledge with anyone."

"Detective Lavino will be on your tail like mustard on a hot dog."

"By the time anyone discovers I'm gone, it will be too late. And there's nothing to connect me to Swathers's little accident. I'm meeting my stunt double later tonight. He's going to disappear on an…uh…extended vacation."

"Too bad. His only crime is looking like you."

Someone knocked on the door.

Previn stepped outside, and I heard hushed tones.

I scanned the room. Nothing I could use as a weapon. It wouldn't do me any good against a trained Special Forces killer anyway.

I had to stay alive to alert Lavino.

Jennifer would be calling him, but would he act in time? She'd make Lavino aware of the stunt double, but could Lavino prevent another murder, capture Previn before he left the country, and save me? None of these things was apt to happen in time.

I opened the door a crack and saw Previn speaking with

the dance troupe of women in sheep costumes and men in shepherd outfits holding crooks. I had to act quickly.

"Help," I bellowed.

All heads turned toward me.

I stepped out of the room, spotted the hall light switch and turned it off.

In the dark I dashed into the crowd of dancers, tripping over a crook and falling to my knees.

I heard Previn shout, "God damn," and then further curses and thumps—the sound of people bumping into each other.

Something wooly smacked into my face and knocked me flat on my butt. I flailed like a swimmer trying to gain traction. My hand struck another piece of wool. I grabbed it and heard a tearing sound and found a hunk of cloth in my hand.

"Help! Someone's tearing my costume off," a female voice screamed.

"Sorry," I said as I crawled down the hallway on all fours.

I heard further thumps and clanks of people and shepherd crooks falling.

"Where's that goddamn old man?" Previn shouted.

I placed the piece of cloth over my head and continued doing a crab crawl, feeling like a drag version of Little Bo Peep as I scrambled away from the tumult.

I rounded a bend in the hallway, stood up and found a door that I opened onto a lighted hallway.

Faster than you can say flying geezer, I pedaled my feet toward the exit and found myself in front of the hotel. I spotted a cab, dashed over, opened the back door, jumped in and said, "Move."

The cabbie flinched, started the engine and roared out of the parking lot.

NINETEEN

"FIND ME A PAY PHONE," I said to the cab driver.

"Should be one over by the gas station on Arapahoe."

It was only then that I noticed the cabbie's full beard, wire-rimmed glasses and shiny bald head. "You're the art history PhD."

He smiled. "That's me."

"You gave me and my date a ride to the mall and Flagstaff House last night."

"That's right. You stopped at the Pitman exhibit along the way."

"It was the pits."

He pulled into the gas station. First order of business—call Jennifer. She answered on the third ring.

"Did you reach Detective Lavino?"

"Yes, Grandpa. I did. I told him about Previn's stunt double, Matt Larson, at the library and gave him the phone number, but he was very skeptical at first."

I slumped down onto the seat in the phone booth. "So he's not doing anything?"

"I didn't say that. He needed some persuading."

"How'd you accomplish that?"

"Simple. I told him he'd better act on this immediately or I'd be calling my friend, Chief of Police Atkins."

"You know the chief of police?"

"Yes. He came and spoke at our school in March. I was selected as one of the two students to have lunch with him.

We talked law enforcement, and he invited me to visit him anytime I wanted."

"So you could have pulled strings when Lavino brought me in for questioning?"

"I didn't have to. He released you. I was saving my contact for a time when you really needed it, so I used my trump card with Detective Lavino and he paid attention to me."

"The wonder of school programs."

"Detective Lavino agreed to investigate Previn and Matt Larson."

"May I speak to your mom or dad?"

"No can do, Grandpa. A little while after you called earlier, they decided to go to a movie. I wouldn't expect them back for a while."

"Crap."

"Grandpa, don't be so upset."

I sighed. "You're right. Say, while you're on the line, give me Lavino's number. I have an update for him."

She read the number to me, and I committed it to memory.

Next I called Lavino. He wasn't available so I left a message on his voicemail. Told him I'd be home in fifteen minutes and to call me.

When we arrived home, I asked the cabbie to pull into the driveway. The lights shone on the front of the house. I handed the cab driver a twenty-dollar bill, thanked him and rushed to the door to let myself in. I put my key in the lock, opened the door as the light from the cab's headlights disappeared and took two steps into the entryway when I felt a vice-like grip on my arm from behind.

"About time you got here, Mr. Jacobson," Previn said, his hot breath in my ear.

I staggered forward with Previn clenching my arm.

Max came running, wriggling with delight to see us both. Totally oblivious to the menacing hostility emanating from the stranger, he jumped up joyfully. Here I needed a Doberman to sic on Previn and, instead, I had a licking rag mop.

Previn kicked at Max, who slunk away with a hurt look. "This is as good a spot as any," he said. "I'll do you, then find Larson."

"You spend an awful lot of time trying to murder people. Why don't you just leave the country like you were planning?"

"I killed Reynolds and Swathers each with a single blow, and I'll do the same to you now."

Out of the corner of my eye I saw Jennifer sneaking up on Previn with a tennis racquet in her hand. I kept my reaction to myself.

Previn raised his hand.

Jennifer raised her racquet and delivered a ringing blow to the back of Previn's head.

He crumpled to the floor.

I stood there stunned, looking at Previn's blood seeping onto the entryway tile. Allison wasn't going to be happy about this.

"You should have called 9-1-1, Jennifer."

"I did when I saw Previn push you into the house. But the police wouldn't arrive in time, so I had to do something."

Moments later I heard a siren. I opened the door as an athletic-looking police officer raced up the walkway.

"We received an emergency call—an intruder. Then the phone cut off."

I pointed to Previn. "This man killed two other people and tried to kill me this evening."

"What happened to him?" the policeman asked.

Jennifer strolled into the entryway still holding her tennis racquet. "Nobody gets away from my forehand. Nobody."

TWENTY

"YOU BETTER CUFF HIM GOOD," I said to the policeman as I pointed to the unconscious Previn. "Both my granddaughter and I heard him confess to killing two men with deadly martial arts blows, and he intended to do the same to me."

"I can handle him," the swarthy cop replied as he placed handcuffs on Previn.

"I don't know," I said. "He still has his feet free. Be careful."

"I'll keep an eye on him, too," Jennifer said, hefting her tennis racquet.

I staggered into the kitchen to guzzle a glass of tap water and, when I returned to the entryway, heard moans emerge from Previn as his eyes fluttered open. The policeman bent over to examine him when suddenly Previn pivoted his body, whipped his legs in a lightning fast arc and knocked the legs out from under the policeman whose chin crashed into an end table in the entryway. The end table splintered into smithereens as the cop crumpled to the floor.

Previn staggered to his feet, his bloodshot eyes focused on me. "You," he said with a snort.

I stumbled backward as he lurched toward me.

Jennifer brought her tennis racquet swinging around and into Previn's right kneecap.

He yelped with pain and collapsed into a heap, holding his leg.

For good measure she bashed him on the noggin again.

She blew on her tennis racquet. "Nobody gets away from my backhand. Nobody."

"Find some duct tape," I said to Jennifer.

She ran off to the panty and returned with a pristine roll of gray tape.

I removed the cellophane cover and wrapped tape around Previn's legs.

"That should secure him." I stepped back to admire my work.

"We need to wake him up," Jennifer said, pointing to the policeman who lay unconscious in the remains of the shattered table.

Max, who had apparently regained his courage, scampered into the entryway and began licking the policeman's face.

At this moment Denny and Allison returned home to find Jennifer with her tennis racquet over her shoulder, me with a roll of duct tape in my hand, Previn unconscious in a puddle of blood, and the policeman rising onto his elbow amid the pieces of the destroyed table.

Allison shrieked.

"Take it easy," I said. "Jennifer and I have everything under control."

Denny shook his head. "Define control."

"Hey, Jennifer and I had some excitement this evening, but outside of a little mess, we have everything in check."

Allison still had her hand over her mouth with her eyes the size of saucers. "My…my entryway. Jennifer, are you okay?" She gave her daughter a hug.

"It'll all clean up neat and tidy," I said. "I'll even spring for a new table."

The policeman had now moved to a sitting position but wasn't yet able to stand up. "I think my leg is broken," he said with a groan.

I shook my head. "I tried to warn you."

I heard footsteps, and a tall, skinny guy in a dark suit strolled into the entryway.

"You here to repair the table?" I asked.

"It's Detective Lavino," Jennifer said.

Lavino scowled. "What happened?"

"My granddaughter and I collared Gary Previn." I pointed to the cuffed and well-duct-taped limp form on the floor. "He murdered Daniel Reynolds and Randall Swathers and attempted to do the same to me."

Lavino leaned over to examine Previn.

"Be very careful with him, Detective. He's an expert in martial arts and already hurt your policeman."

Lavino stepped back.

Previn's body twitched, and his eyes opened. He turned his head from side to side. He couldn't move anything else. "I've been attacked," he mumbled. "I demand justice. Call my lawyer."

Jennifer stepped forward and shook her fist at Previn. "You're an intruder. Under the Colorado 'make my day' law we can use necessary force to protect ourselves."

"Spoken like a true lawyer," I said.

Lavino made a call on his cell phone while Denny and Allison helped the policeman to his feet.

I picked up a three-foot long chunk of wood from the broken table and handed it to the limping cop. "Here, use this for a cane until help arrives."

Jennifer hovered over Previn, waving her tennis racquet as if daring him to give her cause to deliver another blow.

Shortly, a crowd of people arrived. Two paramedics brought a stretcher for the injured police officer, and two burly cops carted Previn away.

Lavino regarded me with a serious expression on his face. "Now, Mr. Jacobson, I need to take a statement from your granddaughter and you. Separately."

"Why don't you interview her first so she can get to bed?"

"Oh, Grandpa. I want to stay up to see everything."

Several crime scene investigators arrived, and Lavino moved us all out of the entryway so they could take pictures and do their magic.

"I need a place to speak with Jennifer," Lavino said.

"You can go in the dining room," Allison said and pointed.

Lavino and Jennifer headed there, and Denny, Allison and I plopped down on the living room couch. I could see Lavino and Jennifer but not hear their conversation.

"You certainly bring a new element of excitement into our quiet home, Dad," Denny said.

"Only doing what I can to contribute to Jennifer's legal education."

"I'm so nervous. I need to do something with my hands," Allison said. She reached for a pencil and a puzzle book.

"Hey, I thought you swore off those Sudoku puzzles," Denny said.

"I'm only going to do one."

I patted Denny on the thigh. "Cheer up. It's better than smoking."

"I don't know," he said. "They're pretty addictive."

I lifted myself up and ambled into the bathroom to wash my face. In my pocket I discovered some balloons and Matt Larson's crumpled business card. I sneaked up to Jennifer's room and inflated the balloons. With some masking tape I stuck them to the mirror over her dresser.

HALF AN HOUR LATER Allison was still working Sudoku puzzles, and Lavino and Jennifer entered the living room.

"Your turn, Mr. Jacobson," Lavino said.

"We can use my room this time," I said and led him to my suite.

I parked my fanny in one chair, and Lavino scraped another one up so that he faced me.

"Why don't you tell me the whole story of your escapades tonight, Mr. Jacobson?"

"I went to the Colorado Mountain Retirement Properties promotional shindig at the Millennium Harvest House and saw Gary Previn in action. He had this routine with a stunt double. I took the opportunity to interview the look-alike, a man named Matt Larson." I gave Lavino the somewhat-worse-for-wear business card.

"I noticed that Larson had a tattoo of a surfboard on his wrist. When I interviewed the checkout clerk at the Boulder Public Library, she remembered the guy she thought was Previn checking out a book on the day Swathers was murdered. She said he had a surfboard tattooed on his wrist."

"The things you come up with, Mr. Jacobson."

"If you contact the library again, you'll hear the same story. Unfortunately, the clerk didn't report this to the police at first. She only recalled it later when I spoke with her."

"Go on."

"So after I determined that Previn hadn't been at the library that afternoon, but Larson had, I clued Larson in on Previn. I really don't think he knew. Larson planned to meet Previn later, but I warned him not to. Then I confronted Previn and accused him of killing Swathers in the Community Center parking lot."

"Pretty risky thing to do, Mr. Jacobson."

"Hey, I'm an old fart who won't be around much longer anyway. But I needed to clear my name."

"And then?"

"Previn rigged the raffle drawing so I'd be the one to win the Alaskan cruise. When I went on stage to receive my prize, he dragged me off to a back room. We had a conversation where he admitted committing the two murders and told me he planned to do in Larson and then skip the country. He relieved me of the cruise tickets and planned to kill me, but I escaped his attempt to do me bodily harm."

"Please, Mr. Jacobson, stick to the facts without the embellishment."

"Then I caught a cab home."

"I was pretty skeptical when your granddaughter called about this stunt-double gimmick, and your message sounded strange too."

"I don't blame you, Detective. This whole thing seems so crazy even now. Did you try to call Matt Larson?"

"I did, several times. No answer, not even a machine. He must've run scared after talking to you. But I'm still amazed you confronted Previn on your own. You knew he was a confirmed killer."

"I thought I could somehow expose him and prevent another murder."

"At the expense of him almost killing you?"

"As I said, I'm half-way dead anyway."

Lavino regarded me and a smile crept across his face. "You have more life in you than a dozen thirty-somethings."

"Anyway, when I returned home, Previn grabbed my arm and pushed me into the house. He was furious and itching to kill me. In the entryway he admitted his murders once again. Jennifer overheard this so she can corroborate it."

"Yes. She already has."

"Good. So you have two witnesses to his admission of guilt. Previn was going to kill me when Jennifer walloped him over the head with her tennis racquet."

Lavino sighed loudly. "You and your granddaughter make quite a pair."

"Yup. She's a chip off the old block. Then Previn assaulted your police officer, and Jennifer bashed him again. We bound his feet, and then you arrived."

"A very busy evening for you, Mr. Jacobson."

"Yes. I'm ready for a little shut-eye. I'd appreciate it if you could clear my good name so I can leave the state in the near future. I'm engaged to be married."

Lavino's mouth fell open.

"That's my fiancée Marion's picture on my dresser."

Lavino turned and regarded the picture.

"Well, you don't expect me to go without female companionship, do you, Detective?"

"Tell you what, Mr. Jacobson. You and I can have a long chat tomorrow to deal with all the various crimes you've witnessed or been involved with. I agree that you've had enough excitement for one night."

"As long as we get everything wrapped up, I guess I can wait one more day."

We returned to the living room.

"Is everyone done in the entryway so I can clean up?" Allison asked.

"I'll check," Lavino said. When he returned, he informed us that the investigators were nearly finished.

Within fifteen minutes we had the whole place to ourselves again.

I wandered into the living room. Max was sacked out.

"That was so cool tonight," Jennifer said.

"Time for bed," Denny said.

"Aw, Dad. I'm still too hyped up. I'll never fall asleep."

"You need your rest," Denny replied. "You have your club tennis tournament coming up next week."

"And I got in some practice tonight." Jennifer picked up her tennis racquet, gave it a vicious swing and skipped up the stairs.

"She may have all that energy left, but I'm pooped," I said. "If you'll excuse me, I'm dead tired."

"Not a good choice of words, Dad," Denny said.

TWENTY-ONE

I WAVED GOOD NIGHT to Denny and Allison and headed to my room. In spite of feeling utterly exhausted, I sat down to chronicle the events of the day. What a life I led. But no matter how dramatic, I knew my sex-induced memories wouldn't be with me by the next day.

I had just started when someone knocked on my door.

"Come in."

Jennifer pranced in.

"I thought you were supposed to be in bed," I said.

"I went to my room and found balloons on my mirror. I bet you put them there, Grandpa."

"How could you tell?"

"It was either you or Detective Lavino, and he doesn't seem like the type."

"You got that right."

"Thanks." She gave me a hug and scampered out the door.

THE NEXT MORNING I woke up tired and wondering where the hell I was. I spotted the note atop a journal on my nightstand. It read: "You're lucky to be alive, you old goat. Read this before you do anything stupid."

After reliving the adventures of Paul Jacobson of the Geezer Enforcement Squad, I sat on my bed and contemplated my strange existence. I used to be this mild-mannered guy who minded his own business. Now I was nabbing crooks and getting married. And it seemed to all be happening to someone else.

At breakfast Jennifer bounced up and down in her chair. "We nailed him, Grandpa. That was the coolest thing."

"If you say so. I'm still trying to adjust to you being twelve and no longer six years old."

"That's why you have your journal and me to remind you, Grandpa."

"I'll take all the help I can get."

I was preparing for a day of trying to figure out what to do next when the doorbell rang.

Max danced underfoot as Jennifer opened the door to a tall, skinny guy in an undertaker's suit.

"Hello, Detective Lavino," she said.

"I'm here to see your grandfather," Lavino said.

"Come on in," I shouted. "You here to harass me some more?"

"No, Mr. Jacobson. I'm here to settle a number of questions."

"Then have a seat." I patted the couch cushion next to me. "And do tell me to what I owe the pleasure of your company, Detective?"

"Mr. Jacobson, you and I have had numerous chats."

"Yes. I've been one of your favorite suspects."

"After last night, that's all changed."

I raised an eyebrow. "Oh?"

"Gary Previn is safely behind bars for the murders of David Reynolds and Randall Swathers and the assault on a police officer, the attempted murder of one Mr. Paul Jacobson and the theft of four point six million dollars from Colorado Mountain Retirement Properties. We recovered all the money including one un-cashed check for two hundred thousand dollars."

I whistled. "That's a lot of moolah. You should be able to add fraud for what that sleazy outfit represented."

"Actually, with the return of the money Previn stole, the company has done nothing illegal. You'll be interested to know that they did receive zoning approval and will be breaking ground for construction within two weeks."

"You mean the operation is legit?"

"Apparently. But a number of agencies in the state will be watching them very carefully."

"Amazing."

"In fact, Peter Kingston, the president, asked to speak with you. I will pass on your contact information with your permission."

"Sure. I'm willing to talk to the head honcho."

"And I received a call from Matt Larson this morning. He spent the night with an actor friend in Denver who encouraged him to call me. He's relieved that Previn's under arrest and says he'll testify."

"That should give you a solid case against Previn."

"And I have some other news for you, Mr. Jacobson."

"Are you returning my Alaskan cruise tickets?"

He laughed. "You can speak with Mr. Kingston concerning that. No, this should be better news for you than a cruise. All the crimes that you were connected with or witnessed have been solved."

My eyes widened. "Will wonders never cease?"

Jennifer, who had been hovering around the couch, jumped up and down and shouted, "Hurrah!"

"My lawyer's enthusiasm speaks for me too."

Lavino wrinkled his brow.

"It's a little family joke," I said. "My granddaughter has been handling my various alleged criminal cases."

"It's no joke," Jennifer said, putting her hands on her hips. "Grandpa, you owe me a zillion stuffed animals for my fee."

"You're right. I'll settle up after the detective leaves. Now I'd like to hear the specifics of the various cases."

Lavino cleared his throat. "This may take awhile, given the large number of crimes you've been connected with."

"I have all day, all the rest of my life or whichever comes first."

Lavino chuckled. "First, the kidnapping of Katherine Milo. Thanks to the lead you and your granddaughter provided, we finally tracked down the missing girl and her father. He did have her at the mountain cabin. He's now facing trial, and Katherine Milo has returned home to be with her mother."

"I'm so glad," Jennifer said. "I've missed her. I'll have to call right now." She scampered away.

"And how is Katherine?" I asked.

"She's fine," Lavino replied. "Her dad told her he had permission for her to miss the end of the school year for an early summer vacation. He took her hunting and fishing so she didn't even know she'd been abducted."

"That's good. It could have been pretty traumatic for her."

"Now, the bank robbery."

"I wasn't involved."

"I know that. We found marked bills at Benjamin Slade's toy store, grilled him, and he confessed to the robbery."

"I don't understand that guy giving change with marked bills," I said.

Lavino shrugged. "He thought he could distribute a few of the bills at a time without being detected. He only used them around kids and old people. That was his mistake. He never figured on you, Mr. Jacobson, and your granddaughter."

"But then he was going to use a whole caboodle of the marked money to buy Beanie Babies."

"He planned to skip out and set up shop in another state. Also, under further questioning, he admitted working alone, so you're off the hook, Mr. Jacobson."

"You're good, Lavino. Cleaning up criminals all over Boulder."

"That's not the end of it."

"Do go on." I winked at Jennifer, who had returned to the room.

"Two boys accused you of indecent gestures in the bathroom at Marshall Middle School. Following up on the tape your granddaughter gave me, the boys also admitted to me making up the story. One more off the list, Mr. Jacobson."

"And the theft at the swim meet bake sale?"

"Mr. Jacobson, you shouldn't remember that…oh, yes, your journal."

I wagged my finger at him. "I was beginning to think you had a memory problem, Detective."

"Again, the boy who stole the money confessed. All these kids seemed relieved when they admitted what they'd done."

"They probably had some strong persuasion to 'fess up.' "

"Then there's the matter of the drug bust when you placed a brown bag in a trash container moments before a known drug dealer picked up a similar brown bag from the same container."

"And I described to you the exact contents of the bag," Jennifer said.

Lavino sighed. "I feel outnumbered here. Call off your pit bull, Mr. Jacobson."

"Let's hear the detective out, Jennifer."

She crossed her arms and gave him her evil-eye stare.

"Regarding the drug bust you witnessed," Lavino said, "we subsequently caught the courier who had placed the heroin in the garbage can.

"And finally, we arrested Mr. Mallory Pitman for sawing down trees in Mr. Fisher's yard. Once again thanks to your efforts."

"I'm always willing to help. The public will be happier without his artwork littering the landscape."

"He's sworn off sculpture and has been ordered to complete a community service project by painting over graffiti throughout town for the next two weeks."

"Just make sure he doesn't get inspired by the graffiti and do some of his own."

He gave me a tolerant smile. "Now, Mr. Jacobson, we're down to one last set of charges against you, a dog not under control and not picking up after your dog."

"It wasn't my dog."

Lavino held his hand up to stop me. "I understand. Given all the assistance you provided, I've been able to have this charge dropped. You're now free of all accusations."

"Thank you, Detective."

"And I have a little present for you, Mr. Jacobson. After all the time we've spent together, I thought it only appropriate to leave you a little memento." He pulled something out of a brown paper bag. "It's a picture of the county jail. You seemed so interested in the picture of the jail in the interrogation room at police headquarters that I thought you'd like your own autographed copy. A reminder to stay on the right side of the law."

I held it up to admire it. "I'll be sure to do that. And one thing, Detective. I noticed when you handed me the picture that your fingernails have grown out. You've stopped chewing them."

He smiled. "Yes, thanks to you, I've been so busy wrapping up crimes that I haven't had time to chew my nails. Within a week I've eliminated a fourth of my case load."

"Happy to be of assistance, Detective."

After Lavino left, Jennifer accompanied me to my room where I placed the picture of the county jail on my dresser next to a butterfly collection and the photograph of Marion.

I stood back to admire my fiancée. "Now I'm free to go to California to marry Marion. That appeals to me much more than ending up in that place." I pointed toward the jail picture.

"You're not free yet, Grandpa. You still owe me my fee. I've calculated it at eight additional Hawaiian stuffed animals."

"Tell you what. You and I can catch the bus right now to the mall. You can pick out the ones you like best."

"Cool."

"But, Jennifer, I'm still puzzled by the butterflies on my dresser. That's a hobby I've never pursued."

"You received a present from a detective in Hawaii. You helped him like you did with Detective Lavino."

"I'll be damned. Don't remember it."

"That's why you need to keep writing in your journal, Grandpa."

I sighed. "I guess you're right. Particularly since, if I move to California, I won't have you to remind me."

Jennifer's smile disappeared. "I'm going to miss you, Grandpa."

"You'll have to come visit me once in awhile. Plus we can talk on the phone, and there's always writing letters."

"I wish you'd learn to use email, Grandpa."

"In my next life, Jennifer. In my next life."

WE CAUGHT THE BUS downtown and strolled the short distance to the Pearl Street Mall.

"Look, Grandpa. The store we went to before is still open."

We entered the shop, and a bell rang, signaling our presence. From behind the counter a woman in her twenties, clear complexion, slightly pointed nose, straight short black hair and wearing large oval glasses looked up.

"May I help you?" she asked with a pleasant smile.

"Yes, indeed. I need to purchase a whole raft of Hawaiian stuffed animals for my granddaughter."

She put her right index finger to her chin. "I'm just getting familiar with the stock. I think I have two or three on display. Let's look."

She sashayed out from behind the counter and led us to a shelf. She lifted up a pig and a goose. "Here's what I have."

I frowned. "That won't do. I need more."

Then the woman's eyes lit up. "There's a possibility I have

additional ones in the back room. I haven't gone through all the boxes yet."

Jennifer bounced up and down. "We'll help you look."

The woman motioned us into the back room. It resembled Dorothy's house after the tornado hit. Brown boxes were scattered everywhere.

"How do you find anything here?" I asked.

She gave me a wan smile. "I'm new to this. It'll take me some time to organize the stockroom."

Jennifer launched into ripping open boxes like Max tearing meat off a bone. I bent down and rummaged through cartons as Jennifer shoved boxes aside like a whirling dervish.

I inspected a box of matchbook cars and another with Cabbage Patch dolls. I had just opened a container of Legos when Jennifer shouted, "Bingo! I found it."

She scooted a large box over toward me and pulled the tabs open for me to see. It was crammed full of stuffed animals.

Jennifer began unpacking the box and setting the animals down on the floor. "Grandpa, you owe me for nine cases, but you've already paid me one, the orange crab, so that leaves eight."

"You can round it up to ten," I said. "That's your tip for services performed."

"Okey dokey, Grandpa."

After ten minutes she had a line-up that would rival anything Detective Lavino could put together at police headquarters.

Jennifer couldn't contain her enthusiasm, and I thought she'd bounce clean through the floorboards. "Here, Grandpa, look at this. Umo, a barking Hawaiian monk seal; Nui Loa, a humpback whale; Momora, a Hawaiian pig; Unele, a nene goose; Mele Pumaiko'I, a lucky bullfrog…"

She had to pause to catch her breath. "And He'e Waihe'e, little octopus; Ka'inapu, a prancing horse; a cat, Nihi; Oeha'a, a waddling duck." She danced it around on the floor. "You'll like my final one." She lifted up a yellow and black stuffed animal with black bead eyes and black antennae. "Pualele, a monarch butterfly. The same kind as in your collection in the glass case on your dresser."

"I'm glad you're pleased." I pulled out my wallet and forked over my life savings.

"How long have you been in this store?" I asked the woman as she rang up my purchase.

"Two days. The previous owner had some kind of legal problems, and I bought the shop for a steal."

TWENTY-TWO

WHEN WE RETURNED TO the manor, Jennifer scampered up to her room to install her new friends in a place of honor on her bookshelf.

I settled in an easy chair for an afternoon of trying to figure out what a soon-to-be-married coot in his eighties thought he was doing.

Before I could reach any constructive conclusions, the doorbell rang. Allison put down her Sudoku puzzle and, with Max at her heels, greeted a muscular, dapper man with neatly creased tan slacks, white polo shirt under a blue blazer and closely-cropped white hair. He strode right up to me, grabbed my right hand and pumped it like he wanted to make water shoot out of my mouth.

"Mr. Jacobson, it's a pleasure to meet you."

"I don't know if the pleasure is mutual. Who the hell are you?"

He snapped out a business card. "Kingston. Peter Kingston, the third."

My mind did one of its blips, and all I could think of was Peter Kingston, the turd. I suppressed this thought. "You're the president of the retirement property company."

"The same. And I owe you my deepest gratitude."

Given what that company had represented, I didn't know how deep he could go.

He cleared his throat. "You stopped my ill-selected, ex-friend Gary Previn from destroying my company and sending me to jail."

I raised an eyebrow. "To tell you the truth, Mr. Kingston, I've had my suspicions concerning your outfit since I first heard a pitch from one of your salesmen."

"Understandable. Very understandable. I let the sales force run amok, not realizing what Previn planned to do. He was responsible for all sales and marketing while I focused on operations, finance and completing our zoning applications." He bit his lip and shook his head. "I was unaware that Previn had instructed his sales force to solicit two hundred thousand dollar deposits. He was supposed to be lining up prospects so that when we received our zoning approval, we could make concrete offers."

I regarded him carefully. "You mean you didn't know of this embezzlement scheme?"

"No, otherwise I would have fired Previn and stopped it immediately. I've set everything straight, though. We now have zoning approval, and I've sent letters to the twenty-three people who invested money. I've offered to either honor the promise that Previn shouldn't have made or to refund their money completely. Their choice. We have to return to an even keel with our operation."

"From what I understand, you and Previn spent time in the Special Forces together."

He nodded. "That's correct. Previn had the concentrated drive and sales experience I needed when I started Colorado Mountain Retirement Properties. Unfortunately, I was blind to his greed, corruption and violence."

"But isn't violence a characteristic bred in the Special Forces?"

"True, but a very focused type. It's meant to be used to protect, not take advantage of the general population."

"Didn't you become suspicious when two of your sales people died under mysterious circumstances?"

"I should have paid more attention. Being in the middle of delicate negotiations for the zoning approval, I suppose I kept a pretty single focus. Didn't see the wheels coming off the bus. Previn set me up to take the fall while he prepared to waltz off with a huge chunk of illegally collected money. I understand he even took away the two Alaskan cruise tickets you won in a raffle."

I chuckled. "I didn't deserve those anyway. Previn rigged the drawing as a way to entice me onstage so he could attack me."

"I disagree. Everyone in that room heard you announced as the winner. Even if Previn had ulterior motives, we stand behind our public promises." He pulled a leather pouch out of his inside jacket pocket. "I want to present you with an all-expense-paid cruise package for two. Previn had set it up originally for a cheap inside lower deck cabin. I've upgraded that to a balcony suite. You can choose any shore excursions, which will be charged directly to my account." He slapped the folder into my hand. "Go and enjoy yourself with a companion. It's the least I can do for you in appreciation for saving my hide and my company."

I stared at the packet resting in my hand. "Much obliged. I must say I'm very surprised by this. I read that you were a lawyer."

"That's right. I started my career as a corporate lawyer. Then moved over to the management side."

"I've never seen a lawyer give anything away."

He patted me on the back. "You come from the old school where you classify all lawyers as scum."

"Something like that."

"We're not all that way."

Jennifer, who had been listening, jumped in. "Remember, Grandpa, I want to be an attorney. And your friend Meyer Ohana in Hawaii. He was a lawyer, and he's nice, and he helped you a lot."

I shook my head. "This will take some getting used to."

"I'll also pay for your plane fare to Seattle and back. You

pick the starting point. Call the number on my business card, and my admin will take care of all your arrangements."

"It will probably be from Los Angeles."

"Wherever. You can fly from Paris if you like. It's a small price to pay for what you've done for me. Now if you'll excuse me, I'll take my leave and let you get back to your family."

As he left, I must have been standing with my mouth open.

Jennifer looked at me. "As Dad always says, close your mouth or you'll catch flies."

I chuckled. "That's what I always told him when he was a little squirt."

"Grandpa, you can take Marion on the Alaskan cruise for your honeymoon."

"You're right. That's one aspect of getting hitched I would need to take care of. Now with Lavino off my back, I can start the ball rolling on wedding plans."

I moseyed into my room and admired the picture of Marion next to the butterflies and Boulder County jail photograph. What an eclectic collection I had on my dresser.

Marion was a handsome woman. And she seemed willing to be stuck with me for as long as I stayed alive and kicking. What a world.

I found Andrea's cell phone number and decided to give Marion a call.

After Andrea put Marion on the line, I said, "Is this the young chick who's willing to settle down with an old fart?"

"Paul, it's wonderful to hear your voice."

"Yes, at my age it's still wonderful to be able to speak."

She tisked. "You have to quit obsessing about your age."

"Only a statement of fact. I called to discuss wedding plans."

"Well, first I have to convince you to come to L.A."

"I'm ready to take the plunge. I've wrapped up all my… er…obligations here, so I'm free as a bird."

"If you fly out within the next week or so, I think we can complete plans in a month. Say a late July wedding."

"No sense delaying at my age."

"There you go again."

"All right. No sense delaying when I have such an attractive young bride."

"That's better."

"Is your family ready to be invaded by an old coot?"

"They're all very excited that you're coming."

"All right. I'm ready to get this show on the road. And by the way, I have our honeymoon all set."

"Oh?"

"An Alaskan cruise in August."

"Then we'll definitely have to have our ceremony in July. I've never been to Alaska."

"I've never been on a cruise, so it will be a new experience for both of us."

"Didn't you do a tour of duty in the Navy?"

"Sure. I've been on destroyers and cruisers but never a love boat."

AFTER I HUNG UP, I returned to the living room. Before I could even relax again, the doorbell rang.

"I'll get it," Jennifer shouted as she and Max raced to the door. She flung it open.

A stocky woman dressed in a business suit entered, accompanied by a girl Jennifer's age.

"I'm here to see your grandfather," the woman said.

"Grandpa, Mrs. Milo and Katherine are here!"

Uh-oh, the savage mother lawyer.

Katherine and Jennifer hugged each other and started gabbing a mile a minute.

Mrs. Milo strode right up to me and looked me straight in the eyes. "Mr. Jacobson, I owe you an apology."

I blinked. "I'm not used to lawyers apologizing."

"I made a bad mistake. I accused you of being at fault when my ex-husband abducted my daughter. I found out that you actually helped the police find her."

"Just doing what I thought was right."

"It's more than right. I promised a reward of five thousand dollars to anyone who helped locate my daughter." She whipped a checkbook out of her purse. "I'm going to write you a check for that right now."

I help my hand up. "Wait a minute. I don't want your money."

"A promise is a promise." She extracted a pen.

I placed my hand on hers. "I have a better idea." I turned my head. "Katherine and Jennifer, come over here. I need your opinion on something."

The girls skipped over with their arms around each other.

"Grandpa, Katherine told me how while she was up in the mountains she caught six big trout."

"Sounds pretty fishy to me," I said.

The girls groaned.

"Now pay attention you two young ladies. Mrs. Milo has offered me a reward. I think it would be better if she made a contribution to your school. What do you both think would be a worthwhile expenditure for five thousand dollars?"

Jennifer and Katherine looked at each other and giggled.

"The computer lab is a mess," Jennifer said.

"They don't have enough disk storage," Katherine added. "We keep asking to have more added, but the teachers say there's no money. You could buy some new disk drives."

"I know about disc brakes, but I have no clue regarding disk drives," I said. "But if that's what the school needs, Mrs. Milo, please make a contribution on my behalf."

"Are you sure you don't want the reward money yourself, Mr. Jacobson?"

"Absolutely. If you insist on writing a check, make it out

to the school so your daughter and my granddaughter can benefit instead."

"Agreed." She grabbed my hand and gave it as hearty a shake, as had Peter Kingston the third.

I stood there in amazement. I'd never be able to trust an attorney again. Just when I had pigeonholed all lawyers, these two had ruined my negative impression of the legal profession.

I flopped down in the easy chair to catch my breath while Mrs. Milo and Allison chatted and the girls swirled around the house like two crazed gerbils.

Eventually, Mrs. Milo collected Katherine, and they departed amid shouts back and forth between the two girls.

"I'm putting Max out in the backyard," Allison said. "With all this excitement from visitors I don't want him having an accident." She led him away into doggy exile.

"Katherine seems in good spirits for a kidnap victim," I said to Jennifer.

"Like Detective Lavino mentioned, she didn't know she had been abducted. She enjoyed the mountains, but now she's glad to be back with her mom."

I sank back into my easy chair. I didn't know if my old ticker could survive the idea of two lawyers giving money away.

My shock and awe was interrupted by the damn doorbell ringing again. "What is this, Grand Central Station?"

"You seem to be very popular today, Paul," Allison said, having returned from putting out Max. She took her turn at opening the door.

I gazed up from my command seat to see two women accompanied by two tow-headed, sullen boys Jennifer's age.

One of the women—a short, slender lady who obviously didn't eat many hot fudge sundaes—stepped forward. "I'm Maggie Bishop, and this is Clarice Buchanan. Our sons have come to apologize to Mr. Jacobson."

"Paul's sitting there in the living room. Please come inside."

The quartet traipsed in.

"Teddy and Randy, what do you have to say to Mr. Jacobson?" the other woman, who must have enjoyed sundaes with extra fudge, asked.

Neither boy raised his eyes. They both scuffed the carpet with their feet.

"Teddy?"

Teddy gulped and, still not looking up, said, "I'm sorry."

"Randy?"

Randy mumbled, "I won't do it again."

"Boys, look at me," I said.

Their heads jerked up.

"If you're really going to apologize to someone, look them in the eyes and mean it."

They both made eye contact and said simultaneously, "I'm sorry."

"That's better. See it wasn't so bad. I'm not going to bite you or anything. What you did caused me some trouble, but it's all been set straight. What do you think you should do to make up for the problems you caused me?"

The boys shrugged.

I regarded them thoughtfully. "I think a public service project should be in order. Do you know computers?"

For the first time since they entered the house, their eyes lit up.

"Yeah," Randy said, scratching his arm. "I work with computers all the time."

"Me too," Teddy replied, stretching up on his tiptoes. "I even taught my mom how to build a webpage."

"Your middle school will be receiving some new equipment in the fall. I think you should volunteer to help set it up and make sure the new students learn how to use the improved computers."

"Cool," Randy said. "We can do that."

I pointed an index finger at each of them. "Now, go and lie no more."

"Yes, sir," they replied in unison.

"Boys. Go wait outside," the roly-poly Mrs. Buchanan said.

Teddy and Randy shot out the door like they had rockets up their asses.

"Mr. Jacobson, we feel we owe you some type of compensation for what our sons did," Mrs. Buchanan said.

"Are either of you lawyers?" I asked.

She looked at her companion quizzically and turned back to me. "Why no."

"Then don't worry. Your sons have apologized. They have a project to work on, and I feel they've learned their lesson."

"Thank you for being so understanding, Mr. Jacobson."

"I remember being a boy in the distant past. I did some pretty dumb things at their age."

As the mob dispersed, I decided I needed to take in a breath of fresh air when the blasted doorbell rang again. I thought fleetingly of ducking out the back, but instead reached out to open the front door.

A man and woman in their seventies stood there.

"Hi, Paul," the woman said. "Nate and I hoped to catch you at home."

The name clicked. These had to be my friends Nate Fisher and Helen Gleason. "Come on in. Everyone else in the world has been here today."

I noticed they each held a box.

"We have some presents for you," Helen said. She opened her box to reveal a luscious chocolate cake. "I baked this as a thank you for bringing Nate and me together."

"I'll be damned. It looks delicious."

"And I have a present for Max," Nate said. He opened his box to reveal a large steak bone. "Thanks for tracking down the tree-cutting culprit, and I apologize again for ever suspecting you."

"There have been a lot of apologies today. I'm glad that you and Helen are so happy together."

"That's something else I want to discuss with you. Helen and I are having our wedding ceremony next week. Paul, would you stand up for me?"

I clapped Nate on the back. "Damn straight. I'd be happy to witness the event."

SO THERE I WAS, decked out in a sports coat and tie, standing next to Nate Fisher while a minister read the vows. Helen looked ravishing in her blue gown, with her daughter next to her in a pale blue floor-length dress.

I watched all the events carefully. I supposed this would be good practice for me on what I would be going through in California with Marion in the near future. Not that I would remember one iota about it. I had to admit that I never had a chance to be bored by anything being repetitive.

After Nate kissed the bride, music blared and we all adjourned to the church courtyard for the reception. Jennifer and Helen's granddaughter, Lauren, came running up to me.

"Grandpa, Lauren and I plan to play tennis together next week. I've invited her over to the club."

"You can teach her that wicked forehand of yours," I said.

They charged off again, and I watched them stuffing food in their mouths, giggling together and racing from one corner to the other. Ah, the wonders of youth.

And here I was, launching into a new adventure of my own. What would be in store for me in Venice Beach with Marion? How would I handle it as a married man again? What would it be like waking up with a new wife beside me who I wouldn't recognize unless we had had a little hanky-panky the night before?

Ah, the wonders of old age.

TWENTY-THREE

THE NEXT DAY I PREPARED for my magic carpet ride to the airport. Max came up and nestled his snout against my trousers. I scratched him under the chin, and he looked up at me with his sad little eyes.

"You take good care of my kids, Max," I said. "And leave Nate's lawn alone."

LATER, I STOOD with Denny, Allison and Jennifer at the airline check-in counter at Denver International Airport. I handed over my ticket, identification and two suitcases, one of which displayed my bumper sticker that read, "Old age is not for sissies." The attendant clicked away on the computer. After a moment she looked up at me.

"There's an indicator record that a bag with your name has been saved in the lost and found."

"Grandpa, it could be the carry-on bag with your Hawaiian journal that you were supposed to have when you arrived here."

"Well, let's go check it out," I said.

After being given an identification number and following the attendant's directions, we found a door that led to a huge room, crammed full of luggage.

"I'm here to retrieve my bag," I said to the man standing behind a counter as I showed him the identification number.

"One minute please."

I looked around the room to see a bin full of cell phones and shelves lined with laptop computers, purses, wallets, pens, keys and eyeglasses. I wasn't the only one around with a bad memory.

The one-minute stretched into ten, making me thankful we had allowed lots of time before my flight took off. Finally, the guy returned and dropped a blue sports bag on the counter. "Here you go."

I unzipped it and pulled out an ear-marked pile of hand-written pages.

"It's your Hawaiian journal, Grandpa."

"I'll be damned. I'll have to read it on the plane."

I consolidated the contents into my other carry-on and gave the blue sports bag to Jennifer.

Outside the security line, Jennifer gave me a hug.

"Thank you for helping clear me of all the legal poop I stepped in," I said.

"Oh, Grandpa. I enjoyed your visit so much. I'm going to miss you."

"Well, I'll be seeing you soon when you come out for my wedding."

"That will be so cool. I can't wait. It'll be even more exciting than the wedding yesterday."

"You're becoming quite the party-goer. Two weddings within a month."

"And, Grandpa, I've been rethinking my decision to become a lawyer."

"Oh?"

"Yes. After solving all those crimes, I think I want to be an investigator like Detective Lavino."

"You're good at it. But you don't have to make up your mind now. Wait until you're in college, and then you can decide what career to pursue."

She nodded. "I know. I like to have a plan."

"And keep playing tennis, Jennifer. It's a good way to stay in shape as you age."

"I'll enter some more tournaments too, Grandpa, although I didn't win the club tournament for my age group last week."

"Oh, I guess I forgot. I apparently didn't write it up in my journal."

"I was pretty disappointed at first. I lost in the finals. In the tiebreaker I missed a forehand setup and then an easy backhand. Can you believe it?" She shook her head and then a smile returned to her face. "But with more practice, I'll do better."

I put my arm around her. "Don't worry about missing a few points. You made the shots on Previn when it really counted. With your powerful strokes, you could develop into quite an athlete."

Her eyes lit up. "You're right. If I keep improving, I might even receive a sports scholarship."

Allison gave me a hug. "I've sworn off Sudoku puzzles again," she said.

"With me out of your hair, you won't have to stay around the house as much."

"Oh, Paul. I enjoyed having you here. I'm going to miss all the excitement."

"Don't worry. Jennifer will keep you hopping. She's entering the wonderful world of becoming a teenager."

Allison rolled her eyes. "Yes, we're in for a whole new stage."

Denny grabbed my hand.

I pulled him close and gave him a hug.

I noticed the expression of surprise on his face. Then he relaxed and squeezed me as well. "Dad, thanks for seeing me through my memory concerns."

"Any time, Son. I think you should take up the Sudoku puzzles. It will keep your brain cells in shape."

I waved to everyone as I entered the security line, ready to be frisked. I patted my carry-on bag containing my personal items. I hoped the metal frames on my butterfly collection, photograph of the jail and picture of Marion wouldn't set off any alarms.

ON THE PLANE I buckled my belt, grumbling that I had a middle seat. The window seat was already occupied by a skinny man who appeared to be sleeping. I only had to wait to see how big a problem I was up against in the aisle seat.

My question was soon answered when a jovial, moderate-sized man in a suit sat down. He extracted a book of Sudoku puzzles from his briefcase.

"You ever done these?" he asked me.

"I tried one once."

"Quite addicting, but they pass the time on a flight. You live in Los Angeles or heading there for a visit?"

"I'm moving there."

He gave me a large grin and handed me a business card. "You look like a discerning gentleman. I represent a new concept in independent retirement living. We're now taking reservations for our facility being constructed in the mountains above Los Angeles, near Big Bear."